MICROBIOLOGY OF OCEANS AND ESTUARIES

Elsevier Oceanography Series

MICROBIOLOGY OF OCEANS AND ESTUARIES

BY

E. J. FERGUSON WOOD D. Sc., B. A.

Professor of Marine Microbiology
Institute of Marine Science
University of Miami
Miami, Fla.

ELSEVIER PUBLISHING COMPANY
AMSTERDAM — LONDON — NEW YORK
1967

ELSEVIER PUBLISHING COMPANY
335 JAN VAN GALENSTRAAT, P.O. BOX 211, AMSTERDAM

AMERICAN ELSEVIER PUBLISHING COMPANY, INC.
52 VANDERBILT AVENUE, NEW YORK, N.Y. 10017

ELSEVIER PUBLISHING COMPANY LIMITED
RIPPLESIDE COMMERCIAL ESTATE
BARKING, ESSEX

LIBRARY OF CONGRESS CATALOG CARD NUMBER 67–10468

WITH 37 ILLUSTRATIONS AND 19 TABLES

PRINTED IN THE NETHERLANDS

PREFACE

The publication of this book so soon after my Marine Microbial Ecology is an indication of the rate of progress of the study of marine microbes. It is also an indication of world interest in the oceans as a source of food and other requirements for a world with an exploding human population, and the realization that the microbes and their behaviour control the food web in the ocean. I have endeavoured to consider the taxonomy and nutrition of marine microorganisms in more detail than I did in my previous book, and have reverted to an earlier interest that I had in the economic implications in marine microbiology. These, as well as the role of microbes in the food web of the seas, are of great importance to humanity, and their effects will increase as we turn more and more to the oceans for our subsistence.

I cannot at this moment entertain the optimism of some that we shall, in measurable time, be able to farm the oceans. We have not yet, except in isolated areas such as Java and Japan, succeeded in farming our estuaries with any degree of success. Even in these places problems of efficiency arise. As for the oceans, our ignorance is so colossal that we have barely touched on the exploitation of existing resources despite the warnings of some students of so-called population dynamics in the oceans. It is our lack of understanding of marine biology and not our fishing efforts that is limiting our ocean fisheries.

My sincere thanks are due to my colleagues Drs. J. S. Bunt, S. H. Hunter and Claude E. ZoBell for some valuable suggestions and criticisms. Their help is greatly appreciated. I wish especially to thank my secretary, Mrs. Claire Edelstein for her assistance in the preparation of the manuscript for publication. She has been particularly helpful with suggestions resulting in a more readable treatise.

E. J. FERGUSON WOOD

CONTENTS

CHAPTER I

INTRODUCTION

MARINE MICROBIOLOGY AS A DISCIPLINE

This book is intended to introduce students to the discipline of the microbiology of oceans and estuaries, to aid the researcher who desires a brief resumé of the many aspects of this microbial world and to guide him in modern trends of thought regarding the many activities of microorganisms in physical and chemical phenomena in the seas of the world. It is not intended as an exhaustive treatise. There are other publications in preparation or in press, written by people more competent than I am, which are designed to present an up-to-date picture of the many-faceted investigations that are going on at the present time concerning microbial activity in the other three fourths of the world we live in.

When my dear friend and colleague ZoBELL wrote his textbook on *Marine Microbiology,* which appeared in 1946b, there were many who shook their heads at his presumption. When I entered the almost virgin field in 1937, it was made clear to me that I would not be able to make marine microbiology a full-time study and I was expected to cover a wide range of activities including the preparation of commercial marine products from material available in the Southern Hemisphere. ZoBell was merely a voice crying in the wilderness, and rather a hostile wilderness at that. For one thing, it was widely believed that microbes did not exist far below the photic zone— temperatures were too low for any appreciable microbial growth and anyway pressures were too great for enzyme activity.

Another fact that must be considered when we look back at those early, pioneering days: our knowledge of biological processes was unbelievably naive, the close relation between microbes and their physical and chemical environment unrecognized, and the methods of study crude and unsophisticated by modern standards. Some of the experiments tried on the microscopic plants by ZoBell and myself and the other few workers, such as Harvey, Atkins, Braarud and Steemann Nielsen, would appear amusing to us today. But a start had to be made, and luckily for us, it was made, though often with ends in view that would be childish today.

The development is due entirely to the tremendous scientific progress of the last four decades. Less than two years ago, I finished and sent for publication a small book on *Marine Microbial Ecology* (WOOD, 1965). It is far more up to date than anything that has been published during the last 15 years except for a few reviews of particular aspects, yet I have for inclusion in this book a large sheaf of material which is not included in that book, research which has been published since it was written. No doubt this volume will be incomplete in many ways when it appears, even if I revise certain sections until the very last moment.

However, as the work of ZoBell inspired me and a few others, so has the interest grown in marine microbiology until all other branches of oceanography and marine biology are looking increasingly to the microbiologist for help and information. One difficulty is that we are expected to be a deus ex machina and provide microbiological explanations for all sorts of processes, some of which are in fact chemical or physical. It is so easy, for example, for a geologist to say "oh, that must be microbiological" when the laws of thermodynamics would show that microbes are not needed. In fact most bacterial transformations derive their energy from exothermic chemical reactions, e.g., anaerobic sulfate reduction, sulfide oxidation. Anaerobic sulfide oxidation, an endothermic reaction, occurs photochemically with iron as catalyst, though it is more usually attributable to purple and green sulfur bacteria in which it is photocatalytic or to chemoautotrophic bacteria such as *Thiobacillus dentrificans*. One naturally wonders how many other photocatalytic reactions occur in shallow-water sediments, since studies of such reactions seem to be unfashionable.

Definition of the subject

Let me say at once that I am including as marine microbes essentially all organisms that occur in the seas and their offshoots and are unicellular or functionally undifferentiated, in their vegetative stages. Thus I would include *Volvox* but exclude the *Chlamydomonas*-like spores of *Ulva* or *Enteromorpha*, and the filamentous algae such as *Ulothrix* or other organisms forming a thallus. The limitations are, of course, arbitrary, and some may disagree with them, but an author has privileges which I intend to use. If I am unduly dogmatic, it is for the sake of brevity, as so many of the questions in marine microbiology are wide open and will remain so for a very long while.

Our main concern will be with the status of micro-organisms in the seas at the present time, their taxonomy (in brief), physiology and ecology and to some extent, their relationship with human economy. We are also interested in the micro-plankton organisms which occurred in past ages as they appear as fossils through geological periods, the development of certain groups and the disappearance of others, and the effect of these early organisms on the environment of their day. It would be good to consider the early ecosystems, little as we know about them, in comparison with those of our time in order to find the reason for the microbiological systems of today.

Importance of marine microbiology

The importance of marine microbiology lies in the fact that the oceanic ecosystems constitute such a large part of the earth; they represent over 70% of the earth's surface and a proportionately much greater volume than the land, as the sea is on the average much deeper than the land is high, and the whole depth is now known to be available for living organisms. Apart from the seaweeds around the coasts, the major part of the plant life in the water is microbial, and even in sea-grass beds, the microbial epiphytes represent a biomass of the same order as the accompanying sea-grasses and larger seaweeds. There have been a number of arguments as to whether the biomass of land or sea plants is greater, and even as to their order of magnitude; it would seem that the standing crops represent much the same order of magnitude, but the rate of turn-over in the sea is much more rapid than on land so the total energy transformation is much greater.

The microbial elements

The microbes we have to consider in this book include the bacteria, fungi, yeasts, flagellates (including microflagellates, coccolithophores, dinoflagellates, silicoflagellates, chrysomonads, cryptomonads, chlamydomonads, Haptophyceae, and euglenids), ciliates (including tintinnids), Sarcodina (including Radiolaria and Foraminifera), diatoms and unicellular and multicellular algae. Of these the diatoms, tintinnids, Radiolaria, Foraminifera, silicoflagellates and coccolithophores are of geological significance owing to their possession of calcareous or siliceous skeletons or tests which can persist after the death of the organism and may form bottom oozes. Such oozes are at times of great thickness and are important constituents of marine and fresh water sediments. This will be discussed in greater detail in a later chapter. Bacteria and, to a lesser extent, fungi have also great geological significance, but theirs is an active rather than a passive role. We get few identifiable fossil bacteria, as they have no hard parts except possibly for the iron bacteria, but the bacteria are the chief microscopic organisms that assist chemical changes of a permanent character. Apart from the photosynthetic bacteria which collect solar energy, the chemical role is one of catalysing at low temperatures reactions which occur without bacteria only at higher temperatures or at greater pressures. Coal is in part due to bacteria, and oil (petroleum) is almost certainly due in some measure to the activity of marine bacteria, possibly related to the action of sulfate-reducers and fat-splitters. Not so well recognized are the roles of bacteria in the formation of laterites, sedimentary sulfur deposits, ore formation, and in nitrogen fixation, which, in the early days of our planet, must have played a great part in the lush growth of plants in the Carboniferous Period. As these reactions occurred in marshes, bogs, shallow seas and estuaries, they come within the purview of the hydrobiologist, particularly of the microbiologist.

MICROBES IN PRIMITIVE AQUEOUS SYSTEMS

It seems to be generally agreed that the first living organisms must have been anaerobes living under reducing conditions in the primordial aqueous organic slime or soup—the "Weltschlamm"—, that is, the organisms were aquatic. Amino-acids have now been synthesized from such substances as paraformaldehyde and potassium nitrate, hydrogen cyanide and other simple inorganic substances under primitive earth conditions. Such syntheses would have been easier in the rare atmosphere of those times, with a correspondingly higher penetration of ultra-violet light to provide the extra energy; and we may deduce that polypeptides, proteins and even DNA and ATP were gradually built up. YCAS (1955) suggested that self-propagating matter could arise by a series of primary valence-bond catalysts, catalysing a series of rate-limiting reactions, forming a series of interlocking cycles all operating at a maximum rate. Such self-generating catalysts would meet the definition of minimal life. There would be no discrete organisms but merely a metabolizing slime in the ocean of that time. The further evolution of this system would, according to Ycas, result in the production of catalysts of high molecular weight similar to peptides. The bubbling of gases such as nitrogen or hydrogen through this oceanic slime could result in the accretion of organic particles such as those described by RILEY et al. (1963) and the separation of a distinct water phase with organic aggregates (coacervates) therein. The formation of a membrane with selective osmotic properties is not difficult to imagine or explain. The life cycle of *Streptobacillus, Bacterioides* and other organisms producing filterable stages, suggests a method for the formation of bacteria. This would have to be preceded by the formation of cytochromes, catalase, porphyrins to produce organisms as we know them, and later the photosynthetic pigments would have appeared. Most of the primitive microbes possessed motility, which would be of the greatest advantage to free-living water bacteria, and algae. Further development, leading to multicellular organisms would mean the loss of motility, which loss would be an advance in morphology. Strangely enough, while many bacteria have locomotor organs (flagella), more developed motile algae such as the Oscillatoriaceae and the diatoms *Coscinodiscus* and *Rhizosolenia* do not. This is supported by the non-motility of the actinomycetes and many corynebacteria at the higher end of bacterial development, and also by the loss of motility in the development of the green algae. Following on from the cytochromes and porphyrins come the chlorophyll pigments, including the bacterial chlorophylls, and photosynthesis.

I incline to the opinion already expressed by microbiologists such as WINOGRADSKY (1949) and OMELIANSKY (1922) that the autotrophs would precede the heterotrophs in time and the photosynthetic bacteria would appear before the motile, chlorophyll-bearing flagel-

lates. We are here, however, in a field of pure but interesting speculation. To me, the idea seems attractive that the bacteria of the sulfur
cycle were the first to make their appearance, although the morphol-
ogists would regard these pleomorphic organisms as coming rather
later in the phylogeny of bacteria than the spherical, non-motile
cocci. It is interesting, and perhaps significant in this connection, that
Desulfovibrio and the thiobacilli have thermophilic representatives;
thus *Thiobacillus thiooxidans* can grow at pH —0.5, while *T. dentrificans*,
Desulfovibrio and the purple and green sulfur bacteria are strict
anaerobes. Several workers with this group of organisms (including
myself) have found that some strains of sulfate-reducers can exist
in a purely inorganic medium, and with the Thiobacilli and the green
and purple sulfur bacteria can give rise to a whole cycle of sulfur
reduction and oxidation which can be repeated ad infinitum as long
as carbon dioxide is present. The hydrogen required by the sulfate-
reducers *Desulfovibrio* and *Clostridium nigricans* would be derived in
the first place from the interaction of magmatic iron and water. The
sulfides would then be oxidized by the Thiobacilli, which can act
anaerobically with their nitrogen in the form of ammonia, and as
soon as photosynthesis emerged, by the purple and green sulfur
bacteria which, along with *Desulfovibrio,* have the power to fix dissolved
or atmospheric nitrogen. BAAS BECKING and WOOD (1955) have
shown that the sulfur cycle occurs in and often controls the chemistry
and biology of the estuarine sediments which are probably the
modern equivalent of the primordial ooze.

As the environment was anaerobic, one would expect the obligately
anaerobic bacteria to be the most primitive, instead of a rather advanced
group producing resting spores (the Clostridia). There is recent
evidence discussed by WOODS and LASCELLES (1954) that microbial
autotrophic and heterotrophic pathways are essentially similar, and
STANIER (1961) and HOLM-HANSEN (1962) point out that the essential
difference is in the mode of formation of ATP. The former authors
conclude, however, that it is not possible to decide on present evidence
whether the autotrophic chicken preceded the heterotrophic egg or
vice versa.

The effect of oxygen on the development of primitive organisms

So far we have hydrogenations and dehydrogenations but not oxidations, in the sense of combinations with molecular oxygen. These begin with plant-type photosynthesis, which once established, leads us to the world of plants and animals which we know today. Bacterial photosynthesis, exemplified by the purple sulfur bacteria is, in its first stage, dehydrogenation ($H_2S \rightarrow S$), but the second stage ($S \rightarrow SO_4$) is an oxidation. The blue-green alga *Lyngbya* can grow at an Eh of —170mV at pH 7.5–8.0, i.e., anaerobically; NAKAMURA (1937) stated that the diatom *Pinnularia* and the blue-green *Oscillatoria* can utilize hydrogen sulfide for photo-reduction of CO_2, a system analogous to that of the purple sulfur bacteria, although these are normally regarded as true photosynthetic algae. FRENKEL et al. (1949) record photo-reduction for *Scenedesmus* and HUTNER and PROVASOLI (1951) consider that this form of nutrition may be quite common among the microscopic algae including the flagellates. SPRUYT (1962) states that certain algae can, in the dark, evolve hydrogen, take up hydrogen from the atmosphere high in H_2 and oxidize it. In the light, they can evolve hydrogen and oxygen without normal photosynthesis and assimilate CO_2 with H_2, H_2S or an organic substance as hydrogen donor. As the oxidation-reduction potential rises, i.e., conditions become aerobic, these algae continue to photosynthesize in the normal manner of the higher plants, by reducing carbon dioxide with water as the hydrogen donor and the evolution of oxygen. One will call to mind that the "bacterium" or "colorless blue-green alga" *Beggiatoa* and its allies can also play an oxidative part in the sulfur cycle.

BERKNER and MARSHALL (1965), in an interesting and somewhat provocative paper, consider the relative effects of ultra-violet radiation and oxygen production on the early formation and maintenance of life. The authors have, however, ignored the probability that the first photosynthetic organisms were the anaerobic photosynthetic sulfur bacteria, which could oxidize sulfides anaerobically without the production of free oxygen. These organisms would thus be working in a reducing environment (to —300 mV) and would be followed by photosynthetic microorganisms such as *Scenedesmus* which can use H_2S as well as H_2O as a hydrogen donor. These authors considered that the oceans would not be available as a habitat for living microbes at this stage because of a high sinking rate, and of the activity of convection currents which would carry the organisms upward into the lethal region of ultra-violet or down below the compensation point. One must remember that the ability to use

H_2S as hydrogen donor allows the organism to photosynthesize by a mechanism which requires $1/10$ the light energy required by oxygen-producing photosynthesis, thus giving it a greater depth range. Further, most of the organisms concerned, especially the more primitive ones, have various efficient mechanisms for locomotion and could thus maintain themselves against considerable convection currents. Moreover, the lower limits for net gains from photosynthesis using H_2O would appear to be much less than is generally believed, e.g., less than 5 foot-candles in the case of some Antarctic micro-algae. The presence of algal forms corresponding to *Chlamydomonas* types, Siphonales and blue-green algae in pre-Cambrian sediments as recorded by BARGHOORN and SCHOPF (1965) make it certain that the micro-algae were well-developed in these strata.

It is interesting, and no doubt significant, that all plant processes are already in evidence in the few primitive groups we have discussed, though the metabolic pathways may not necessarily have been the same in the past as they are today. While it is easy to follow a chain of biochemical and physiological development in these primitive organisms, the morphological and phylogenetic gradations are not so clear. There is a great deal of argument as to where the differentiation into cytoplasm and nucleoplasm began. An apparatus allowing of gene recombination has been demonstrated in bacteria and there seems no doubt that bacterial heredity is similar to that of higher organisms with sexual processes. Perhaps one day the cytology and phylogeny of these primitive organisms will have been worked out, and thus allow certainty to replace speculation. One deduction, however, we can make, that the bacteria of the aqueous environment are the representatives of the original bacteria of our earth and that it is only after the development of the photosynthetic plants that parasitic bacteria came into existence, though the bacteriophages may have preceded them. This will be an unpleasant thought to the medically trained bacteriologists who have for so long dominated the science, and have created an anthropomorphic bacteriology in which all bacteria must be grown on blood and bile media and separated by serological tests using rabbit serum. This blood and bile bacteriology has seriously hampered the study of general microbiology in ways which I have discussed in a previous volume (WOOD, 1965). I believe we must accept the fact that terrestrial and aquatic microorganisms possess a variability pattern of which we usually see a single facet. This conception teaches us that a parasite is merely a selected strain which has grown for so long in its specialized environment that it finds it difficult or impossible to regain its original characters. Facultative pathogens would be strains which have been unable to attain a truly parasitic existence. This conception allows us to presuppose that new strains of disease-producing and other organisms may easily arise, and that even diseases new to science are not impossible. KEOSIAN (1960) suggests the possibility that conditions still exist for the biogenesis of viruses and bacteria, especially parasites, and that this may in part account for the difficulty in bacterial classification. If we accept Keosian's thesis, a microbe with primitive characters need not be phylogenetically older than a more complex organism.

There appear to be two possibilities for the occurrence of specialized strains—by mutation, and by repeated selection of certain characters by the environment. The mutant strain should, in theory, be characterized by stability, the selected variant by a tendency to revert towards the norm. However, a mutant strain may mutate again and thus retain a certain variability, while a variant may become stabilized by repeated selection. Strains may likewise be selected by environmental factors for resistance to changes in salinity, temperature or other factors. *Desulfovibrio*, for example, though at first intolerant of large changes in salinity, can be trained to grow at greater or lesser salinities than those of its natural environment. I have cultivated strains isolated from Lake Eyre where the salinity was saturating and acclimated them to grow in sea water media, and grown also in sea water at room temperature other strains from a fresh water lake on Macquarie Island in the Antarctic Ocean. The occurrence of strains of diatoms such as *Corethron criophilum*, *Biddulphia mobiliensis*, *B. chinensis* and *Dactyliolen mediterraneus* in separate populations restricted to distinct temperature ranges (WOOD, 1964) must be a natural example of such ecological selection. The eco-forms of these species occur in the Pacific, Indian and Atlantic Oceans.

There are traces of bacterial life from the Algonkian period of geological time; THODE et al. (1953) consider that bacterial activity was present at least 800,000,000 years ago, deducing this evidence from the microbial fractionation of isotopes of sulfur. Fragments of what are regarded as fossil microbes have recently been described from the Precambrian rocks of Australia (BARGHOORN and SCHOPF,

1965). As far as we can tell from the geological record and from the nature of chemical reactions in the sediments, there has been little change in the physiology and not very much in the overall morphology of microorganisms throughout the ages. Once cells began to unite and become specialized, differences became more important and there is a phylogenetic succession paralleling to a large extent the geological succession. Among the microbes, however, their small size, large surface-volume ratio, and flexibility of metabolism have ensured their survival with little modification, from the primordial biological slime to the present day, and have permitted them to remain the dominant organisms in much of the world throughout that period, especially in their original if greatly modified home, the sea.

The relation of the fungi to the marine habitat is curious. I. M. WILSON (1960) asks two questions concerning the origin of the fungi found in the marine habitat; did they originate in the sea which they now inhabit or are they terrestrial species which have secondarily adopted the marine habitat? Of the Phycomycetes, the marine representatives belong to families and genera which have numerous terrestrial and aquatic counterparts, though some have developed or maintained primitive characters conducive to their life in the marine habitat. The Pyrenomycetes in marine habitats do not show primitive characters, which one would expect if they were derived from these environments. On the other hand, the marine forms do appear to be well adapted, suggesting that they have been in this environment for a considerable period. The evidence at the moment seems to indicate that the marine fungi represent in the main an invasion of the marine habitat by terrestrial and aquatic forms. As most of the species studied (except for the wood-inhabiting ones) are parasitic, they have become somewhat specialized in the marine environment, but this may be secondary to their host-specificity. This hypothesis is supported by the tolerance of most fungi to a large range of salinities and temperatures. One would expect an autochthonous flora to have limits fairly close to those of the environment.

WHY MARINE MICROBIOLOGY

In this heading, the accent is on the word "marine", but, because of some traditions that have grown up, mainly in the United States, it has become necessary to define *microbiology*. In that country, the word is too often used as a synonym for bacteriology and this is very unfortunate as it leaves no word to describe under a general term the study of microscopic organisms other than the bacteria. We shall therefore use the term microbiology to include all unicellular algae, such as the blue-greens or Myxophyceae, and the diatoms, the flagellates (called by zoologists Phytomastigina) and also the colorless flagellates (or Zoomastigina), the Ciliata and Sporozoa as well as the bacteria and the fungi (Schizophyceae) and myxomycetes, although to the last mentioned have been ascribed the genera *Labyrinthula* and *Dermocystidium* which are more usually regarded as Protozoa.

Peculiarities of the marine environment

We can, in point of fact, find all these groups in the fresh water and in the soil environments, though in very different proportions and differently distributed. In other environments we shall find some, but by no means all of them, and they will not have the same significance. Thus the *marine* environment differs in having a different *assemblage* of microorganisms. Another difference is in the relative importance of macro- and micro-organisms. In terrestrial environments, and to some extent in fresh water, the higher plants are far more important in biomass than the lower plants, particularly the microbes. In the marine environment the reverse is true, as one can realize when one considers that the only macroplants are the seaweeds and sea-grasses and that these are confined to very shallow water and estuaries, i.e., close along the coast. The rest of the plants in the marine environment are microscopic, even those which form felts and are known as tapetic organisms. We have now learned that the marine environment differs from others in the relative importance of the microbes, and in the kind of community which they form. This is, as may have been deduced, due to conditions which are peculiar to the marine environment. Together with the habitat of pathogenic microorganisms, the aqueous environment is peculiar in having water universally present, and except in the intertidal zone, desiccation does not occur. The abundance of water in the environment is important in controlling the equilibria of chemical reactions and thence in certain phases of plant metabolism. It controls also the ratios and abundance of gases, depending on their solubility and utilization by organisms and on other chemical processes, mainly confined to shallow waters, and it governs interaction between sediments and the water above. Because of the aqueous environment and the universal presence of particulate matter, adsorption is probably more important and constant than it is in terrestrial environments. Many of these conditions are common to fresh and salt water, and the real difference between the marine and all other environments lies in the concentrations and ratios of the salts in solution in sea water. Finally the oceanic environment is far more constant than any other. Changes do occur, but they are relatively slow in time or extended in · space. Ocean currents tend to have the same properties (*conservative properties* they are called) over long distances and to have been in a relatively steady state for a long time, sometimes hundreds of years as with the deep antarctic water of the ocean bottom. In estuaries, where land, sea and rivers meet, we do get considerable variation, but the changes are of degree rather than of kind, and one can separate out the different influences.

We shall speak throughout this book of marine species and floras, and of marine environments, and the reader will find that certain microbial processes are considered as being essentially marine, such as "red tides".

A parameter to which the terrestrial microbiologist will not be accustomed is depth, at least to the extent to which it influences organisms in the oceans. The deepest part of the ocean is about 32,000 ft., and sunlight penetrates effectively down to about 300 or 400 ft. with feeble light to about 1,000 m at the maximum so there is a huge dark world of water which is lit only by the feeble glow of bioluminescence and which is part of the environment we must study. Moreover, water is almost (though not quite) incompressible, and has weight so that the hydrostatic pressure increases about 1 atm (roughly 15 lb./sq. inch) for every 10 m (30 ft.) of depth. Thus the organisms in deeper water have to be able to adapt themselves to pressures that are vast by terrestrial standards. In fact it was long thought that life could not exist at such depths because of these pressures. Another important feature which the oceans have in common only with the atmosphere is currents, and like those of the atmosphere they are four-dimensional, since time enters the equation. In fact, time is often of great importance as water movements are often slow.

The approach to marine microbiology

The reader will see therefore, that the marine microbiologist has to consider simultaneously more factors than has a microbiologist studying any other environment. This is reflected in the methodology which is far more difficult, and leads to the acceptance of sampling procedures which would be considered inadequate in other branches, although even in the latter, quantitative microbiology is only relative. Take for example the problem of microbial counting. In microbiology, generally, we can use plating techniques (viable counts), slide counts (which depend on the ability of certain microorganisms to attach to things like glass slides), or direct counts in which the organisms are made to settle on a filter or a slide and counted there irrespective of their ability to grow or to perform certain tasks. If we can sample readily, have several techniques which support each other, and have ample assistance, we can make useful quantitative observations. When as in the marine world, sampling is made even more difficult, and it is almost impossible to take two consecutive samples from the same spot because our water is never still, adequate sampling becomes very difficult indeed. In oceanographic sampling, ships such as the Miami research vessel "Pillsbury" (Plate I) are required, and as these cost from a minimum of say $400 to somewhere over $1,000 for one sample, quantitative marine microbiology becomes a very expensive luxury. One must take advantage of ships traveling for other purposes to supplement the observations one can make from one's own ship. The reader will see that such sampling needs careful planning so that the ships cover as many disciplines and take as many samples as possible on a given course and in a given time; also required are careful techniques, so that the methods will be adequate for the job in hand, and not so complicated as to delay the ship overlong for any one sample.

The marine microbiologist must therefore be trained in the ordinary aspects of microbiology, have a rather wider acquaintance with the whole concept of microbiology than his terrestrial colleague, and also have great practical ability to plan and carry out observations under considerable difficulties. It is not that he needs special attributes, but he does need adaptability and the ability to improvise as well as considerable enthusiasm. It is this enthusiasm which enables him to study his microorganisms under a high-power microscope in the

Plate I. R.V. "Pillsbury", an ocean-going marine research ship. Note two A frames, one on port, one on starboard side crane for heavy gear, hydrographic winch on upper deck forward of bridge. (Photo by D. Heuer.)

cabin of a small ship at sea, to collect his material in heavy weather at sea or in the estuaries (which can be even more uncomfortable), and to insist to his colleagues that his work is of paramount importance. This is very necessary on a multi-purpose cruise, that is to say, on most cruises.

SOME GENERAL CONSIDERATIONS

The oceanic environment is usually divided for ecological study into two regions, *planktonic* and *benthic*, the former representing the milieu of the floating or free-swimming organisms, the latter that of the epontic (Greek: ἔπι = on, ὄντος = existing) (attached) organisms also called "Aufwuchs" or *periphyton* and the sedentary organisms or true *benthos* which live in the bottom; the microbes in this habitat are sometimes called *epipelic* (Greek: ἔπι = on; πέλη = mud; literally living on the mud). This has been a convenient division, and also represents a characteristic difference in the flora and fauna. The plankton was previously regarded as restricted to depths from which the organisms could migrate to feast on the plant material. This was considered to be confined to the illuminated region of the seas called the *photic zone*. Certain terms are extensively used in these connections; as plants gain energy by photosynthesis and lose it by respiration, there will be a light intensity at which these two processes will balance and the plant will neither gain nor lose energy overall. This point is known as the *compensation point* and the depth at which the light is so reduced is known as the *compensation depth*. It does not follow that the compensation depth for every species will be the same, as some make more efficient use of light than others, while some require very little light indeed (of the order of 5–20 foot-candles), and cannot live in even moderate intensities. The depth at which total photosynthesis per unit of water surface is equal to the total respiration has been called the *"critical depth"* and applies to a body of water and not to individual organisms or strains.

These terms have to an extent lost their significance since several authors have found potentially photosynthetic microorganisms at depths to 5,000 m, and other organisms which can supplement their photosynthetic diet by *heterotrophy* or *phagotrophy* (utilizing dissolved or particulate organic matter as food). It has been found too that there are organisms, sometimes very numerous, at depths which preclude their ever reaching the photic zone except by chance through upwelling or other occasional phenomenon. The animals of this group presumably feed on the quasi-autotrophic, heterotrophic or phagotrophic plants and form a distinct community in what may be called the *aphotic* or *sub-photic zone*. We have little information as to the biological importance of this zone, rates of growth and metabolism, and even the trophic levels at such depths.

DEVELOPMENT OF MARINE MICROBIOLOGY

It is probably true in all sciences that fashion has dictated the trend of scientific advances. At the moment, marine microbiology is fashionable and it is comparatively easy for institutes to obtain money for research in this field. Accordingly progress has recently been very rapid and is still accelerating. Even so, it is far behind other developments, especially as on the results of our researches may depend the adequate feeding of the world population in the not very distant future.

The development of microbial taxonomy

From the work of Linnaeus, it appeared that all plants and animals in the world could be placed in definite categories which would indicate the course of phylogenetic development of organisms and groups of organisms throughout geological time. This very happy hypothesis led to a great enthusiasm for taxonomy as giving us a key to both the present and the past; the present, in that it should show up the relations of organisms to each other and allow comparative studies, the past in that the present could be related back through geological time and conclusions made as to biological conditions in past ages. Thus the aim was primarily ecological, but more and more taxonomy became an end in itself, especially as it grew at a rate which threatened to engulf the other disciplines. Moreover, taxonomy of the then-known microbes was easy in that it required a microscope and a few instruments, whereas ecology and physiology became hampered by the limited techniques that were then available. It became fashionable for schoolmasters and the like to kill their idle time at the microscope naming and classifying organisms of all types, in many cases with a rather gay abandon, and a readiness to describe new species naming them (hopefully reciprocally) after a friend. The criteria selected for classification were usually those easiest to discern through the microscope, and were not often critically assessed. This resulted, after the naming of vast arrays of species, genera and families, in taxonomy becoming a rather despised pastime, an unfortunate trend which has persisted until very recently. Thus, fashion led the biologist of the latter half of the last century into creating thousands of "species", mostly delimited by descriptions of type specimens, often with complete Latin diagnoses, but no account of possible variation. Incidentally, the requirement of Latin diagnosis for validity of a species is a ludicrous anachronism indulged in by the taxonomic botanist; it is rare these days for the writer or the reader to have any familiarity with Latin. Such diagnoses can be misleading if they are written by one classics scholar and translated by another, both being ignorant of science; for this to be apparent, one has only to remember one's own ludicrous errors when using the wrong synonyms for translating Vergil or Ovid into English during one's schooldays. I have in fact used in my own Latin diagnoses homonyms which made the translation impossible, and have never been questioned about them, which would suggest that all my readers have been more at home in English than in Latin. Nowadays, but only recently, we have a new approach to taxonomy, not as a phylogenetic approach which would end all genetic arguments, but as a dynamic study leading to a better appreciation of the ecology and physiology of plant and animal associations and individuals. It is not much use studying the physiology and ecology of what is regarded as a single species only to find that we are dealing with a number of entities, or to find that our distinct entities belong to a single species with a diverse habitat. An example of this is to be found among the Japanese oysters as related to me by Dr. Takeo Imai. What had been regarded as a single species, proved by culture tests and fertilization experiments to be several species, while strains from different areas which had been regarded as separate species proved on assembling them in one area to be mere eco-forms of a single species.

Difficulties of microbial taxonomy

This makes it no longer possible to separate species on artificial criteria chosen for the convenience of the taxonomist; in the new taxonomy, physiological and ecological features have to be taken into account even though the classification may be phylogenetic. It is no longer sufficient to define a type by a certain dried and probably broken specimen known to be in a certain institution; we must also know how this type can be varied by the effect of the ecosystem upon it. The organism must be studied through the whole range of its potential environment, its response to these changes observed and recorded, and the future path of change must be assessed. Words such as family, genus and species take on a new connotation as living and possibly mutable things, and not convenient and unalterable pigeon holes. Unfortunately, in the meantime, would-be-taxonomists have turned to other avenues of research and there are now too few to make the necessary observations, and even too few to teach those who would take up the subject.

We are now faced with the almost impossible situation of a vast taxonomic literature concerning microbial species in particular, and the necessity to eliminate a majority of these, if only we can find criteria and justification for doing so. Since, in several of these groups of organisms, we have found individuals which bridge genera and even families, and have learned that some forms are mere stages in the life history of other closely or distantly separated ones, it would seem that a phylogenetic taxonomy is impossible in these groups at the present time. It may be necessary to provide an interim classification to suit the physiology and ecology as well as the morphological differences, and then try to correlate this with the original, purely morphological taxonomy.

Another trend was set in the latter half of the last century by the work of Pasteur, Koch and Ehrlich, who led us into the study of bacteriology; these brilliant men were, naturally enough, interested primarily in the curing of human ailments, although Pasteur did at one stage suggest the use of fowl pox to rid Australia of rabbits. The medical bias introduced by these men led us to a bacteriology which relied on serological tests and on the study of bacteria on a limited series of media related to human pathogens and their relatives. Their methods were adopted in all bacteriological studies and the efforts of Beijerinck and Winogradsky to study microbial ecology in mixed cultures were regarded with suspicion.

This medical bias led to attempts to classify all bacteria in terms of forms which were associated with humans, e.g., to grow them on blood and bile media, to test their agglutinins against prepared rabbit sera, to grow them at 37 °C, and test their biochemical reactions on media which had been adopted with medical ends in view. I remember on one occasion that my work was criticised because I found bacteria which fermented galactose and mannose but not glucose; this was considered unlikely because more terrestrial bacteria ferment glucose than any other sugar. I was able to point out that galactose and mannose were far more common in the marine environments I was studying than glucose. This type of argument shows the extent of the bias which has had to be overcome in developing marine microbiology.

Microbial variability

I must mention here the potential variability of marine species of bacteria. They are far more pleomorphic than most terrestrial bacteria, particularly in their natural environment, though they lose much of this pleomorphism in culture. They tend to vary too in their relations to temperature, salinity and nutrient concentrations. Some strains have a wide range of temperature and/or salinity, others have a narrow range, but one can often select strains from a single-cell culture which will differ widely in their optima and which maintain such differences. Thus, the presence or absence of an agarase, for example, may well be characteristic of a strain and not of a species which makes absurd the creation of such genera as *Agarbacterium*. One cannot stress too strongly the necessity for studying a large number of strains from identical and similar habitats, and testing their variability and the range thereof before ascribing a generic or specific name to them. While morphology of bacteria is of limited use as a criterion, since overall shape and flagellation are all that we have to use, marine bacteria do have a peculiarity in the degree of polymorphism that they show, and this made me ascribe them to the genus *Mycoplana* rather than *Pseudomonas*. It is difficult to apply the Adansonian principles used in bacterial taxonomy by COLWELL and LISTON (1961) and others to assess degrees of variability, when some strains tend to maintain a norm with regard to a property, and other strains tend to depart from the norm in different directions, giving curves with several peaks which allow one to select strains differing widely from the parent strain. Such strains would be classified as different species by the Liston-Colwell system. Unfortunately, I can suggest nothing to take its place, and believe that we have no reasonably clear picture of bacterial classification, or just how to go about making one.

Fortunately, it is probably relatively unimportant to know the species of a bacterium for ecological studies; it is the physiology and function that really concern us, and so many properties are non-specific. For example, it is more important to know an organism's relationship to cation ratios of sea and fresh water than to know whether it is a *Pseudomonas* or a coccus.

Bacterial physiology has usually been studied by selecting some property such as malic dehydrogenase activity or the Krebs cycle and studying this, often with washed cells in a Warburg respirometer. For marine studies, *Escherichia coli* is frequently used because of the large backlog of studies that have been made on this organism. The researchers then extrapolate from the behavior of *E. coli* to make deductions regarding the marine environment. There seems to have been little effort to determine the significance of certain enzyme systems in marine environments.

Despite the criticisms I have voiced, we have a large amount of information regarding the kind of marine microorganisms which occur in the seas, but because of the influence of terrestrial examples, this information tends to be biased in certain directions, and to have large gaps which gravely limit its use. We badly need to reassess all the information available in the light of modern knowledge of the biology of microorganisms and of modern ideas and developments in taxonomy. The difficulty arises in knowing what must be discarded and what retained and in overcoming a number of prejudices and upsetting some theories that have been regarded as axiomatic.

Quantitative investigations

ZoBell, Wood, and others have tried to enumerate bacteria in the ocean by making counts of viable organisms on nutrient media, sometimes on enrichment media. At the same time, they realized the weakness of viable counting and tried to support such information by direct counting methods. They found that the ratios between direct and viable counts were not constant but tended to depend on the concentration of organisms in the samples (WOOD, 1953; Fig.1). Such dependence was not direct enough for a factor to be introduced, and moreover, even on a large number of culture media one cannot reproduce the environment enough to even guess what the actual role of these bacteria may be in the ecosystem. We shall discuss this and allied problems in greater detail in a later section.

Plant assemblages were estimated by so-called "net counts". Hensen and others assumed that if nets of certain dimensions and with certain mesh sizes were towed for a given time, a reasonably constant amount of water would be filtered and the catch of animals in the net could be considered as a rough representation of the population of the region. This theory was also applied to plants or phytoplankton which made things easy, as plant and animal collectors could be towed at the same time. The Discovery "N 50" net was extensively used for quantitative phytoplankton study. This net was attached to a ring 50 cm in diameter with 200 mesh/inch bolting silk. It was in fact an exceedingly inefficient net as it pushed most of the water ahead, and filtered only a small portion even if the net were new; when it was old and clogged it hardly fished at all. Samplers which trapped a quantity of water were banned because the

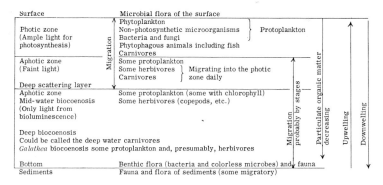

Fig.1. Oceanic zones and their biocoenoses. Depths are only approximate and vary considerably in different localities.

samples caught in this manner had to be filtered or centrifuged. Filtration in days before the molecular filter was crude, and lost and destroyed many organisms, and centrifugation was done in buckets which resulted in a resuspension of many organisms by inertia when the centrifuge was stopped. The criticism leveled at this type of centrifugation was later applied generally, even when continuous centrifuges came into use, and this delayed until very recently their acceptance for concentration. This in turn delayed the acceptance of closing samplers such as depicted in Plate II and Fig.2 and 3 as an adequate replacement for nets. It took a long time for the importance of the micro-flagellates to be recognized due to the fact that these organisms passed through the nets almost quantitatively. It is known that these small organisms are frequently more numerous than the net phytoplankton, and may even provide a greater biomass. Such findings as these have produced a greater interest in the *nano-plankton*, *micro-plankton* or *ultra-plankton* as this group of organisms is called.

Partly because of the discredit into which phytoplankton taxonomy has fallen, or because it was considered that the necessary taxonomic work had been done, the number of taxonomists sharply decreased so biochemists and others took over the role of the biologists in studying quantitative phytoplanktology. This resulted in the acceptance of measurements of such parameters as chlorophyll, oxygen production, carbon assimilation and phosphate and nitrate content. It could probably have been deduced on biological grounds alone that these chemical parameters would tell a very imperfect and probably a false story. Unfortunately, the biologist issued no warnings and ship cruises were planned and expeditions organized with the main aim of making supposedly quantitative determinations of productivity of seas, oceans and later of estuaries. From these it was hoped to make "guesstimates" of the productivity at each trophic level and thence determine the amount of fish food in the oceans. Such "guesstimates" were to be correlated with calculations made from fishery statistics of available fish stocks. So far we have been unable to accept even the available figures for primary productivity as accurate within one order of magnitude.

Plate II. Paired Van Dorn samplers, open. Note wire clamped to centerpiece and trigger mechanism at top. (Photo by R. Breach.)

Fig.2. Putting a Niskin sampler on the hydrographic wire. This gives an aseptic sample for microbial study.

This was of course inevitable in programs in which the biology of the organisms was continuously ignored. Now we are faced with the necessity of making intensive studies of the biology of all organisms in the trophic web, and determining from these the measurements we should make. It is unfortunate that the recent advances

Fig. 3. Loading a Van Dorn-type sampler on the wire.

in the accuracy and ease of measurement of physical entities should have led biologists and others into the trap of measuring for measuring's sake. Financial baits were much to blame, e.g., justification for budgets of such instrumentalities as the Food and Agriculture Organization of the United Nations, and the Special Committee on Oceanographic Research sponsored by UNESCO.

Physiological studies

Arising from the belief in the efficiency of pure culture studies, which I have already referred to, it has become customary, both in working with the bacteria and with the algae, to isolate the organisms in test tubes and preferably in pure culture. Physiological tests and biochemical studies have been made on such cultures or, since the devotion of biochemists to the Warburg respirometer, on washed cells from such cultures. This has given us a lot of information on specific enzymes under a number of conditions, some more, some less artificial, and on the behavior of many organisms under strictly controlled conditions. It has been shown for example that certain organisms require certain compounds as macro- and micro-nutrients, and has particularly shown the importance of growth factors and antibiotics in marine ecology. What has not been recognized by many workers in this field is that the test tube may or may not closely represent the real behavior of the organisms in their natural environment. ZoBELL (1946) earlier warned us of the effects of adsorption on microbial reactions and microbial growth; cultures are usually far richer in nutrients than natural environments, organisms in such cultures are usually far more concentrated than they are in nature. Thus, information gained by such methods as axenic culture are, as a rule to be taken as guides only, and must always be checked by field observations. The latter have been sadly neglected, probably due to the difficulty of making intelligent observations in natural and complicated environments, and partly to difficulties in interpreting our observations and correlating them accurately with the conditions of the environment.

The study of plant and bacterial extracts such as the pigments, cytochromes, amino-acids and other constituents has been accelerated by technical developments over the last 20 years, such as spectrophotometry, polarography, chromatography, electrophoresis techniques, mass spectrometry, etc. It seems a far cry from the chlorophyll units devised by Harvey for estimation of phytoplankton to the rapid separation and estimation of plant pigments by the spectrophotometer, and from the time-consuming and not-too-sensitive Winkler oxygen method to the mass spectrometer determination of production and consumption of oxygen and other gases. Likewise, advances in the study of morphology have been rapid due to improved techniques of electron microscopy. In some cases, advances have been so rapid that we have not had time to assess the full meaning of certain data or the implications of our measurements, before new methods have appeared.

We are gradually building up a picture of the chemistry and physiology of many of our microorganisms, as well as the knowledge of their life histories, sexual phases and genetics, but progress has been along certain rather popular lines of research rather than on a broad front, and a great deal of work is still required to connect various aspects and thus form a more complete picture.

SIGNIFICANCE OF MARINE MICROBIOLOGY IN OCEANOGRAPHY

In any system, organisms interact with the environment with the result that the environment modifies the organism to some extent and the organism modifies the environment. Marine microbes are of the greatest importance in the oceans from their numbers and biomass and from their activity in a number of chemical and physical processes. As has been said, apart from the seaweed beds along the coasts of continents and islands and the Sargasso Sea, the plants of the ocean are almost entirely microscopic. Even in the estuaries and intertidal zones, microbes are extremely important, even if only for their rapid rate of turnover of nutrients. In addition to the plants, we have the microbial heterotrophs and phagotrophs which belong to the second or third trophic levels.

Microbes and the oceans (Fig.1)

The most important role of the microorganisms in the oceans is the reception and conversion of solar energy into biological energy; this energy, collected by the plant process of photosynthesis is available for further biological use and some of it is ultimately released to the system as heat or light. Light, heat and radioactive energy are the three great external sources of energy which make up for losses through entropy at various energy levels, in this earth of ours. While much of the energy collected by photosynthesis passes through various trophic levels, and some may remain indefinitely in living tissues, the rest is gradually converted to simpler substances, yielding energy at each step until it is discarded from the animal or plant as particulate or dissolved organic matter. There are many estimates of the quantity of particulate organic matter in the oceans; some authors believe it is negligible but most consider that it is at least of the same order of magnitude as the phytoplankton and possibly one or two orders higher. It is likely to be more stable than the living microorganisms and to consist largely of refractory matter such as chitin, cellulose, degraded plant pigments, or agar. It represents therefore stored or potential rather than kinetic energy, and will not release energy at the rate that rapidly-reproducing phytoplankton will. It is doubtful however whether much of it remains in existence long enough to represent more than transient storage, except for some refractory materials such as degenerated plant pigments.

Dissolved organic matter produced largely by microorganisms is found in all types of water at all depths. It is used as food by heterotrophic bacteria, flagellates, diatoms and other organisms which can live a saprobic existence. PÜTTER (1907) believed that it served an important purpose as food for many of the zooplankton animals, but KROGH (1931) believed he had completely disproved Pütter's theory. However, latest works show that many species belonging to a number of orders can directly utilize a large amount of dissolved organic matter, so that Pütter may have been right to a large extent, though possibly from the wrong motives. Dissolved organic matter then is an important component of water at all depths, and its constituents are available to add to the inorganic content when broken down by organisms with suitable enzyme systems. The implication of this is that such inorganic components can be found in situ instead of being derived by turbulence or diffusion from other waters, and we no longer have to suppose an external source for bodies of water with a high organic content.

One method of estimating fertility of water has been the estimation of nitrate therein, on the assumption that this was the main source of nitrogen used by the phytoplankton. It is now known that many of the organisms use ammonia or organic nitrogen sources and more recently that a number of them can fix nitrogen. Nitrate content of the water probably represents the absence of organisms which can use oxidized sources of nitrogen, rather than fertility. The fixation of nitrogen by phytoplankton organisms, especially by those from large "red tides", may have great significance in oceanography. Such organisms, occurring at the surface, will produce a nitrogen gradient from air to water and consequent solution of atmospheric nitrogen as the plants remove it from the water. We do not know the significance of nitrogen fixation at various levels in the oceans, though we do know that potential nitrogen-fixing microorganisms are widely distributed therein.

The phosphate content of sea water is often used to define water masses which have similar conservative properties. Phosphate is used, of course, by the phytoplankton and has been shown by a number of authors to vary inversely as the phytoplankton population. However, it is true that waters which are uniformly low in phosphorus and have similar conservative properties (salinity, temperature) may be regarded as belonging to the same water mass, and the same applies to waters that have a uniformly high phosphorus content. Further, a uniform change in phosphorus content may indicate a uniform water mass in which there is a uniform change in productivity, i.e., the organisms are using up or releasing phosphorus at a constant rate.

It is usually found that such changes are accompanied by changes in the oxygen content of the water, due of course to the fact that phosphorus assimilation or dissimilation is accompanied by photosynthetic or respiratory activity. Oxygen can be used to detect biological activity in intermediate and bottom water as well as in the photic zone. D. J. Rochford (personal communication, 1963) found a gradually diminishing oxygen content and increasing inorganic phosphate in a current running southwest from Fiji towards New Zealand and considered it as evidence that the same biological community was involved. Microbiological studies confirmed his supposition.

Salinity and temperature as factors

Microorganisms vary in their tolerance to salinity and temperature. The relation to salinity is not as a rule osmotic, but related to cation ratios in the water. Temperature relations tend to be governed by rate of change rather than actual temperature of the water, though most organisms appear to have a definite maximum and minimum temperature for continued existence. These facts can be made use of by considering suitable organisms as *indicators* of the water mass in which they occur. Some species are confined to narrow limits of salinity *(stenohaline)* or temperature *(stenothermal)* and others can tolerate wide ranges *(euryhaline* and *eurythermal)*. Organisms which can tolerate high salinity are known as *halophils*, those with low temperature maxima are called *psychrophils* (0–15 °C, maximum around 20 °C), with the usual temperature range (about 15–37 °C) *mesophils*, and from 40–60 °C in the vegetative stage *thermophils*. There is some dispute about these figures, but the ranges are those generally agreed upon at Princeton in January, 1966. In marine environments we have little to do with halophils or thermophils since sea water has a salinity around 35.5‰ and only in comparatively shallow water does the temperature rise above 30 °C. In the Arctic and Antarctic Oceans the temperature drops below 0 °C, and even in tropical waters does not often exceed 15 °C below the *thermocline*. A *thermocline* is a temperature (and usually a salinity) boundary between two water masses. Thus, many of the organisms found in the colder waters are within the range we have defined as psychrophilic.

I have found (WOOD, 1964) that Antarctic and sub-Antarctic protoplankton organisms have a circumpolar distribution and extend towards the equator to the vicinity of the sub-tropical convergence, thus fulfilling the requirements for psychrophily. Even in the Antarctic bottom water, Antarctic species of diatoms have been identified when this water is forced to the surface by upwelling. Thus such species may characterise a water mass even when it has moved thousands of miles from its source. Tropical species occur from the tropics towards the sub-tropical convergence, the more stenothermal ones disappearing first, as the waters move away from the equator. The oceanographer can thus use these indicator species to confirm his chemical and physical data in plotting the course of ocean currents.

From the summary of information which I have given, it can be seen that microbes can be of great importance in defining and in altering the characteristics of ocean water. Later, we shall discuss the effect of the oceanic environment on the organisms.

Microbes and oceanic sediments (Fig.4)

ZoBELL (1952) was the first to show that microorganisms could and do exist in the deepest ocean sediments. He found most of the bacterial

Fig.4. Bringing in a gravity corer.

transformations which we are accustomed to finding in terrestrial environments, and isolated aerobic and anaerobic heterotrophs or saprotrophs, sulfate-reducers, methane bacteria, *Hydrogenomonas* and bacteria important in the nitrogen cycle. Strangely enough, he did not find sulfur-oxidizing bacteria nor have I succeeded in doing so. In the shallower sediments of the California Basin, RITTENBERG et al. (1955) have also recorded the same bacterial niche. It would seem from their work, which has been more detailed and quantitative, that the bacteria of the sediments control the equilibrium between the bottom and the water above. Thus, bacteria in sediments restore to the water most of the nutrients that sink to the bottom. The rate of restoration depends on the rate of sedimentation. In oceanic sediments it would seem that all but the most refractory organic materials are decomposed, for example, in the red clays which form about 40% of the ocean bottom. Only where a large occurrence of living organic material is suddenly killed and sinks to the bottom do we get large concentrations of organic material remaining in the sediments. BRONGERSMA SANDERS (1948) stated her belief that such deposits are the precursors of petroleum formation. They are usually associated with deoxygenation caused by and causing the toxic killing of fish and other animals in shallower waters of the continental shelf as in the Walvis Bay region off the west coast of Africa, or the west coast of Florida and the Gulf of Mexico. It is interesting to record that the world's largest petroleum deposits are found in areas adjacent to those where there are periodic fish kills associated with what are known as "red tides". These red tides are composed of millions of marine microbes, the color being due to carotenoid pigments.

Microbial oozes

The origin of large deposits of siliceous and calcareous oozes will be discussed in detail in the chapter on the activity of microbes in geology. Meantime, we can point out that the skeletons of minute organisms form vast beds of ooze which later consolidate into limestone, flints and cherts, and occur throughout the geological ages. I have studied a very large number of plankton catches from many parts of the world, but I have never seen organisms such as the Radiolaria and Foraminifera in quantities which would account for the vast beds of fossil tests that we find in our sedimentary rocks. The important question arises; do these deposits represent conditions which differ from those of our times? I have not seen any figures which would show the rate of precipitation of silica represented by such deposits, or relate it to the present silica content of the oceans and the rate of contribution of dissolved and particulate silica from the land. This question of silica balance in the ocean is important to those organisms which secrete silica in their skeletons such as the silicoflagellates and the diatoms. DEFLANDRE (1952a) believes that the former have definitely declined in importance, but the diatoms still represent an important part of the plankton in cold waters and close to shore in warmer waters.

Calcium carbonate precipitation

Calcium carbonate equilibria in the oceans and sediments have a particular importance in shallow tropical waters. These equilibria are associated with photosynthesis and respiration of plants including the calcareous red and green algae, coccolithophores, and with denitrification and chemical secretion in the bacteria and Foraminifera. In the ocean waters, the organisms are not concentrated enough to overcome the buffering of sea water, but in shallow waters, the limit of precipitation of calcium carbonate is reached in the vicinity of pH 9.4 and we get a precipitation and re-solution of carbonate at the surface of the sediments. DREW (1914) believed that bacteria were a major source of calcium carbonate precipitation in tropical waters, and this was strenuously denied by LIPMAN (1924) and the question left open by BAVANDAMM (1931). The coccolithophores are oceanic so their activity in sediment formation is confined to the precipitation of their calcareous coccoliths after the death of the organisms. The red coralline algae, calcareous greens such as *Halimeda*, *Penecillus* and more especially the blue-green algae or Cyanophyceae are important in the formation of calcareous sediments in shallow tropical waters. From the physico-chemical point of view, precipitation in a semi-colloidal state may well result in co-precipitation of other inorganic nutrients, and could well account for the lack of phytoplankton in the Florida Everglades (fresh water) and in the Straits of Florida where the incipient Gulf Stream flows through a 40-mile channel with a maximum depth of about 800 m, from the Yucatan Channel and Old Bahama Channel north to the Abacos. This hypothesis is currently being tested. If true, it means that currents which have their origin in shallow tropical waters will have to regain their fertility through upwelling or merging of nutrient-rich waters. At the same time, the calcareous sediments are provided with a source of nutrients, including particulate, adsorbed and adsorbing organic matter which is available for the sedentary animals of the reef and the plants which accompany them.

Mention must be made here of zooxanthellae, which are associated with the corals and other animal groups, especially in shallow calcareous areas. Zooxanthellae are flagellates living in symbiosis with animals to their mutual advantage. They will be discussed in a separate section; they are necessary to coral reef formation. Their rate of photosynthesis is probably sufficient to raise the pH and thus assist the coral polyps in forming their calcareous skeletons.

Microbes in the estuaries (Fig.5)

In the estuarine environment, the relations between organisms and the environment are more complicated than in the environments we have been discussing, partly because the spatial relations between water and sediment are so much closer and partly because the environment is affected by terrestrial as well as oceanic factors. Thus the organisms are far more tolerant of change in physical and chemical factors than oceanic organisms. BAAS BECKING and WOOD (1955) believe that the microbes of the sediments, particularly those concerned with the sulfur cycle and photosynthesis, control the estuarine environment. Marine plants cease photosynthesis at a pH of about 9.4 because they require carbon dioxide or bicarbonate and these are virtually absent at that pH in the presence of the excess of calcium ions which exists in sea water. At night, respiration reverses the carbon dioxide–bicarbonate–carbonate equilibria and reduces the pH. The change in pH affects the solubility of phosphates as well as many other chemical equilibria in the water, so the chemical and biological changes resulting therefrom will be controlled by the extent of the

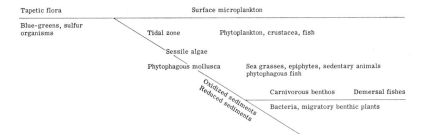

Fig.5. Distribution of microbes in estuaries and their relation to the food web.

pH change, i.e., the activity of the photosynthetic plants, especially the microorganisms.

Microbes in estuarine sediments

In the sediments, we have photosynthetic activity at the surface largely due to micro-algae such as the blue-greens and the flagellates, though in certain areas such as Barnstable Flats in Massachusetts and the *Spartina* Flats of Sapelo and other islands off the Georgia coast, diatoms may be important in photosynthesis, especially between tides in the intertidal zone. Also at the surface we find the sulfur oxidizing bacteria of the sulfur cycle such as the Thiobacilli and the purple and green sulfur bacteria, and below these are the sulfate-reducing bacteria. BAAS BECKING and WOOD (1955) showed graphically the effect of these organisms of the sulfur cycle on the oxidation–reduction potential of the estuarine system. There is sufficient sulfate in sea water to allow for an extensive reduction, and this occurs, provided that there is sufficient saprotrophic digestion of organic matter to reduce the redox potential of the seawater system (pH about 8.3) to about $+100$ mV, after which sulfate reduction or extensive anaerobic digestion can further reduce the environment to about -300 mV. This low potential eliminates many organisms but allows the growth of others and thus modifies the reactions and rates occurring in the sediments. Where sulfate reduction is high, phosphate content of the sediment will be low owing to the release of phosphoric acid from phosphates by hydrogen sulfide and the consequent precipitation of iron sulfides. It is probable too that the oxidation–reduction potential *(redox* or *Eh)* will affect the adsorption of organic matter on particles of montmorillonite and also the kind of organic matter adsorbed. It is certain that muds with a low Eh and high sulfide content are more thixotropic than those with a high Eh and low sulfide content. Both photosynthesis and sulfide oxidation raise the Eh of sediments and the water above them, so that it is usual for the surface of the sediments to be oxidized and the water may have an Eh up to $+650$ mV, though it is more usually around $+450$ mV. The most significant characteristic of biological phenomena in estuaries is the potential rate of change. The maximum rate is reached only in parts of an estuary and may never be reached anywhere in estuaries of a different character. One has only to cite

the possibility of a pH change of over 5 pH units in 12 h, a change
in redox potential of water from +450 to −250 mV in a matter of
days or one from supersaturation with oxygen to complete deoxygenation in a similar period to show how organisms (mainly microorganisms) can alter the environment for chemical and physical
reactions.

SIGNIFICANCE OF MARINE MICROBIOLOGY IN MARINE BIOLOGY

As, in the oceans, the micro-algae take the place in the food web of
trees, grass and other crops in terrestrial environments, their role
is that of food for the phytophagous animals, particularly the copepods, those small crustacea which in turn serve as food for so many
marine animals. The quantitative information we have regarding
the daily or annual consumption of phytoplankton by animals in the
oceans is sparse and unreliable, as we know little concerning the
factors involved. True, some estimates of the daily consumption of
diatoms and flagellates by copepods have been made by CLARKE and
GELLIS (1935), MARSHALL and ORR (1955a,b) and others, but these
have not been made in the natural environment and merely designate
trends; in fact, some authors believe that the copepods ingest the
microbes irrespective of their digestion rate, and others that they
are selective. My own observations, admittedly meager, suggest that
feeding is selective to the extent that, for example, *Coscinodiscus* is
preferred as food to the spiny *Rhizosolenia*, that the feeding rate
depends on the intensity of the deep scattering layer and its mobility.
In areas such as the southern Tasman Sea and the Tongue of the
Ocean, where the deep scattering layer can scarcely be defined, the
nocturnal minimum of phytoplankton is about half the number
found at the daily maximum. In the Benguela and Guinea Currents,
where the deep scattering layer is intense and migrates to the surface
in waves just about dusk (Fig.6), there is a sudden drop in phytoplankton numbers following this migration to about $^1/_{10}$th the daily
maximum if the dominant forms are coccolithophores (probably a
matter of size) and about $^1/_3$–$^1/_5$ if they are diatoms. The minimum
appears to be reached rather rapidly, and the rate of feeding must
therefore fall off to zero. This may be due to satiation of the animals,
or to the search for food being uneconomical for them. In all studies

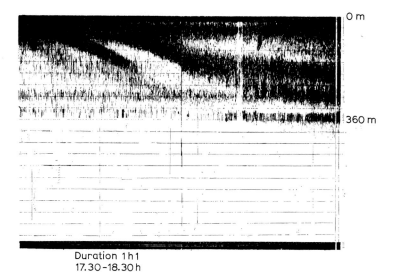

Duration 1 h 1
17.30 –18.30 h

Fig.6. Vertical movement of the deep scattering layer in the Gulf of Guinea.

made in the Pacific and Atlantic Oceans, the plants have succeeded in replenishing the population by the next afternoon, not necessarily with the same species. Thus, selective grazing may be a cause of the succession of phytoplankton species.

Phytoplankton blooms

There are times of course, when plant reproduction exceeds the grazing rate, and we then get blooms of phytoplankton which, in extreme cases of rapid reproduction, may result in "red tides", those gigantic blooms in which the milliards of microorganisms actually color the water with their living cells. These red tides seem to be inimical to fish and other organisms, due to active toxins as with *Gymnodinium brevis* and *G. splendens*, or to inhibitory substances such as are apparently produced by *Trichodesmium*, *Goniaulax polygramma*, *Prorocentrum micans* (GRINDLEY and TAYLOR, 1964) and *Rhizosolenia*. We have no definite evidence of these inhibitory substances from the second group of microorganisms, but copepods and fish avoid these blooms, feeding around the edges, presumably on the Protozoa

Fig.7. Hardy plankton sampler. This sampler can be towed from a ship at speeds up to 15 knots, and, using a fine-mesh screen in the barrel, can be used for qualitative samples from merchant ships and ships in rapid transit.

(including flagellates) which apparently live on the dying and dead cells of the plants. On the other hand, it may be that the reduction of oxygen tension owing to nocturnal respiration of the algae may discourage the copepods and fish from the red tides. This is an important part of the oceanic food web which has been little studied. The Animal Exclusion hypothesis of HARDY (1935) maintained that plankton blooms and animal swarms were mutually exclusive. HARVEY (1934) considered that the lack of coincidence between phytoplankton and zooplankton blooms was due to grazing of the plants by the animals. The evidence from *Trichodesmium* and *Gymnodinium* blooms is in accordance with Hardy's hypothesis; my own evidence from tropical waters conforms with the grazing theory of Harvey. I would guess that where moderate abundance of edible plants occur, grazing controls the population of phytoplankton, where abundance of phytoplankton is greater, to the extent of producing red tides, the animals are excluded by toxic or deterrent substances. This is supported by the verbal statement made to me by the late Dr. Baas Becking that the milkfish *Chanos chanos* feeds on *Oscillatoria* when this alga is present in small quantities and is young, but avoids it when it is abundant.

In our studies of marine productivity, we have assumed for no valid reason that the relations between the protoplankton and such animals as the copepods was purely one between photosynthetic organisms and crustaceans. In fact, non-photosynthetic microorganisms are frequently an order of magnitude more numerous than the photosynthetic ones, and are rarely of lesser importance. These include bacteria, colorless flagellates and tintinnids (ciliates), and are almost certainly ingested along with the true phytoplankton by members of what is usually regarded as the second trophic level, but which, because the colorless Protozoa and the bacteria are phytophagous or heterotrophic, is in this case, the third trophic level. Because this group of microorganisms can and does ingest particulate, though not necessarily living, organic matter or can assimilate dissolved organic matter, it represents a large proportion of the primary material. By this I mean that, when the plants die, their protoplasm disintegrates into particulate or dissolves into assimilable organic matter and that these as well as the living plants are used by the colorless protoplankton. JOHANNES (1964a) believes that it is at this level and by protoplankton, rather than at subsequent levels and by bacteria, that nutrients are released into the sea water.

Because of the intensity of grazing in the first 450 m or so of the oceans, it is doubtful whether any appreciable part of the protoplankton sinks below this depth. There exists however, down to 5,000 m and probably to the greatest depths, an eco-system consisting of protoplankton (including chlorophyll-containing microorganisms) and crustaceans and other forms; this ecosystem would appear to be distinct from that extending from the photic zone to the bottom of the deep scattering layer.

CHAPTER II

MARINE MICROORGANISMS

(bacteria and fungi)

This chapter will be devoted to consideration of the taxonomy and nutrition of the bacteria and fungi which are most widely distributed in marine environments. There is often considerable difficulty in defining the difference between marine and nonmarine microorganisms as they frequently have the same morphology, and many of them, the same enzyme systems. A big difficulty also is that there are insufficient morphological characters for defining a large number of species, their genetics are insufficiently known and there is often considerable overlapping of characters. In my book on *Marine Microbial Ecology* (WOOD, 1965), I have dealt with the species concept as applied to the bacteria, diatoms and dinoflagellates. *Bergey's Manual of Determinative Bacteriology* (BREED et al., 1961) lists well over a thousand species of bacteria, and much of the work that has been done has been very superficial and based on preconceptions. The diatoms are described from their skeletons *(tests* or *frustules)* as we have stated, and once again, no attempt was made to evaluate the genetic value of the criteria adopted. It is perhaps a pity that the Linnean species concept has been transferred to these unicellular organisms and that in consequence type specimens are required for the bacteria and non-planktonic diatoms. Types are of necessity rigid and any deviation from the type is far too often regarded as a new species, or even a new genus without any attempt to consider possible degrees of variation.

In the case of the bacteria, type cultures are kept at a number of centers such as the national collections of type cultures in the United States and Great Britain. I have found repeatedly that such cultures, though derived from a single cell, can and do vary in morphology and in biochemical characteristics after being kept on artificial media for a length of time. A difficulty is that some strains of the same organism, e.g., *Desulfovibrio* vary much more than others with regard both to morphology and enzyme reactions, so that it is often impossible to demarcate a norm. A thermophilic strain of sulfur bacteria may contain a few variants which are mesophilic in character and these can be selected to give a mesophilic strain. The mesophilic strain may breed true, or vary again, so we cannot use this character to define a species. The same applies to salinity tolerance in the case of *Desulfovibrio* and to certain slow-lactose fermenting coliform bacteria. Some strains of these will take weeks to form acid and a small bubble of gas, and others will revert, under continued sub-culture, to *Escherichia coli* or to *Alkaligenes* types according to the selective methods used. The hydrolysis of carbohydrates is another selective property. Some strains will hydrolyse agar even if other carbon sources are supplied, others will do so actively only if no other source is present, while still others hydrolyse agar only very slowly. The majority of strains isolated from a single environment are intermediate in activity but would not be classified as *Agarbacterium* if grown on nutrient agar. Further, some strains lose the property of agar digestion on prolonged subculture. This, in my opinion, makes the use of such generic names erroneous and misleading and it is high time they were dropped. For the same reason, *Xanthomonas*, *Cellulomonas*, *Alginomonas*, *Microbacterium*, *Gaffkya*, *Arthrobacter* and probably *Streptomyces* are undesirable, if one requires a pragmatic classification.

The bacteria

The primary criterion in the taxonomy of the bacteria is morphology: firstly according to their shape, and next according to the number and position of the flagella, if these are present.

The cocci

The spherical forms are known as cocci and these are divided up in several ways according to different classifications. The older classifications contained the genera *Micrococcus* and *Sarcina* of interest to marine microbiologists; these were separated according to the association of the cells: most cocci are non-motile, but some marine forms are flagellate, and one motile species also forms heat-resistant spores. Some of the rod forms of bacteria which are regarded as a development from the coccoid form tend to revert, e.g., many marine Corynebacteria.

Modern taxonomists tend to the opinion that the mode of division in two planes is not sufficiently constant a character to separate the genus *Sarcina* from the micrococci and streptococci. BAIRD-PARKER (1965) has reduced the large number of species of micrococci to only eight groups, which may be regarded as species, independently of their origin.

Baird-Parker (1965) recorded two out of four of his *Staphylococcus* groups from marine sources, as well as all eight of his *Micrococcus* and *Sarcina* groups. He separates *Micrococcus* from *Staphylococcus* because the latter ferments glucose anaerobically while the former does not.

The difficulty of classifying the Micrococcaceae is emphasized by the work of SILVESTRI and HILL (1965), who used "taxometric" methods (i.e., methods based on computer programming of the results of chemical tests). They found that the DNA base composition thus analysed divides the *Staph. aureus–saprophyticus–lactis* sub-group *(Staphylococcus)*, from the *S. roseus–afermentans* sub-group. However, they hasten to point out that "divisions of such systems can only be achieved by considering many phenic characters", and propose certain principles: (*1*) Phena or groups based on overall similarity which satisfy criteria for stability, can be confirmed by use of experimental criteria independent of taxometric criteria. (*2*) Conversely, when members of a monothetic group (i.e., a group defined by the obligatory possession of one or a few characters) show heterogeneity in DNA base composition, it may be expected that the group would become split in taxometric analysis, yielding sub-groups which coincide with the base ratios. They suggest that only stable and homogeneous groups be accepted as autonomous taxonomic entities, thus greatly simplifying bacterial taxonomy and removing many of the thousands of "species". The authors suggest too that the staphylococci as a group are phylogenetically heterogeneous and the catalase positivity and coccoid shape and gram reaction are due to evolutionary convergence. During my own studies of marine micrococci and corynebacteria I found evidence of such convergence, one group being apparently true micrococci and the other having strong affinity with the corynebacteria.

Rod forms

The rod-shaped bacteria may be divided according to whether they form heat-resistant spores. Those which do so are called *Bacillus* if they are aerobic or facultatively aerobic in nutrition, and *Clostridium* if they are obligate anaerobes. The non-sporing rods are primarily divided according to whether they do or do not hold the gram-stain. The gram-negative rods, especially those with polar flagella (Pseudomonadaceae) predominate in aqueous environments. It is usual to divide these further on the form of the rods, straight rods being called *Pseudomonas*, curved rods *Vibrio* and spiral rods *Spirillum*. These morphological divisions have some biochemical correlations, many of the straight rods producing a greenish fluorescent water-soluble pigment, many curved ones being pathogenic, but these differences are not absolute and there are many intergrades. Marine pseudomonads (Fig.8) are typically pleomorphic in the natural environment, so much so that they fit the morphology of

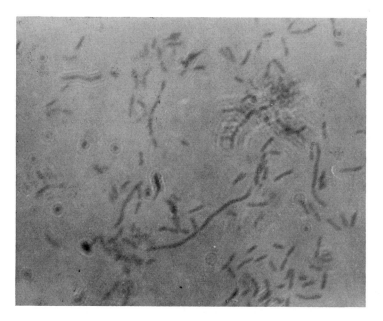

Fig.8. The varied morphology of a marine bacterium *(Pseudomonas)*. (Photo by J. Buck.)

the highly pleomorphic genus *Mycoplana* described by GRAY and THORNTON (1928). Unfortunately, the bacterial taxonomists do not seem to have made up their minds as to whether morphological, biochemical or physiological characters should be used in consecutive order, so the criteria for identification are somewhat confused. It is probably futile to criticize taxonomists especially when they are using computers for greater efficiency, but much modern bacterial taxonomy does not take into consideration variability of strains and the spectrum of microbial adaptability to changes in the habitat.

INGRAM and SHEWAN (1960) give a historical discussion of the non-pathogenic non-sporing gram-negative bacteria, and cite the different arrangement of these difficult organisms in different classifications, and the confusion that has arisen therefrom. They point out the shortcomings of the existing classifications and the reasons for bandying so many strains about among the recognized genera and species. The conclusions of these authors are very interesting:

"In all this, little has been said about the separation of species, because the more experienced workers in this field have for the present ceased trying to identify them. It seems certain that most of the *Pseudomonas* and *Achromobacter* species described in the current lists of Bergey or Brisou are illusory; in this connection, one may recall the recent monograph by Rhodes in which he suggested that the species of *Pseudomonas* (exclusive of plant pathogens) should be reduced to three, not very readily separable. With *Achromobacter* species the situation is even worse, for these have been little investigated, and the type species cannot be found.

Overshadowing all this are the difficulties in defining even genera, which spring from misgivings about the validity of characters like flagellation and pigmentation, long thought to be stable and fundamental. It is a situation ripe for agnostic application of the Adansonian techniques of Sneath; and it appears that, in this group of bacteria especially, it may be necessary to relinquish the old conception of a genus as a distinct systematic unit characterized by basic homogeneity in morphology and metabolism."

HOBBS et al. (1964) endeavoured to compare *Pseudomonas, Achromobacter, Vibrio* and *Aeromonas* by serological tests, but found that such tests cut across the accepted taxonomic divisions. SHEWAN et al. (1960a,b) studied further the non-sporing gram-negative rods from marine environments and produced a scheme for determining these organisms with some measure of reproducibility, and which seems sufficiently definite to be used for ecological studies of marine bacteria. COLWELL et al. (1965) state that their Adansonian computer species-clusters agree well with the DNA base composition analyses, and it will be interesting to compare their final determinations with those which Shewan and his school have devised from ecological considerations.

The Bergey classification partially separates autotrophic bacteria from the heterotrophs; the motile pseudomonads of the sulfur cycle have generic names such as *Thiobacillus*, *Desulfovibrio*, and hydrogen users are called *Hydrogenomonas*, methane users *Methanomonas* and so on.

Gram-positive non-sporers are regarded as being higher in the developmental scale than the gram-negative species because they tend to form primitive mycelia, and one can follow an apparently phylogenetic development in complexity of the mycelium from *Corynebacterium*, through *Mycobacterium*, *Nocardia*, to *Actinomyces*. Some of these forms have been found in marine environments.

The filament-forming *Beggiatoa*, *Thiotrix*, *Leptothrix*, etc., are usually regarded as colorless Myxophyceae (Cyanophyceae) (e.g., PRINGSHEIM, 1949, p.91), but PRESCOTT (1964) believes that the Cyanophyceae should on the evidence produced by electron microscope studies be included in the Schizophyceae. The fact that chlorophyll in the Cyanophyceae is in bodies in the lamellae, at least in the Oscillatoriaceae (HALL and CLAUS, 1962), suggests a relationship with the higher algae, as does the presence of ellipsoid formed bodies within the centroplasm, and these bodies may, according to Hall and Claus, represent nuclear material.

We shall now discuss briefly the genera of bacteria which are commonest in marine environments. The list of families and genera given here does not represent all those which have been recorded, but should be sufficient to satisfy the immediate needs of the marine ecologist. Because of the confused taxonomy, the marine biochemist and physiologist are usually content to study given reactions, e.g., calcium precipitation, without trying to identify the organisms responsible; this is the logical approach, as the results are independent of bacterial taxonomy or degrees of microbial variation.

Classification of marine forms

In the marine environment we do not find all the families of bacteria that are listed in *Bergey's Manual of Determinative Bacteriology*, so only those which do or might be expected to occur will be listed here:

I. Pseudomonadales

A. Autotrophic

(*1*) Thiorhodaceae (purple sulfur bacteria). Anaerobes using hydrogen sulfide as hydrogen donor for reduction of carbon dioxide; contain bacterial chlorophyll and sulfur granules.

Commonest genus *Chromatium*.

(*2*) Athiorhodaceae (purple non-sulfur bacteria). Anaerobic, facultative often heterotrophic.

Commonest genus *Rhodospirillum*.

(*3*) Chlorobacteriaceae (green sulfur bacteria). Anaerobes using hydrogen sulfide as hydrogen donor; contain chloroviridin, with external sulfur granules.

Commonest genus *Chlorobium*.

(*4*) Nitrobacteriaceae. Variable morphology, motile or non-motile, gram-negative, utilize oxidation of nitrogen compounds as energy source. Aerobic. Genera *Nitrosomonas* and *Nitrocystis* oxidize ammonia to nitrite. *Nitrobacter* oxidizes nitrites to nitrates.

(*5*) Methanomonadaceae. These oxidize methane to carbon dioxide, e.g., genus *Methanomonas*, or hydrogen to water, viz. genus *Hydrogenomonas*.

(*6*) Thiobacteriaceae. Pleomorphic gram-negative bacteria, polar flagellate or non-motile; oxidize sulfides or sulfur to sulfate; frequently associated with sulfur granules. The following genera belong to this family:

Thiobacterium: non-motile, rods forming bladder-like masses; estuarine.

Macromonas: polar flagellate; contain calcium carbonate and sulfur granules.

Thiovulum: large (5–20μ), round organisms, flagellate, forming striated bladders with internal sulfur granules; appears to require organic carbon.

Thiobacillus: pleomorphic gram-negative bacteria with polar flagella or non-motile; oxidize sulfides to sulfur and sulfates. *T. thiooxidans* grows at low pH (to – 0.5) normally below pH 4, aerobic. *T. thioparus* does not grow below pH 5, aerobic. *T. denitrificans* utilizes reduction of nitrate to nitrogen as source of energy, and oxidizes sulfides anaerobically.

B. Heterotrophic

(7) Pseudomonadaceae. The commonest bacteria in marine environments, most strains being strongly pleomorphic in the natural environment, less so if at all in old or prolonged culture. Most of the strains found fit morphologically into *Mycoplana* or appear as Spirillae on primary isolation, and later become morphologically *Pseudomonas.* The genus *Alginomonas* is based on a non-specific reaction which can easily be lost by many strains and so cannot be maintained. The genus *Photobacterium* should also be discarded as the property of bioluminescence is frequently lost on sub-culture, and presumably also under natural conditions. *Azotomonas* is designated from its ability to fix atmospheric nitrogen, presumably due to the presence of a hydrogenase. This is not a generic character, e.g., BAAS BECKING and WOOD (1955) found some strains of *Desulfovibrio* with and some without hydrogenase, and the same difference occurs with *Escherichia coli.*

The following Tables (I and II) taken from SHEWAN et al. (1960a) allow of the separation of the aerobic, heterotrophic gram-negative rods which are found in marine environments. The genera into which they fall fit well with the Bergey classification, and the groups are useful in the study of the microbial flora of fish and fish products.

(8) Caulobacteriaceae. Of these, the iron bacterium *Gallionella* has been recorded from estuarine environments. The cells occur at the end of twisted stalks composed of pectic material impregnated with ferric hydroxide. Many organisms which appear as *Caulobacter* on slides fail to produce stalks in peptone, and it is probable that the failure to culture these stalked bacteria is due to a change in morphology, i.e., *Caulobacter* in culture is ascribed to other genera.

TABLE I

AN OUTLINE OF THE DETERMINATIVE TESTS APPLIED TO CERTAIN GRAM-NEGATIVE ASPOROGENOUS ROD-SHAPED ORGANISMS

Motility	Morphology	Colony appearance*	Penicillin†	Behaviour in Hugh and Leifson's medium‡	Kovacs' oxidase test‡	Growth at 37°	Genus, species or type
−	Short stout rods 0.8 × 1.0–1.5 μ and coccal forms	Grey to greyish-white, slightly opaque	++ or +	Alkaline or oxidative	N.A.	−	Achromobacter Alkaligenes
−	Slender rods, occasionally filamentous	Yellow to orange	−	N.A.	N.A.	−	Flavobacterium
+	Slender rods	Yellow-orange	−	N.A.	N.A.	−	Flavobacterium
+	Slender, straight or curved rods	Translucent, colourless, diffusible fluorescent pigment ±	−	Oxidative	+	or +	Pseudomonas
+	Slender, straight or curved rods	Translucent, colourless, occasionally pigmented	−	Alkaline or no action	+	−	Pseudomonas
+	Slender rods, straight or curved	Translucent, colourless	−	Fermentative, gas abundant	+	+	Aeromonas
+	Slender, straight or curved rods	Translucent, colourless, occasionally yellow pigmented	−	Fermentative with no gas or (very seldom) traces	+	−	Vibrio (marine origin)
+	Straight rods	Translucent, colourless	−	Fermentative, gas abundant	−	+	Paracolon E. coli

* ±, may or may not be present. † Sensitivity to 2.5 i.u.; +, very sensitive; +, sensitive; −, insensitive. ‡ N.A., test not applied.

TABLE II

AN OUTLINE OF THE BEHAVIOUR OF CERTAIN MEMBERS OF THE FAMILY
PSEUDOMONADACEAE, AND OF THE GENUS *Spirillum*, IN CERTAIN DETER-
MINATIVE TESTS

Genus or group	Behaviour in Hugh and Leifson's carbohydrate medium	Sensitivity* to		
		Penicillin	Terramycin	Comp. O/129
Pseudomonas group I, green fluorescent pigment formed	Oxidative, acid only	—	—	—
Pseudomonas group II,† no fluorescent pigment	Oxidative, acid only	—	+	—
Pseudomonas group III,‡ no fluorescent pigment	Alkali formed aerobically	—	+	—
Pseudomonas group IV, no fluorescent pigment	No action aerobically or anaerobically	—	+	—
Aeromonas (Kluyver and Van Niel)	Fermentative, acid with abundant gas	—	+	—
Vibrio	Fermentative, but acid only	—	+	+
"Gut-group" vibrios (Liston) and related luminous types (Spencer)	Fermentative, acid with little gas	—	+	+
Spirillum	No action	+	+	—

* +, sensitive; —, insensitive. Penicillin, 2.5 i.u.; Terramycin, 10 mg.
† *Xanthomonas* spp. give the same reactions. ‡ See text.

(*9*) Spirillaceae. The separation of this family from the Pseudomonadaceae seems to be a taxonomic gimmick, as the morphology of
marine organisms in this group is far too variable to allow one to
distinguish between rods, commas and spirals even in single-cell
strains. The pathogenic members of the genus *Vibrio* seem to be a
well-defined group of organisms and their separation may be justified.

This does not apply to the organisms to be found in marine or even fresh water environments. *Methanobacterium* reduces carbon dioxide to methane and is important in some estuarine habitats. *Desulfovibrio* is to be found in sediments to 10,000 m and occasionally, probably adventitiously, in the water. Cellulose digestion seems inadequate as a generic distinction and this fact should exclude *Cellvibrio* and *Cellfalcicula*.

II. Eubacteriales

(*1*) Azotobacteriaceae. PSHENIN (1963) claims that these occur in the Black Sea in quantity, and mentions that they are found in anaerobic environments, which casts grave doubt on the identity of these organisms. I have not been able to authenticate the occurrence of truly marine *Azotobacter* though a few organisms of the same general morphology have been found in estuaries.

(*2*) Achromobacteriaceae. *Achromobacter* and *Flavobacterium* have been recorded repeatedly from marine sources such as fish and shellfish, but it seems probable that most of these organisms are pseudomonads. *Flavobacterium piscicida* is quite definitely a *Pseudomonas*. Because of the variability of the property of agar digestion, the genus *Agarbacterium* is indefensible. The flagellation of this group as described by ANGST (1929) is not known and they are probably pseudomonads anyway.

(*3*) Enterobacteriaceae. This family is usually regarded as being mainly adventitious in marine environments, but there are records of marine strains of *Escherichia* from India, and this genus is also known from the intestinal tract of warm-blooded mammals such as whales, sea-lions, and seals. *Serratia* is recorded from marine environments by ZOBELL and FELTHAM (1934), but does not appear to be common therein.

(*4*) Micrococcaceae. In this family, *Micrococcus (Staphylococcus)*, *Sarcina* including *Planosarcina* and the doubtful genus *Gaffkya* have been recorded from marine environments. *Methanococcus* occurs in sediments and produces methane from organic materials.

(*5*) Corynebacteriaceae. Members of this family occur in marine environments, particularly in certain estuary sediments and in and on elasmobranch fish. I have ascribed them to *Corynebacterium* doubting whether temperature optima are sufficient grounds for separation of such genera as *Microbacterium* and *Arthrobacter*. In connection with *Arthrobacter*, SIEBURTH (1964b) records an organism which is pleomorphic and gram-negative below 16 °C, but gram-positive above that temperature. He does not state, however, that the strain tested was derived from a single cell, so contamination cannot be entirely ruled out. I have pointed out (WOOD, 1953) that there appear to be affinities between *Mycoplana* and *Corynebacterium* from marine sources, and if Sieburth is correct in his observations, the records of WOOD (1950b) and VENKATARAMAN and SREENIVASAN (1955c) that corynebacteria were found in estuarine environments and elasmobranch fish would be consistent with the failure of other workers to find these organisms in colder waters such as Japan and the North Sea.

(6) Bacillaceae. The genus *Bacillus* is quite frequent in sediments. It is characterised by having either central or terminal spores, being aerobic or facultatively anaerobic, and gram-positive. Many of the marine strains are pigmented, pink and yellow being the commonest. WOOD (1953) described a pink *B. subtilis*-like organism as frequent in some east Australian estuarine sediments.

Clostridium. The genus *Clostridium* is strictly anaerobic, gram-positive with terminal to central spores. The biochemical reactions vary from proteolytic to saccharolytic, and some at least of the species can fix dissolved nitrogen. Catalase is generally absent. *Cl. nigrificans* produces hydrogen sulfide from sulfur-containing organic matter and may be important in reduced environments, though it has not so far been recorded from marine sediments. It was formerly mistaken for *Desulfovibrio* and named *Sporovibrio*. *Cl. botulinum* is toxic and has been found in sediments, and the intestinal tract of some marine vertebrates, although the type occurring in marine environments is not that associated with canned or frozen fish. Recently *Cl. botulinum* type F has been found in marine sediments off the west coast of the United States (ECKLUND and POYSKY, 1965). *Cl. tetani* was also recorded from fish guts by SHEWAN (1938).

III. Actinomycetales

(*1*) Actinomycetaceae. A number of Actinomycetes have been recorded from estuarine sources and some have been found to produce antibiotics. These organisms are aerobic, with non-septate mycelium later becoming septate, breaking up into rods or spheres with sometimes aerial hyphae bearing spores. *Nocardia* resembles a simple Actinomycete but has no aerial hyphae and two species have been recorded from marine sediments in shallow water and from algae. The genus *Streptomyces* does not fragment and conidia occur; it has been recorded from estuarine sediments, e.g., GREIN and MEYERS (1958), DEMNY et al. (1961).

IV. Beggiatoales

(*1*) Beggiatoaceae. These occur in trichomes and resemble colorless members of the Oscillatoriaceae with which they are now homologised. They obtain their energy from oxidation of sulfur or organic matter, seem to require organic matter for nutrition and to be able to do without sulfur. *Beggiatoa* is apparently heterotrophic and partially autotrophic. It also occurs in films very similar to those of *Thiovulum* but these are not streaked like the latter. Like *Thiovulum* also the beggiatoas seem to be gradient organisms in the sense of BAAS BECKING et al. (1956). The genera found in marine habitats are *Beggiatoa* and *Thiothrix* and occasionally *Thiospirillopsis*.

PRINGSHEIM (1964) found he could not distinguish species in *Beggiatoa*. He concluded that some of the longer forms are strictly autotrophic, that halophily is not a species characteristic, and that cell diameter and mode and rate of locomotion are relatively constant for each clone. He found that the one marine strain he used could not grow in fresh water and most of his fresh water strains would not grow in sea water media. Two strains from Florida, one from sewage and one from seaweed were euryhaline. Many of his heterotrophic strains produced sulfur granules, apparently from organic sulfides. Pringsheim stated that *Beggiatoa* grows best when oxygen and hydrogen sulfide are easily available.

(*2*) Vitreoscillaceae. These organisms are motile by gliding, and similar to blue-green algae such as *Oscillatoria*, but without sulfur granules. The doubt as to the necessity for sulfur in *Beggiatoa* makes the validity of this family doubtful. *Leucothrix* is marine and resembles a colorless *Rivularia*.

Achromatiaceae. These are spherical to ovoid organisms which contain sulfur, and at times calcium carbonate granules, and move in a jerky fashion if at all. They are associated with reduced sediments with hydrogen sulfide.

V. Myxobacteriales

(1) Cytophagaceae. These are long, flexible rods which move with a gliding motion. They have occasionally been found in estuarine environments, usually associated with seaweeds; some attack cellulose.

Nutrition of marine bacteria

It will be noticed that, in our consideration of the families and genera of bacteria which we have commonly recorded from the marine world, a large number of families are completely or virtually absent from the sea. The absence of human and plant pathogens is to be expected, but there is a large number of genera which occur in soils and other terrestrial environments which one might expect to find in the sea. One would not expect the symbiotic rhizobia as there are no legumes in marine environments, but the apparent absence of *Azotobacter* despite PSHENIN's (1963) claims is not so easy to explain. The overall processes of chemo-autotrophic, photo-autotrophic and heterotrophic growth are similar in marine and terrestrial forms and for a time Wood and ZoBell disagreed as to whether there were true marine bacteria. ZoBell, working at that time in Californian waters where upwelling is frequent and deep water occurs close inshore, was studying bacteria from a truly oceanic environment, Wood, working close to estuaries on the Australian coast and studying bacteria from the continental shelf with much turbulence and mixing and from fish and other substrates associated with shallow waters, found a bacterial flora which was much more catholic in its requirements. Also, ZoBell's was a cool water flora; Wood's was derived from tropical and sub-tropical water masses with strong shore influences. Thus ZoBell's flora was much less euryhaline than Wood's and this for a time obscured the issue. When Wood studied a more truly marine flora, his findings were closer to those of ZoBell. WIEBE and

Liston (1965) found that of 452 randomly-chosen strains, 99 could grow only in seawater and the growth of all the strains was enhanced in that medium. One may still argue whether the marine flora represents strains or separate species, but this question is largely academic. MacLeod and his colleagues in a series of papers spread over some years have shown that the essential difference is due to the effect of cations rather than the osmotic pressure of the dissolved salts. In the sea, the sodium/potassium ratio is higher than in fresh water and so are monovalent-divalent cations and calcium/magnesium ratios.

Specific requirements of marine strains

MacLeod and his co-workers (1954–1960) have found that the marine bacteria studied by them have a specific requirement for sodium, potassium and magnesium ions, and that calcium and magnesium have sparing or antagonistic effects according to their concentrations. Magnesium is required for endogenous oxidations but not for exogenous, and can be replaced by bivalent manganese to prevent cytolysis. Chloride ion is also required by marine bacteria. Iron was required by one of their test organisms but could not be replaced by nickel or cobalt which were toxic at the levels required. It seems that the truly marine strains differ from terrestrial and fresh water bacteria in the optimal ratios of potassium and sodium, and of magnesium and calcium, as well as the ratio between total monovalent and bivalent cations, and the concentration of chloride ions. The ionic requirements for the carboxylic cycle, ability to utilize amino-acids as sources of nitrogen and carbon, and growth factor requirements for marine strains of bacteria do not appear to differ from those of fresh water bacteria.

In his most recent paper, MacLeod (1965) reviewed his former work and pointed out that he has not found any character which could be used to separate marine bacteria from bacteria found in other environments. To summarise his conclusions: those which grow on complex media as heterotrophs possess a wide range of nutritional requirements, from relatively simple to quite complex, and these requirements are met by the plankton and its residues in the water and the sediments. The marine strains have a characteristic preference for amino-acids as carbon and nitrogen sources, and this though rather more pronounced is not confined to such strains. Again, marine bacteria have an absolute requirement for sodium ion but again this is not unique. Magnesium ion is required in higher concentration by marine than by terrestrial bacteria, though the bivalent cation ratios are again not unique, and many terrestrial bacteria can tolerate higher salt concentrations than marine strains. To sum up, the marine bacteria have no features which would justify ascribing them to separate genera from the terrestrial forms.

Recently, BROWN (1964) has reviewed the relations between bacteria and cations. The following account is compiled from his study. He points out that the ionic composition of bacterial cytoplasm is usually different from that of the extracellular environment, and that this can happen through the selective binding of ions within the cytoplasm or by the existence at the cell surface of a permeability barrier or both; in fact, there is evidence of binding and the permeability barrier does exist. The permeability barrier includes a lipoprotein membrane and possibly a second membrane. The unit membrane consists of two electron-opaque layers separated by an internal transparent layer, the overall dimensions being 15Å. Membranes can consist of 15%–30% lipid, from less than 70%–85% protein and some carbohydrate. The formation of this membrane is probably a physico-chemical process. The ionic composition of solutions on each side of the membrane tends to differ and is controlled by the membrane.

Gram-positive bacteria are bounded by a cytoplasmic lipoprotein membrane and a rigid cell wall mainly composed of a carbohydrate polymer (mucopeptide). The cell envelopes of gram-negative bacteria differ from the gram-positive ones by having a delicate semi-permeable membrane and presumably a more or less rigid permeable cell wall, resembling a lipoprotein membrane, with a lipid content of 20%. According to BROWN (1964) the difference in gram-reaction is in the morphology of the cell envelope, and the percentage of mucopeptide and protein lies between 35% and 84%. Gram-positive bacteria require about ten times as much magnesium as gram-negative ones, and it may well be the sparing activity of calcium that allows gram-negative bacteria to preponderate in marine environments. The gram-positive bacteria are most abundant in media of low ionic strength, and diminish in importance as the salinity increases until they are absent in saturated brines. On the other hand, there is no evidence that the gram-reaction is controlled by the ionic strength of the medium.

Brown states that bacteria with a low salt tolerance have two cell membranes with one polygonal layer about 100 Å across, and pleomorphic changes so characteristic of marine bacteria may be ascribed to efforts at stabilization against rupture by ionic components of the sea. The difference between halophils and non-halophils include absence of muramic acid from halophils, more protein in their cell envelopes, low carbohydrate (3.3–5% against 10–30% for non-halophiles), slightly higher protein (11.5–13.5% nitrogen against 6.3–11.4%), with nucleic acids about the same (15.5–25% against 10–30%).

The intracellular concentration of organic ions varies directly in response to changes in the composition of the environment, modified by the salt requirement or salt tolerance of the organism concerned. All bacteria concentrate potassium ion to many times the concentration in the natural environment, and the accumulation of potassium is greatest in the halophils. With this increase in ionic concentration, there is no evidence of changes in metabolic pathways, though these may be limited at high salt concentrations. The mode of motility may be changed by ionic concentrations; for example, the amoeba *Naegleria gruberi* changes from an amoeboid form to a free-swimming flagellate when the cationic strength of the medium is lowered, and this is because the cell membrane is polarized in opposite directions in the amoeboid and flagellate forms.

There is some evidence that there is interrelation between ionic requirements and temperature, increased ionic requirements being associated with increased temperature optima or resistance. The broad limits of salt tolerance and salt requirements are, according to Brown, genetically stable characters of a bacterium, inherited information being expressed in the amino-acid composition and sequence of proteins. The genetic explanation of halophily in bacteria is related to the more acidic amino-acids in the membrane protein of the halophils. The high potassium requirement is required to activate the intracellular enzymes of halophils, and this ion is accumulated by the organism against a strong concentration gradient. The cell envelope controls the response of bacteria to their ionic environments, acting as a selective barrier to the diffusion of ions. Osmotic phenomena seem to be of minor importance in halophily. It would seem that the more halo-tolerant microorganisms have the greater ability to change the regulatory function of the cell membrane.

Temperature relationships

It seems strange that so very little work has been done in connection with the temperature relationships of marine bacteria. ZoBELL (1946) has pointed out certain thermosensitive bacteria that could not be cultivated above 22 °C, but in point of fact, 90% of the marine oceanic environment is colder than 10 °C. MORITA and HAIGHT (1964) have been studying psychrophilic marine bacteria and found their organism grew between −1 and 20 °C, with an optimum at 15–16 °C, but was killed by heating to 28.8 °C for 6.25 h. The lower temperature apparently has some effect on metabolic pathways, though the net metabolic activity is approximately the same, enzyme reactions having lower optima. If this is generally true, it may well be that marine bacteria existing below the thermocline and in arctic and antarctic waters do not have an appreciably lower metabolic rate than those occurring in warmer waters. Most of the studies on metabolic rates have been carried out at temperatures around 22 °C or with organisms with optima around 25 °C.

Recently, WIEBE and LISTON (1965) found only seven obligate psychrophils among some 452 bacteria isolated from sediments, presumably shallow sediments. SIEBURTH (1965) found a difference in the temperature relations of bacteria in cool-temperate estuarine waters between spring (18–27 °C as optimum) and winter (0–9 ° optimum), the latter representing a psychrophilic flora. It is possible that Wiebe and Liston's results might have been very different had their samples been collected at a different season.

SIEBURTH (1964b) found a *Corynebacterium (Arthrobacter)*, which changed its gram characteristics at different temperatures, being gram-negative and pleomorphic below 16 °C and gram-positive and frequently coccoid above that temperature. This may account for the frequency of Corynebacteria in the warm waters of the Australian region and India, and the absence of gram-positive forms in cold waters. Sieburth found that, at intervals in the vicinity of 8–9 °C, 16–18 °C, 24–27 °C and 32–36 °C, conditions appear to be unfavorable for the growth of certain marine bacteria. DROST-HANSEN (1956) stated that there are certain "kinks" in the temperature dependence of certain properties of liquid water and that these occur near 15, 30, 45 and 60 °C, and there is also a discontinuity 5.3 ° below 15 °C, i.e., at 9.7 °C. Sieburth's discontinuities are at somewhat higher temperatures than Drost-Hansen's, but these may be due to temperature intervals at which Sieburth's studies were made. It is interesting to consider the possibility that certain temperature-dependent changes in the properties of water are reflected in metabolic changes in the microorganisms.

Pressure effects

The effect of pressure on marine bacteria was first studied in some detail by ZoBell and co-workers. ZoBell and Johnson (1949) found that certain terrestrial bacteria were killed at 600 atm pressure and inhibited at 300 atm, but some marine strains grew more rapidly and were more reactive at pressures higher than those of the natural environment of the organisms (p.183). In the case of bacteria isolated from great depths (500–1,000 atm pressure) many strains failed to grow at atmospheric pressure, but they still grew at the pressure from which they were isolated. From this came the concept of barophilic organisms, namely those which require high pressures for active growth, and therefore do not grow at the pressures likely to be met with in the upper waters of the oceans. Since ZoBell's work, and the finding of living bacteria at depths of more than 10,000 m in the ocean abysses, observations have been made on the effect of such pressures on enzyme reactions. It may be generally stated that the reactions under increasing pressure proceed in the direction on which the reactants will occupy the minimal volume. The adaptability to pressure seems to vary with different bacteria. Working at Scripps Institution in 1954, I found that *Desulfovibrio* isolated from the deep abysses by ZoBell reduced sulfates at atmospheric pressure and strains of this organism isolated from the surface produced sulfides at the same rate at a pressure of 500 atm, and there was little retardation at 100 atm (E.J.F. Wood, unpublished).

ZoBell and Morita (1957) and later Morita and his-co-workers have been making a study of the effects of pressure on bacterial enzymes. In *Escherichia coli*, various dehydrogenases were inactivated by pressure (Morita, 1957). Other enzymes such as inorganic phosphatase have their reactivity increased by pressures to 700 atm with rising temperatures.

Growth factors

The necessity for and effect of growth factors has not been studied to any extent in marine bacteria. There is evidence by Burkholder

(1963) and Starr et al. (1957) that certain marine bacteria produce growth-promoting substances and this is the source of much of the vitamin in the oceans reported by Droop (1957a). Burkholder also suggested that the bacteria, in return for these growth factors, obtain many organic nitrogen compounds from the marine algae in exchange.

The bacteria in the oceans are often numerically far below the numbers which could be supported by the available nutrients, and it is probably true that they are limited by the grazing of other organisms including the smaller flagellates.

The fungi

Studies on marine fungi have been almost entirely restricted to estuarine situations, and largely to wood-destroying species. This limits the value of the work which has been accomplished to date. Johnson and Sparrow (1961) have assessed our information, and the following summary is largely derived from their work.

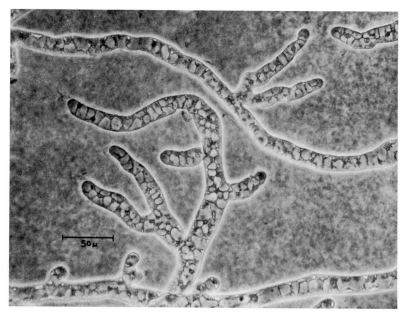

Fig.9. Marine Phycomycetes. (Photo by C. Martin.)

The genus *Labyrinthula* has doubtful affinities, resembling a rhizopod protozoan in some respects and a myxomycete in others. It consists of a series of protoplasmic strands along which move fusiform or spherical bodies. One of these Labyrinthulae was considered to be the cause of the destruction of the beds of *Zostera marina* in northern Europe and America. However, as this organism is to be found in healthy *Zostera* and many other sea grasses and algae, it is doubtful whether it is a primary pathogen.

Among the true fungi, the Phycomycetes and Ascomycetes are most frequently found in marine environments, though some imperfect fungi also occur; one Basidiomycete has been recorded, a smut parasitic on *Ruppia maritima*.

Marine Phycomycetes (Fig.9) may consist of a single cell which includes the reproductive units, one with assimilative rhizoids or an extensive mycelium. The parasitic or saprobic Phycomycetes of the estuaries consist largely of the first two types and include the orders Chytridiales, Hypochytriales, Plasmodiophorales, Saprolegniales, Lagenidiales, Peronosporales and Eccrinales. The mycelial Mucorales are to be found in estuarine sediments and littoral zones may be of terrestrial origin and their extent and function in marine environments is unknown.

The Ascomycetes have a septate thallus and non-motile spores, plus an ascus which consists of a cell with a series of spores formed by a meiotic division and subsequent mitotic divisions, providing nuclei for the spores. The asci are usually found within a pseudoparenchymatous ascocarp, or perithecium, with a terminal pore. Most marine Ascomycetes belong to the perithecate Pyrenomycetes. The taxonomy of this group leave a great deal to be desired, so the reader is referred to Johnson and Sparrow for detailed information.

The Protoascomycetes or Hemiascomycetes include the yeasts which have numerous marine representatives, although it seems the general consensus of opinion that none of the yeasts from marine habitats have definite characteristics which would enable us to define a true marine flora. Records of yeasts in marine habitats are, on the whole, to be regarded with some suspicion because the collectors did not use aseptic samplers. This applies to both American and Russian work with the exception of some recent work by FELL (1965), in which sterile samplers were used. The errors occasioned by the use of non-sterile samplers are shown by WILLINGHAM and BUCK (1965).

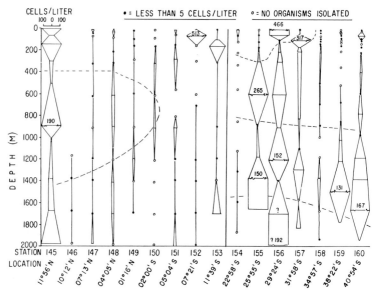

Fig.10. Vertical distribution of yeasts from 12°N to 40°S in the Indian Ocean; note the shore-associated concentrations at station 145, the rarity of yeasts in the tropics and greater abundance in cooler waters.

While Fell found yeasts to be numerically important in Indian Ocean waters at a number of depths (Fig.10), he did not show that they performed an important function in the environment. There is no evidence that the yeasts are essential to the food web of the oceans or are more than adventitious inhabitants thereof, though such a possibility has not been excluded.

Classification of marine fungi

The marine fungi belong to the following major taxa:

I. *Phycomycetes:* Hyphae if present are non-septate except to delimit the spores, if absent the thallus is usually unicellular.

II. *Ascomycetes:* Mycelium, if present, septate; spores (usually eight) produced in an ascus, often within a multicellular *ascocarp*.

III. *Pyrenomycetes.*

IV. *Fungi Imperfecti:* Sexual spores unknown; other characters usually those of Ascomycetes.

Phycomycetes

The following orders can be distinguished:

(*1*) Hypochytriales have uniflagellate motile spores with the flagellum anterior.

(*2*) Chytridiales have uniflagellate motile spores with anterior flagellum.

(*3*) Plasmodiophorales have two flagella of unequal length and a multinucleate plasmodial stage.

(*4*) Saprolegniales have spores with the flagella of equal length, and cleaving within the sporangium.

(*5*) Peronosporales (Pythiaceae) have spores cleaving outside the sporangium and with flagella of equal length; thallus mycelial.

(*6*) Lagenidiales differ from the Pythiaceae in having a rudimentary mycelium.

Of the Hypochytriales, one genus of the family Anisolpidiaceae is recorded from marine sources; the genus *Anisolpidium*.

The Chytridiales are represented in the sea by about twelve genera belonging to five families namely: Chytridiaceae, Olpidiaceae, Cladochytridiaceae, Phlyctidiaceae and Rhizidiaceae.

Among the Plasmodiophorales, two genera *Tetramyxa* and *Plasmodiophora* are recorded from marine environments.

Marine Saprolegniales provide representatives of all the families: Haliphthoraceae, Ectrogellaceae, Saprolegniaceae and Thraustochytriaceae.

The Peronosporales are represented in the marine habitat by the one genus *Pythium*.

The Lagenidiales have all three families represented in the marine environment: Olpidiopsidaceae, Lagenidiaceae and Sirolpidiaceae. In addition there are a number of fungi incertae sedis, which have been described from the marine environment.

Systematic study of the Phycomycetes and their distribution is being made at the Institute of Marine Science, Miami, and collections are being made in sub-tropical waters and in the Antarctic. So far, the evidence suggests a wide distribution of these organisms, and it seems certain that the number of species and genera occurring in oceanic waters will be greatly enlarged in the near future, possibly before this book is issued.

Ascomycetes

Of these, the Protoascomycetes are represented by the yeasts which will be discussed later; the Euascomycetes in the marine environment are represented by the Pyrenomycetes with a porulate ascocarp.

Pyrenomycetes

The families of Pyrenomycetes occurring in marine habitats include the Scolecosporae, of which *Lulworthia* is mainly confined to artificial structures and other genera to mangroves, sea-grasses and macroscopic algae; Amerosporae occurring in seaweeds and artificial environments such as wood; Didymosporae, found mainly in wood, sometimes on mangrove roots and a few species on macroscopic algae. Many species described from marine habitats are also found in the terrestrial environment or in fresh water; Phragmosporae on wood, mangroves or algae; and Dictyosporae which are found on algae such as *Pelvetia* and swamp grasses *(Spartina)*.

Fungi Imperfecti (Deuteromycetes)

Of these, two orders, the Sphaeropsidiales and the Moniliales have marine representatives. The former have conidia produced in pycnidia or cups, the latter on separate conidiophores. The families represented are the Sphaeropsidiaceae with globose pycnidia and the Excipulaceae with rather discoid pycnidia with a very large opening.

The Moniliales provide three families with marine representatives; Tuberculariaceae, Moniliaceae and Dematiaceae.

Most of the Deuteromycetes are associated with wood and therefore possibly of terrestrial origin, though some may have become adapted to marine habitats.

Nutrition of fungi

The fungi are either parasitic or saprobic, i.e., they either invade the tissues of, and cause disease in a host, or obtain their energy from organic compounds derived from a dead or dying organism or from organic detritus. JOHNSON and SPARROW (1961) give evidence that certain fungi, particularly Phycomycetes, are active parasites in algae such as the red algae *Ceramium* and diatoms such as *Licmophora* and *Striatella*, invading the living algae and dying out as soon as the host becomes moribund. Most instances of fungal parasitism of algae lead to the belief that the fungi are facultative rather than truly parasitic, and the degree of severity of the infection depends on the environmental conditions. The Ascomycetes and Imperfect fungi do not appear to parasitize vigorously growing hosts, but do depend for their entry on some debilitating factor. They tend to be saprobic rather than parasitic.

Saprobic fungi

Saprobic fungi require an oxidized environment, and are therefore confined to the water and the surface of the sediments, except when the sediments have a high redox potential. In estuarine waters and sediments, there is ample evidence of the presence of terrestrial types of fungi such as *Penicillium*, *Aspergillus*, *Alternaria*, but there is no evidence of great activity by saprobic fungi, whether terrestrial or marine, in any marine environment. Lignin-digesting fungi (so often referred to by the bastard Latin term *lignicolous*) are known to be common in estuaries, and no doubt are important in digesting lignin of trees, mangrove roots, etc., in such environments. Lignin, however, is not of marine origin, and these fungi and their function must be regarded as a carry-over from terrestrial sources. For some strange reason, there has been no concerted attack on the question of whether true marine fungi actually exist, though MOORE and MEYERS (1959) have already coined a name for them (Thalassio-mycetes). The existence of such fungi could only be established when we know that they require certain cation ratios similar to those required by marine bacteria and phytoplankton. A little work on this has been done by VISHNIAC (1960) and ADAIR and VISHNIAC (1958).

SGUROS and SIMMS (1963, 1964) found that the growth maxima of two fungi which they studied were obtained in salinities from 20–60% of that of sea water. These fungi, an ascomycete *Halo-sphaeria mediosetigera*, and a deuteromycete *Culticalna achaspora*, had also an absolute requirement for sodium ion, this suggesting marine affinity. On the other hand, the only ions that were non-toxic at sea water concentrations were calcium and potassium. These charac-teristics are those of obligately estuarine species, and could not apply to truly marine species. Among the vitamins, *Culticalna* required only thiamine, and *Halosphaeria* both thiamine and biotin. It is probable that such strains of fungi as those studied by Sguros and

Simms are merely estuarine-adapted, and much further work is necessary before we can conclude that these fungi are confined to marine environments.

I. M. WILSON (1960) quotes a number of authors in evidence that most of the chytrid fungi can grow in a wide range of salinities. The situation is apparently similar to that of the benthic diatoms in that the number of species diminishes as we proceed from the land to the deep sea, but those that do persist in the deeper sediments and waters are also characteristic of the shallows and the terrestrial environment. Only some of the parasitic species and maybe a few of the saprobic species are confined to the marine environment, and may be regarded as marine fungi. Other orders of the Phycomycetes including the saprolegnias have species which appear to be confined to marine habitats. These occur as parasites on red and brown algae, diatoms and on marine crustacea.

It seems probable, in the light of the available evidence, that the Phycomycetes are widely distributed in the seas. The only published work on the oceanic Phycomycetes is that of HÖHNK (1959), who found these organisms at all depths to 3,000 m in the North Atlantic. C. MARTIN (personal communication) has found them almost invariably in the samples he has taken in the headwaters of the Gulf Stream, and they are common in the estuaries wherever they have been looked for. I. M. WILSON (1960) discusses the Phycomycetes and recorded parasitic members of this group from a number of algae such as *Ectocarpus*, *Licmophora*, *Bryopsis*, and plankton animals such as the copepod *Calanus finmarchicus*. As this *Calanus* is one of the principal foods of the herring, the Phycomycetes could play an important role in controlling the food web in the cooler waters of the Northern Hemisphere.

KOHLMEYER (1964) lists the number of fungal groups found on various organic substrates in the sea. A basidiomycete has been found on the sea-grass *Ruppia* (brackish-estuarine rather than marine) and another, *Digitatispora marina,* has been described from cellulosic material in the sea. The Ascomycetes have contributed some 39 species belonging to 31 genera, to the flora found on marine algae, 23 species belonging to seventeen genera to that of the sea-grasses, and 66 species to that of wood submerged in the sea; two species are associated with chitin. Among the Fungi Imperfecti, thirteen species have been found in algae, five in the sea-grasses, 24 in wood, etc., and none in animal substances.

I can find no reports of fungi parasitic on plankton microorganisms, but this may be due to lack of observations. A serious attempt to study the mycology of the oceans has yet to be undertaken.

Fungi as parasites

Active parasitism of algae by some Phycomycetes has already been mentioned, and there are all degrees of parasitism from virulent to commensal. A number of parasitic fungi have been associated with sea-grasses, particularly *Plasmodiophora* with *Diplanthera (Halocordyle)*, and here again we have different degrees of pathogenicity. Whether *Ophiobolus* is actively or passively associated with *Labyrinthula* in the wasting disease of *Zostera* has not been solved. *Ichthyosporidium* species have been found in connection with a number of fish and have been ascribed as the cause of certain diseases and a fungus was considered by Smith (1941) and by Galtsoff (1940) to be the cause of a wasting disease in sponges in the Bahamas. Fungi have also been found in a large number of invertebrates in the seas, many of them as more or less active parasites, the most intensively studied being the oyster mortality due to *Dermocystidium marinum* (Mackin et al., 1950).

An interesting group, not thoroughly understood, is the *composite* composed of a fungus and an alga such as *Guignardia* and *Ulva* which appears to be a true, though not universal symbiosis, and *Blodgettia confervoides* which is a universal *Cladophora-Blodgettiomyces* composite which can probably be called a lichen. In some of these associations, there is evidence of a true symbiosis with no appearance of parasitism or invasion of the algal tissues by fungal hyphae. In some cases, the two organisms sporulate simultaneously.

It will be seen that marine mycology is a much neglected field, despite suggestions by a number of authors that studies of marine fungi and their distribution and ecology would amply repay investigation.

Yeasts (Plate III). While a number of terrigenous yeasts are to be found in the estuarine environment, there appears to be a group which may be regarded as endemic in the oceans. These belong to two genera, *Candida* Berkhout and *Cryptococcus* Kützing. The species

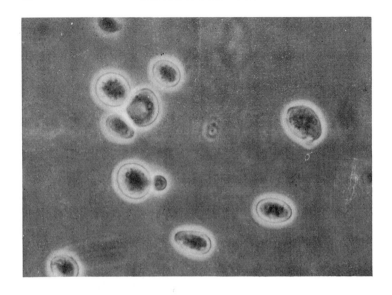

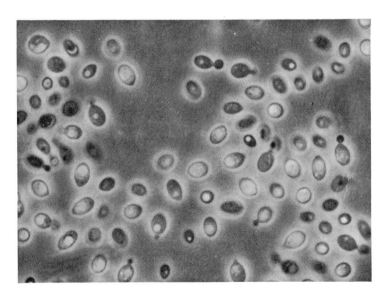

Plate III. Marine yeasts. (Photo by J. Fell.)

associated with estuaries may belong to the genera *Rhodotorula*, *Torulopsis*, *Debaromyces* and *Trichosporon*, while still other genera may be represented by "guest" species.

Quantitative studies made by FELL (1965) give figures up to 500 cells/l from the Indian Ocean and to 5,000 cells/l in the region of the Bahama Banks. Fell has observed that when the number of micro-algal cells increases, the number of yeast cells tends to diminish and he ascribed this tentatively to antibiosis by the algae. The Russian quantitative work, using glass slides is subject to some criticism, though it may give an indication of relative abundance.

Fell's work, largely in the Indian Ocean, shows an interesting distribution. Terrestrial influences raise the yeast content of the water considerably, and increases and decreases of populations can be ascribed to water masses. The equatorial waters of the Indian Ocean were poor in yeasts, but the Antarctic intermediate water showed large yeast populations which might well be an important source of food for the zooplankton populations in this habitat (Fig.10).

TABLE III

CRITERIA FOR DISTINGUISHING ESTUARINE AND MARINE YEASTS
(After FELL, 1965)

Estuarine	*Marine*
Animal-associated	Not animal-associated
Numerous species	Few species
Maximum growth temperature 37–44°C	Maximum growth temperature 26–30°C
No growth at 5°C	Growth at 5°C
Fermentative	Oxidative
Limited utilization of organics	Versatile

FELL (1965) appears to have established that yeasts as a group are halotolerant, and therefore one cannot distinguish marine from terrigenous yeasts on their salt requirements. His criteria are given in Table III.

Fell also reports that some yeast species are indicative of certain water masses.

Viruses. Wood (1965) discussed the reports of viruses in the marine environment. There is little work at present on these, and no indication that they play an important part in the ecology of the oceans. At the same time, the work which has been done is insufficient to prove such a radical difference between terrestrial and oceanic environments. The lack of interest in marine viruses is partly due to the somewhat negative preliminary results. It should be remembered however that the earlier yeast studies were not encouraging.

CHAPTER III

MARINE MICROORGANISMS

(the algae)

The first anomaly we meet in diatom taxonomy is the rigid requirement of type specimens for the pennates and some of the centric
forms but not for other centrics. The reason is that the more delicate
centric species cannot be preserved permanently on slides without
disintegrating, owing to the weakly silicified skeletons. This applies
to many species of *Chaetoceros*, *Rhizosolenia*, to *Guinardia*, *Bacterias-
trum*, etc. The other anomaly is that described by WOOD (1959c) in
which two valves of the same cell belonged to two different *families*,
a genetic impossibility. This occurred in several specimens in the
same sample from the Antarctic and a similar frustule has been
photographed by Mr. John Walsh from material collected on the
research ship "Eltanin" in October 1965. Frustules of this kind have
also been found in other samples from tropical waters, so there must
be some closer relationship between the two genera, namely *Coscinodiscus* and *Asteromphalus*, although the contour of the valves is
quite different. *Coscinodiscus-Actinocyclus* crosses have been seen by
several workers and *Schimperiella* is probably another instance. What
then are we to think of the recognized species of *Coscinodiscus*? We
know that the markings may differ on the two valves of the cells and
R. W. Holmes (personal communication) has found up to four
"species" of *Coscinodiscus* in unialgal culture. Thus it seems that we
must take existing classifications with extreme caution.

In the case of the dinoflagellates, we have been luckier as it is not
possible to preserve these organisms indefinitely. There is also a
limited number of characters available for identification so that the
species of this group still represents a finite number. I believe that
there are too many species of *Prorocentrum* and probably of *Oxytoxum*
and some species of *Ceratium* and *Peridinium* should probably be

abolished. PRAGER (1963) has suggested that *Glenodinium* must be discarded and I fully agree with him. Recent work has shown that some of the coccolithophores are alternate generations of other branches of the Haptophyceae or stages of other species or genera of the coccolithophores, i.e., that the shape of the coccoliths cannot always be used to separate genera (see PARKE and DIXON, 1964).

The taxonomy of the organisms we are considering must therefore be regarded as being in a state of flux, and differences in taxonomy, especially above the genus level, must be regarded as personal opinions. I shall later list two classifications of microscopic algae: one from Great Britain and the other from America. For myself, I prefer whichever is the simpler if I must use families or orders.

The algae: classification

Algal systematics, though somewhat more orderly than those of the bacteria, can still provide almost as many arrangements as there are algologists. The classification is so far mainly subjective and fluid. As an example of this, PRESCOTT (1964) and CHRISTENSEN (1964) in the same publication, list the following phyla or classes: Prescott: Cyanophyta, Chlorophyta, Chrysophyta, Euglenophyta, Pyrrhophyta, Rhodophyta, Phaeophyta, Cryptophyta and Chloromonadophyta; Christensen: Cyanophyceae, Haptophyceae, Craspedophyceae, Baccillariophyceae, Dinophyceae, Raphidophyceae, Euglenophyceae, Rhodophyceae, Phaeophyceae, Xanthophyceae, Cryptophyceae, Loxophyceae, and Prasinophyceae. SILVA (1962) has a classification which differs slightly from these two, and PARKE and DIXON (1964) stay close to the classification of Christensen.

All are agreed that the Cyanophyceae are the most primitive group; they are separated from the photosynthetic bacteria by the presence of chlorophyll *a* and the lamellate chromoplasm. In this group, cell division takes place by an invagination of the cell wall, the invagination of the inner layer meeting to divide the cells.

The Rhodophyceae have an affinity with the Cyanophyceae with regard to pigments, but the position of this group within the algal assemblage is still the subject of much discussion.

PRESCOTT (1964), in the review mentioned above has discussed the areas of research which may be expected to give greatest aid to an improved systematics. They include:

(*1*) Life histories, studies of phylogeny and evolution.

(*2*) Microscopy (light and electron).

(*3*) Physiology including studies of toxins, antibiotics and extra-cellular metabolites.

(*4*) Limnology, hydrology, chemical and physical aspects of ecology.

(*5*) Distribution ecology.

(*6*) Physiology from bioassays and culture studies.

(*7*) Physiology of oxidation wastes, aeration.

(*8*) Economics, including use of algal products.

(*9*) Taxonomy per se.

He makes several interesting observations, pointing out that life histories have shown in some cases that plants which had been placed in separate taxa proved to be stages of the same organism. This has been demonstrated by the recent work of Parke and her colleagues (PARKE et al., 1955, 1956, 1959, 1962; PARKE and DIXON, 1964; PARKE and RAYNS, 1964) on coccolithophores and the Haptophyceae. The electron microscope has been very useful in clearing up a number of taxonomic points in certain cases, for example in emphasizing the relationship between the Chrysophyceae and the coccolithophores from the structure of the plates. Another example is the suggestion of a relationship between *Oxyrrhis marina* and *Exuviaella* by similarities in their nuclear structure. On the other hand, the basing of taxonomy on electron microscope studies which cannot be confirmed by the light microscope is introducing an impossible situation, as the electron microscope cannot be used in routine studies of the microscopic algae. PRESCOTT (1964) suggested that toxin production might be used as a taxonomic character. Species such as *Gymnodinium brevis* or *Goniaulax catenella* seem to produce toxins as a constant character, but different strains of the blue-green alga *Microcystis aeruginosa* have different toxin levels, and some are non-toxic. The brown seaweed *Sargassum* in the Sargasso Sea produces a strong antibiotic preventing the attachment of other organisms, but the same species moving with the Gulf Stream have completely lost their antibiotic effects when they reach more northerly and colder waters (SIEBURTH, 1964a). These examples make it inadvisable to use toxicity as a character except in a few, well-authenticated cases. Hydrology and the relation to water masses have been discussed to some extent. A difficulty here is that we may have cold- and warm-water strains of such species as the diatom *Corethron criophilum*, one confined to Antarctic and sub-Antarctic waters and the other to tropical regions. Culture studies may be difficult, in that many truly oceanic species have not been cultivated, despite considerable effort to get them into cultivation. Further, changes in morphology may be induced by culture methods, and different strains of the same organism may vary in different ways and in different degrees. On the other hand, many of the microflagellates have been described by microscopic observation as different species when cultures have shown that they are merely stages in the life history of a single organism. J. J. A. McLaughlin (personal communication) sent several strains of a single organism derived from a single cell to a taxonomist who described several species from the material. No doubt our taxonomist was justified on taxonomic grounds, using existing criteria. In such cases, where criteria are limited because of the small size and primitive morphology of the organisms, cultures are the only method whereby we can determine the range of variation and conditions of change for each organism, especially under varying conditions of growth. Another method for determining the significance of taxonomic characters is the detailed study of an environment, correlating all the changes that are to be found in a given species or group of species. On genetic grounds, we may assume that if two forms occur in the same ecological niche, and intergrades are to be found, that they may be assumed to represent a single species. This should be insisted upon despite the existence of type specimens in museums. *Navicula brasiliensis* and *N. granulata* were long maintained as separate species merely because the existence of type specimens was believed to overrule the ecological evidence, though intergrades were found in the same localities. At the present time these two forms are united as *N. granulata*.

In the case of the diatoms (Bacillariophyceae) I should like to comment on the families and sub-families given by SILVA (1962) in the lists given below, and to plead for an abrogation of the strict rules of nomenclature in certain cases. The terms Centrobacillariophyceae and Pennatibacteriophyceae may be correct but they are also horrible mouthfuls compared with Centricae and Pennatae and I see no reasons for keeping them. Further, the divisions into Araphidineae for the Fragilariales, Monoraphidineae for the Achnanthales, Raphidoidineae for the Eunotiales, Biraphidineae for the rest of the pennates, do give the non-taxonomist a clue to the characters of these groupings according to the development of the raphé, where the "correct" designations do not. In this, I shall continue to follow HENDEY (1937, 1951) and other British diatomists.

The following table lists the classifications (to families) of SILVA (1962) and PARKE and DIXON (1964), and enlarges the differences which were brought out above. I have no doubt that readers will choose their classification according to their prejudices or their needs, as I have done in my own work. As an ecologist I require a pragmatic classification even if it is not acceptable to my taxonomist friends.

CLASSIFICATION OF ALGAE

SILVA (1962)	PARKE and DIXON (1964)
Cyanophyta	Cyanophyceae
Chroococcales	Chroococcales
Chroococcaceae	Chroococcaceae
Entophysalidaceae	Entophysalidaceae
Nostocales	Nostocales
Oscillatoriaceae	Oscillatoriaceae
Beggiatoaceae	
Thiotrichaceae	
Nostocaceae	Nostocaceae
	Microchaetaceae
Rivulariaceae	Rivulariaceae
Scytonemaceae	Scytonemaceae
Stigonemales	Stigonemales
	Nostochopsidaceae
Mastigocladaceae	Mastigocladaceae
	Chamaesiphonales
	Dermocarpaceae
	Chamaesiphonaceae
	Pleurocapsales
	Pleurocapsaceae
	Hyellaceae
Cryptophyta	Cryptophyceae
Cryptophyceae	Cryptomonadales
Cryptomonadales	
Cryptomonadaceae	Cryptomonadaceae (includes
Senniaceae	Senniaceae)
	Cyathomonadaceae
(Cyanidium)	
Pyrrophyta	Dinophyceae
Desmophyceae	
Prorocentrales	Prorocentrales
Prorocentraceae	Prorocentraceae

(omits Dinophysidae of
Kofoid)

Dinophysiales
　Amphisoleniaceae
　Dinophysiaceae
Dinophyceae   Peridiniales
　Gymnodiniales   　Gymnodiniaceae
　　Pronoctilucaceae   　Pronoctilucaceae
　　Noctilucaceae   　Noctilucaceae
　　Gymnodiniaceae

　　　　　　　　　　　　　　　　Warnowiaceae
　　　　　　　　　　　　　　　　Polykrikaceae
　　　　　　　　　　　　　　　　Amphilothaceae
　　　　　　　　　　　　　　　　Ptychodiscaceae
Peridiniales   Glenodiniopsaceae
　Glenodiniaceae   Glenodiniaceae
　Peridiniaceae   Peridiniaceae
　Gonyaulacaceae   Gonyaulacaceae
　　　　　　　　　　　　　　　　Protoceratiaceae
　　　　　　　　　　　　　　　　Heterodiniaceae
　　　　　　　　　　　　　　　　Ceratiaceae
　　　　　　　　　　　　　　　　Goniodomataceae
　　　　　　　　　　　　　　　　Oxytoxaceae
　　　　　　　　　　　　　　　　Cladopyxidaceae
　　　　　　　　　　　　　　　　Thecadiniaceae
　　　　　　　　　　　　　　　　Podalampadaceae
　　　　　　　　　　　　　　　　Oodiniaceae
　　　　　　　　　　　　　　　　Blastodiniaceae
　　　　　　　　　　　　　　　　Haplozoonaceae
　　　　　　　　　　　　　　　　Syndiniaceae
　　　　　　　　　　　　　　　　Coccidineaceae
　　　　　　　　　　　　　　　　Paradiniaceae
　　　　　　　　　　　　　　　Phytodiniales
　　　　　　　　　　　　　　　　Phytodiniaceae
　　　　　　　　　　　　　　　Dinotrichales
　　　　　　　　　　　　　　　　Dinotrichaceae
Bacillariophyta   (Not considered by Parke)
　Centrobacillariophyceae
　　Eupodiscales
　　　Coscinodiscaceae
　　Rhizosoleniales
　　　Rhizosoleniaceae
　　Biddulphiales
　　　Biddulphiaceae
　Pennatibacteriophyceae
　　Fragilariales
　　　Tabellariaceae
　　　Fragilariaceae

Eunotiales
  Eunotiaceae
Achnanthales
  Achnanthaceae
Naviculales
  Naviculaceae
  Cymbellaceae
  Amphiproraceae
Phaeodactylales
  Phaeodactylaceae
Bacillariales
  Nitzschiaceae
Surirellales
  Surirellaceae

Chrysophyta   Chrysophyceae
  Phaeothamniales   Phaeothamniales
    Phaeothamniaceae   Phaeothamniaceae
                          Phaeosaccionaceae
  Ochromonadales   Ochromonadales
    Ochromonadaceae   Ochromonadaceae
    Dinobryaceae   Dinobryaceae
    Synuraceae   Synuraceae
                          Ruttneraceae
    Coccolithophoraceae   in Haptophyceae
    Phaeocystaceae   in Haptophyceae
  Isochrysidales   in Haptophyceae
    Isochrysidaceae
    Prymnesiaceae
  Chromulinales   Chromulinales
    Chromulinaceae   Chromulinaceae
    Chrysocapsaceae   Chrysapsidaceae
                          Pedinellaceae
    Hyduraceae   Chrysococcaceae
                    Chrysapsales
                          Sarcinochrysidaceae
  Thallochrysidales   Thallochrysidales
    Thallochrysidaceae   Thallochrysidaceae
                          Chrysomeridaceae
                    Dictyochales (Silicoflagellatae)
                          Dictyochaceae
           Haptophyceae PARKE, 1961
             Isochrysidales
               Isochrysidaceae
            Prymnesiales
               Prymnesiaceae
               Phaeocystaceae
               Chrysotilaceae
               Syracosphaeraceae

	Coccolithaceae
	(Braarudosphaeraceae) stages of
	(Thoracosphaeraceae) other forms
	(Ochrosphaeraceae)
	Craspedophyceae
	Monosigales
	Monosigaceae
Xanthophyta	Xanthophyceae
Chloramoebales	Heterochloridales
Chloramoebaceae	Heterochloridaceae
	Rhizochloridaceae
Mischococcales	Mischococcales
Pleurochloridaceae	Pleurochloridaceae
Chlorobotrydaceae	
Halosphaera (placed by Parke and Dixon in Prasinophyceae)	
	Characiopsidaceae
Tribonematales	Tribonematales
Tribonemataceae	Tribonemataceae
Heterotrichaceae	
Vaucheriales	Vaucheriales
Vaucheriaceae	Vaucheriaceae
Botrydiaceae	
	Heterogloeales
	Heterogloeaceae
	(Not treated by Parke and Dixon)
Euglenophyta	
Euglenales	
Euglenaceae	
Astasiaceae	
Peranemataceae	
	Prasinophyceae
	Pyramimonadales
	Nephroselmidaceae
	Polyblepharidaceae
	Tetraselmidaceae
	Chlorodendraceae
	Halosphaerales
	Pterospermataceae
	Halosphaeraceae
Chlorophyta	Chlorophyceae
Volvocales	Volvocales
Polyblepharidaceae	Dunaliellaceae (see also Prasinophyceae)
Chlamydomonadaceae	Chlamydomonadaceae
Haematococcaceae	
Volvocaceae	

Palmellaceae
Tetrasporaceae
Chlorococcales
    Chlorococcaceae

Protosiphonaceae
Hydrodicdyaceae
Chlorellaceae
Oocystaceae
    plus fresh water forms

Chlorococcales
    Chlorococcaceae (may include
    phases of other families)

Oocystaceae
Characiaceae
Endosphaeraceae
Phyllosiphonaceae

NUTRITION OF MARINE ALGAE
(general considerations)

The marine algae, as has been indicated earlier in this work, have widely different nutrition patterns, and the simple concept of algae as obligate phototrophs must be abandoned. It is unfortunate in this connection that so many oceanographers interested in productivity or standing crop of micro-algae have not informed themselves of this change in the basic concepts of algal nutrition.

Metabolic processes

PRINGSHEIM and WIESSNER (1961), FOGG (1963) and others have shown that light may act not only as a source of energy for photosynthesis per se, but may increase the ability of the plant to assimilate organic matter as a carbon source, or may act directly by assisting the organism to assimilate and fix carbon from low-energy reactions with such substances as acetate at low light intensities. Such reactions are economical for the plant because the organic materials used are in a higher energy state than is carbon dioxide, so that more energy can be released by the complete decomposition of such chemical species with less energy required for their assimilation and storage. The utilization of such compounds would not be detected by the Steemann Nielsen ^{14}C method as this estimates only the carbon fixed from carbon dioxide which has been labelled as $Na_2^{14}CO_3$. Estimations of standing crop would also be invalidated, because, with heterotrophy or acetate synthesis, the chlorophyll may be used to give its fullest photo-catalytic action only in part or not at all, so that it can no longer be relied upon as an index of potential assimilation.

Fogg points out a number of errors in studies of rates of organic production in aquatic environments, especially by the Steemann Nielsen method of measuring inorganic carbon fixation.

(*1*) There are errors due to enclosure of the samples in vessels; these arise from adsorption on the walls and from reflection or refraction of light from the surface of the vessel. In limited spaces such as reaction vessels, gross changes can occur in the balance of populations in short term experiments.

(*2*) Oxygen production does not necessarily measure energy flow, for instance, radiant energy used in cyclic phosphorylation results neither in assimilation of carbon dioxide nor in evolution of oxygen.

(*3*) When the Steemann Nielsen method is used, hydrogen chloride is used to wash the filters holding the cells which have theoretically fixed the carbon. This acid will dissolve any carbonate formed by the cells, e.g., the coccoliths of the coccolithophores or the carbonate precipitated by the blue-green algae, and some of this carbonate may contain ^{14}C which has been assimilated by the plants.

(*4*) The organic matter formed may vary in level or reduction, for example carboxyl groups are formed with scarcely any gain in potential chemical energy, while hydrocarbon chains represent large gains in chemical energy.

(*5*) We do not know whether intermediate products of photosynthesis are preferentially used in respiration, or whether intermediates in respiration are used preferentially to carbon dioxide photosynthesis. Such metabolism would represent a short-circuit in the assimilation and dissimilation of carbon dioxide and of course of the labelled ^{14}C used to follow metabolism of marine plants.

(*6*) The radiocarbon method measures only assimilation of carbon from carbon dioxide or bicarbonate. If photoassimilation of organic carbon occurs, or much carbon is assimilated as a carbamide complex, the errors will be great and may represent an order of magnitude.

(*7*) Photosynthesis may result in the formation of soluble organic compounds which will escape from the organisms into the water, and be washed away from the filter which is used to retain the organisms and their assimilate.

(*8*) A certain amount of carbon dioxide (or bicarbonate) is fixed even in the dark, energy being provided by exothermic chemical reactions within the organism. This is known as dark fixation and is a rather complex phenomenon, depending on the condition of the population (rapid growth in the logarithmic phase, slow growth and dissimilation in the stationary growth phase, or dissimilation without growth in the death phase). HOLM-HANSEN (1962) points out that, with previous photo-illumination, the high energy phosphate bonds as in ATP and the reduction of pyridine nucleotides supply both energy and hydrogen for the reduction of carbon dioxide in the dark. Dark fixation can also occur by other pathways, with the formation of such substances as malic or aspartic acids, possibly via the Krebs cycle intermediates. In *Euglena* it seems that carbon dioxide may be assimilated via the photosynthetic pathway, using the energy supplied by endogenous respiration instead of light. The products formed during carbon dioxide assimilation may vary with the external conditions of the environment, for example light may inhibit the incorporation of ^{14}C into the Krebs cycle acids. The amount of dark fixation depends also on the kind or kinds of organism involved.

FOGG (1962, 1963, 1964) has shown, and others such as BURKE, PRAGER and MCLAUGHLIN (1962) have confirmed, that a number of micro-algae may liberate a considerable amount of photosynthate into the water during photosynthesis, and this may be in the form of soluble or particulate matter. Ribulose phosphate is the acceptor of carbon dioxide in photosynthesis, and under certain conditions which are often reached in the natural environment and in culture, glycollic acid is released from this source. This glycollic acid, if it remains accessible to the plant, can be reassimilated using energy from photosynthesis as has been mentioned, and this is economical for the plant. In other words, dissolved, and in some cases particulate, organic matter in the aqueous environment can act as a storehouse of nutrient material for the plant, available at all times, and particularly when the amount of light available is insufficient for normal photosynthesis. STANIER (1961) has pointed out that photo-autotrophic and heterotrophic assimilation differs only in the mode of production of adenosine triphosphate (ATP). In some cases according to DANFORTH (1962), almost any substrate or intermediate in the major pathways of energy metabolism may substitute for photosynthesis; however, this is not true in other cases, for example many of the Volvocales (Chlamydomonads, etc.), some *Euglena* strains and many Chlorococcales, planktonic centric diatoms and some dino-flagellates, e.g., *Gymnodinium simplex*, are obligate autotrophs and cannot use any heterotrophic pathways.

FOGG (1963) refers to conditions in which the growth rate of certain algae on organic substances is greatly increased in the presence of light of low intensity. This may explain the results of RODHE (1963) who found that photosynthetic efficiency is increased at low light intensities. The extreme of this type of nutrition is reached in a *Chlamydobotrys* in which carbon dioxide cannot be used in photosynthesis, and acetate is photoassimilated instead (PRINGSHEIM and WIESSNER, 1961).

Some species, such as *Ochromonas malhamensis* and *O. danica* require organic hydrogen donors for photosynthesis, according to AARONSON and BAKER (1959), though this may be adaptive, and very recent work of WRIGHT (1964) and BUNT (1965) suggests the same requirement for some antarctic algae which are able to grow at very low light intensities (down to 5 foot-candles or less). *Ochromonas* can metabolise by photosynthesis, heterotrophy or phagotrophy; heterotrophy and autotrophy may be linked through hydrogen donors, and phagotrophy of bacteria is believed to supply such growth substances as biotin after enzyme hydrolysis releases these compounds.

In a recent paper FOGG (1964) states: "A single strain of an algal species may show remarkable variation in the intensity and pattern of its metabolic activities according to the conditions to which it is exposed". Very few workers have considered the effects of such factors as temperature or light on biochemical pathways, and have concentrated only on the end products. Fogg believes that in the case of a nitrogen-fixing *Anabaena*, the changes in the rate of nitrogen assimilation with temperature are due to the effect of this factor on the later stages of the reaction rather than on the actual assimilation process as a whole. Changes in the supply or consumption of metabolites may also have a considerable effect on metabolic patterns. He states: "the processes of intermediary metabolism are effected by reversible reactions and although we arbitrarily distinguish sequences of reactions such as glycolysis, the tricarboxylic acid cycle, and the carbon dioxide fixation cycle, they are so intermeshed through common intermediates as to form a single flexible system through which material can flow along various paths, largely according to the law of supply and demand".

"In an algal population growing exponentially, synthesis of proteins and other protoplasmic constituents predominates and directly utilizes the intermediates of the photosynthetic carbon cycle. There is little accumulation of cell-wall materials or of reserve products, nitrogenous or non-nitrogenous. Transfer of such cells to a medium lacking a nitrogen source, as is commonly done for experiments on photosynthesis, does not have any immediate effect on the quantum efficiency or rate of photosynthesis, but results in a drastic diversion of the intermediates produced to pathways other than those of protein synthesis. The enzyme system leading to carbohydrate synthesis accepts a major part of the overflow."

"The availability of particular metabolites in the environment may thus have considerable immediate effects on the metabolic pattern, but nevertheless this pattern will be determined primarily by the relative activity of the various enzyme systems in the organism. The availability of a particular metabolite may however, have a longer term effect by producing alterations in the balance of those enzyme systems."

Metabolic patterns may be changed by the production by algae of adaptive enzymes.

Fogg, in effect, stresses the lability of algal metabolism even within the recognized pathways, and its dependence on external conditions such as temperature and light. This argument makes it very difficult to accept quantitative methods based on the estimation of a given component of the system such as chlorophyll or a single metabolic process. It accents too the ability of an organism of this kind to react to and compromise with the environment, while it simplifies our understanding of the persistence of so many microbes through time and space, e.g., so many diatoms from the Pleistocene to the present day and from the equator to the poles. Organisms with a narrow range would be those in which the balance of enzyme systems would not stand up to rapid or considerable alteration, those with a wide range would have a well-buffered balance. One can observe with many organisms that rapid changes are often fatal, but more leisurely changes of greater magnitude are easily survived.

While it is easy to conceive the resilience of enzyme systems and the alternate channeling of intermediates, as facilitating organisms switching from autotrophic to heterotrophic growth and vice versa, phagotrophy, especially among the smaller and more primitive flagellates requires further explanation. The ingestion of an organism or particle requires tactic responses, a temporary discontinuity of the cell wall or an invagination, and strong enzyme activity to destroy the protective envelope of the ingested organism or particle. This must be followed by selection of certain nutrient materials, and the rejection of unsuitable substances through vacuoles or by permeability changes. I have not come across any modern explanation of these phenomena.

So far, we have considered the nutrition of the micro-algae from the point of view of energy relationships, without however going into any thermodynamic considerations. These also we shall have to leave for future researches, though, in the light of temperature, ionic and pressure differences in the marine environment, they could control many of the processes we have been discussing.

Inorganic nutrients

We must now consider the relation to micro-algae of inorganic nutrients. EYSTER (1964) designates as macro-nutrients those which are required in concentrations between 10^{-2} and 10^{-4} molar. These are carbon, hydrogen, oxygen, nitrogen, phosphate, sulfur, potassium, magnesium and sodium. The micro-nutrients are required in concentrations less than 10^{-5} molar, and these include calcium, iron, manganese, copper, zinc, molybdenum, vanadium, boron, chlorine, cobalt, nickel and silica (see WIESSNER, 1962). Calcium is required in larger amounts by such forms as the coccolithophores. The macro-nutrients are required by the algae as constituents of their protoplasm or essential compounds such as chlorophyll or for osmotic purposes in the cell sap, potassium for example. Silicon is needed for diatoms which use this to form their exoskeletons. It seems that these exoskeletons are necessary for the survival of the diatom. Calcium is required only in small quantities, if at all, by the Chlorophyceae and can be replaced in some cases by strontium. HALLDAL (1957) stated that calcium caused negative, and magnesium positive phototaxis. The minimal value for Ca was 0.005 M $CaCl_2$ and for Mg 0.035 M $MgCl_2$; the other algae require magnesium among other things, for optimum nitrogen fixation. It is more essential for marine than for fresh water algae. Manganese is necessary for photosynthesis, and at lower levels for heterotrophic growth. It is needed for reduction of NAD and for oxygen evolution, regardless of the Hill oxidant used. A manganese deficiency is found at concentrations below 1×10^{-7} M. Iron is also required for autotrophic growth, and at a lower level for heterotrophy; it must be in solution or chelate but not colloidal. It is associated with enzymes such as peroxidase, catalase, cytochromes b and f, cytochrome-oxidase, and photosynthetic pyridinenucleotide reductase, while an iron non-haem enzyme is needed for nitrogen fixation. *Asterionella* requires only 10^{-10} M of iron. Chlorine is required for non-cyclic phosphorylation and for the riboflavin-phosphate pathway of cyclic phosphorylation. Vanadium can replace molybdenum as a catalyst for nitrogen fixation, while molybdenum is necessary for nitrogen assimilation generally. Zinc is needed, especially among the flagellates, in a number of metalloproteins including dehydrogenases and carbonic anhydrase; it also increases photosynthesis in some algae. Boron stimulates nitrogen fixation but is possibly unnecessary per se; it may have a buffering effect. Cobalt is required in cyanocobalamin and is sometimes assimilable in other forms. Copper is required at a level of 10^{-7} M but is often toxic above this level. Some algae, including diatoms can tolerate high concentrations of copper (see later chapters).

Phosphate would appear to be available to most algae in inorganic or organic form, or perhaps we should say in some organic forms. According to PRAGER (1963) *Glenodinium foliaceum* uses glycerophosphate, cytidylic, adenylic or guanilic acids in preference to inorganic phosphate. Nitrogen may be limiting to certain species depending on the form of this substance. Some algae require or prefer nitrate, most can use nitrite, some ammonia and a relatively few, nitrogen; organic nitrogen is available to many algae also, and it may be that nitrogen is frequently recirculated without reverting to inorganic states. Mixed nitrogen sources are preferred to single compounds by *Glenodinium foliaceum* which can use alanine, asparagine, glycine, serine, phenylalanine, leucine and lycine, but not methionine. Proline and ammonia are toxic. Sulfur is assimilated either as sulfate in oxidizing environments, or as sulfide in reducing environments; heterotrophs use organic sulfur compounds which are in the main reduced.

Growth factors

Accessory growth factors have been extensively studied in recent years by a number of authors. Euglenids, cryptomonads, dinoflagellates and Chrysophyceae as a group appear to require cyanocobalamin and many species also require thiamine and biotin; some also require p-aminobenzoic acid. About 50% of diatoms, chlorophytes, and very few blue-green algae are auxotrophic. There appears to be little phylogenetic significance in auxotrophy, as it is spread somewhat randomly through the phyla of the micro-algae, nor is there any general correlation between auxotrophy and heterotrophy according to Droop (1962). Plant growth substances such as indolylacetic acid or giberellic acid are stimulatory for some micro-algae but do not appear to be necessary. Growth promotion by organic substances is not confined to actual assimilation, but may occur through chelation, buffering, or even adsorption, allowing the assimilation of other substances that would not otherwise be available. For example, iron is available to these algae when chelated, as we have mentioned, copper can be removed and rendered non-toxic by the same process, as was pointed out by Fogg (1962b), the alga *Desmarestia* apparently requires a very low pH for its cell sap and gets this by means of sulfuric acid. Further, the complex balance discussed by Fogg and referred to above may be controlled in culture by such substances as soil extract, peptone, casein hydrolysate, and the use of these substances is probably due to such control rather than to specific accelerating substances. This no doubt accounts for the fact that no one has been able to show the presence of a growth-promoting substance in soil extract. Such possibilities are discussed by Hutner and Provasoli (1964).

It has been suggested by several authors that micro-nutrients may be a factor in controlling the succession of species in marine algal blooms. It was believed, and may still be partly true, that vitamin B_{12} (cyanocobalamin) derived from the land is a cause of the dense aggregations of *Gymnodinium brevis* and *G. splendens* which cause red tides and large fish kills on the west coast of Florida.

THE CYANOPHYCEAE, MYXOPHYCEAE OR BLUE-GREEN ALGAE

The blue-green algae (Fig. 11) are exceedingly important in shore-line, shallow sediment and epiphytic communities in estuarine environments and in tropical surface waters in the oceans. Their taxonomy

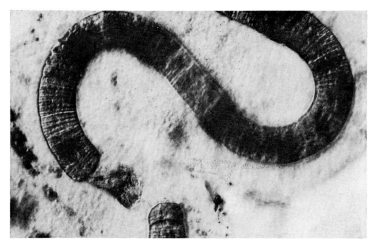

Fig.11. A marine Myxophyte *(Katagnymene)* or blue-green alga.

is very confused, and it is probable that a great deal of simplification is needed. The families recognized by Silva, and Parke and Dixon are listed earlier in this chapter; DESIKACHARY (1960) has a somewhat different listing.

The Chroococcales are unicellular or colonial, without trichomes, and have no differentiation of base or apex. Marine members of this group include *Microcystis, Chroococcus, Gloeocapsa, Gloeothece, Aphanocapsa, Aphanothece, Merismopedia* and *Gomphosphaeria*.

The Chamaesiphonales are unicellular, and are often differentiated with base and apex. Several of these are to be found epiphytic on marine algae.

The Pleurocapsales form a heterotrichous thallus, but do not form a definite trichome; reproduce by endospores formed in sporangia. *Xenococcus* and *Hyella* have been recorded from marine sources.

The Nostocales which form trichomes, and hormogonia, have only false branching, heterocysts, akinetes and endospores. They are quantitatively the most important order of blue-green algae recorded from marine environments, and all families are represented. The marine Oscillatoriaceae include the tropical *Trichodesmium, Katagnymene, Haliarachne* and *Pelagothrix*, all oceanic and planktonic; the estuarine *Lyngbya, Symploca, Spirulina, Microcoleus, Schizothrix, Calothrix, Phormidium* and *Hydrocoleus*. Among the Nostocaceae, *Richelia* is endophytic in certain diatoms, *Nostoc* which occurs on niggerhead corals, and has been recorded from below the photic zone in the Atlantic and Indian Oceans by BERNARD and LECAL (1960), *Anabaena* from brackish Tambak ponds in Java, and *Nodularia*. I do not know of any detailed study of marine blue-green algae, so the list I have given is doubtless incomplete. Distribution studies are urgently needed, and these should later be correlated with the physico-chemical environment. One observation may be of interest here; in the highly calcareous south Florida, blue-greens are far more abundant and widely distributed than other micro-algae in many shallow tidal and sub-tidal areas.

Structure of blue-green algae

The Chroococcales are coccoid, or shortly-cylindrical to fusiform, and cell division may be in several planes. The cells are often contained in mucilaginous capsules and there may be several capsules, one inside another and containing one or more cells. Some genera form grouped patterns such as *Synechococcus* and *Merismopedia*. The Chamaesiphonales are frequently attached at one end, the ends being dimorphic. Filamentous forms may consist of straight trichomes as in *Oscillatoria*, beaded as in *Anabaena*, tapering as in *Rivularia*, with false branching as in *Stigonema*. Most of the filamentous forms have more or less laminated sheaths and many precipitate calcium carbonate outside these sheaths and thus assist in the formation of marl.

The cells have two-layered walls and divide perpendicular to the trichome by invagination of the inner structure of the cell and the inner cell wall. These invaginations meet and fuse, forming a double wall between the cells. The outer wall fills in the area between these walls and forms a double-layered intermembranal wall. The internal chromoplasm shows lamellar structure parallel with the cell walls, each lamella consisting of a double membrane. The lamellae invaginate concomitantly with the division of the cell wall during division. Polyphosphate bodies occur in the interlamellar spaces and occasionally in the centroplasm adjacent to the lamellae. Cyanophycin bodies (chloroplasts?) lie between the cell wall and the first lamella and there are interlamellar bridges. Vacuoles occur at the ends of the lamellae or in the interlamellar spaces. The centroplasm is filled with homogenous material and vacuoles which tend to coalesce. Nuclear material may be represented by ellipsoid formed bodies in the centroplasm. In hormogonium formation, the filaments break up, probably by the cleavage between the two membranes of the interwall which become the outer membranes of the newly formed cells.

Nutrition of blue-green algae

While DROOP (1962) recorded only one out of 25 fresh water blue-greens requiring vitamins, VAN BAALEN (1962) found that 50% of his marine (estuarine) species have an absolute requirement for cyanocobalamine but not for other vitamins. The strains studied by him were not heterotrophic except for one strain of *Lyngbya* which did grow very slowly in the dark on glucose. *Tolypothrix tenuis* was reported by KIYOHARA et al. (1960, 1962) to be able to grow hetero-trophically. Calcium and magnesium ions were necessary for optimal growth, and there is evidence that they spare each other. Sodium seems to be required at approximately the concentration found in sea water. Nitrogen and ammonia were used as nitrogen sources, and it appears that most species can utilize organic nitrogen, though a few, such as *Synechococcus,* require organic sources of nitrogen (FOGG and WOLFE, 1954).

Apart from the workers mentioned above, little has been done to solve the problems of the nutrition of the Cyanophyceae except for the work of PROVASOLI and PINTNER (1954), who found that the alga *Phormidium* had a low light requirement (100–200 foot-candles), was inhibited by 300 foot-candles, and required thiamine, B_{12} and folinic acid. WOOD (1958) reported the close association of many species of blue-greens with the micro-organisms of the sulfur cycle, and stated that *Lyngbya* could grow at −170 mV. SPRUYT (1962) discussed the relation between photoreduction (defined as the assimilation of carbon dioxide with molecular hydrogen with light as the energy source) and anaerobiosis, but did not show whether this method of assimilation was important in natural environments. One would expect from their ecological relationships, that the blue-green algae in particular would be able to photoreduce, using hydrogen sulfide as the hydrogen donor, but this has still to be demonstrated.

The pigments which characterise the blue-green algae include chlorophyll *a* (but not *b* or *c*), and certain biliproteins which allow of considerable color adaptation, which presumably allows these organisms to filter too-strong light and thus live densely on the surface of sediments in the intertidal zone and at the surface of the sea in tropical waters.

Reproduction of blue-green algae

Several reproductive bodies have been reported for the blue-green algae: (*1*) *Hormogones*. These are fragments of the trichome which may consist of one to many cells of uniform size which break off. They are thinly covered with a mucilaginous sheath and are actively motile. They are characteristic of the Nostocales and Stigonemales, which are collectively known as Hormogonales. They are formed by the death of one to several intermediate cells. In certain forms, the hormogones become enclosed in a thick pigmented sheath and are known as *hormocysts*. (*2*) *Endospores*. These are formed within the cell by a quick succession of divisions in three planes and may be contained in the original cell, which thus becomes a sporangium. In *Gloeocapsa* and other Chroococcales these divisions result in a number of very small naked spore cells within the original cells; these spores are known as *nannocytes*. (*3*) Spores constricted from the open ends of sporangia as in *Chamaesiphon* are known as *exospores*. They may germinate in situ. (*4*) *Planococci*. These are unicellular hormogones which show a creeping movement. (*5*) Resting spores known as *Akinetes* are large, thick-walled cells without gas vacuoles.

Motility

The whip-like motion of the Oscillatoriaceae has long been known. Less known is the ability of many trichomes to move rapidly in the direction of the trichome axis and to reverse the motion very rapidly. Several suggestions have been made as to the source of this motion in organisms which do not possess any obvious organs of motility, but the phenomenon is still a mystery. Some centric diatoms have a similar type of motion.

(Plate IV, V and VI)

Because of the relative stability of the skeletons of diatoms and their abundance in recent and fossil sediments, these organisms have been studied in detail from the latter part of the 18th century. Taxonomic studies were made by von MÜLLER (1783), NITZSCH (1817), GRAY (1821), and others between 1770 and 1830, but from 1834 onwards a large number of microscopists made such studies their life-work. The greatest of these were Ehrenberg, Kützing, W. W. Smith, Gregory, Greville, Ralfs, Donkin, Grunow, the Peragallos, P. T. Cleve and his daughter Astrid Cleve-Euler, Van Heurck, and latterly Hustedt, Kolbe, Heiden, as well as many other important workers in the field. About the mid-1800's it was fashionable for retired schoolmasters, clergymen and other leisured persons who possessed microscopes to list the diatom species in their locality naming the forms they found after their colleagues with more courtesy than discrimination. This resulted in the description of about 100,000 species of diatoms of which 10,000 are still regarded as valid. For myself, I would very much doubt if half this number would stand up to studies on variability within the group.

It is only within comparatively recent years that studies of the physiology, reproduction, and anatomy of diatoms have been made to any degree. Even then, most of the investigations have been made on a few species such as *Nitzschia closterium*, *f. minutissima*, now classified as *Phaeodactylum tricornutum*, *Skeletonema costatum* and species of *Thalassiosira* and *Cyclotella*. However, this is now being rectified and studies are being extended to over 100 species of diatoms.

Taxonomy

It is usual and convenient to divide the diatoms into two groups or orders, the Centrales and the Pennales. HENDEY (1937) has criticized this as artifical and has also raised semantic objections. It is, however, possible that the distinction has phylogenetic significance as one can derive the pennate diatoms from the centric ones through *Biddulphia* and *Anaulus* to *Plagiogramma*, *Glyphodesmis* and *Rhabdonema*. It may be significant here that *Rhabdonema adriaticum* is oogamous, having this property in common with the centric forms.

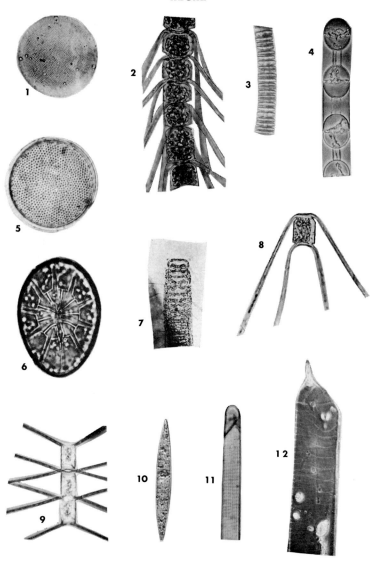

Plate IV. Planktonic diatoms. *1*, *5*. *Coscinodiscus*, *2*, *8*, *9*. *Chaetoceros*, *3*. *Fragilariopsis*, *4*. *Stephanopyxis*, *6*. *Asteromphalus*, *7*. *Chaetoceros armatum* (known only from the coast of Britain and from New Zealand where it is extremely abundant), *10*. *Navicula*, *11*. *Synedra*, *12*. *Rhizosolenia*.

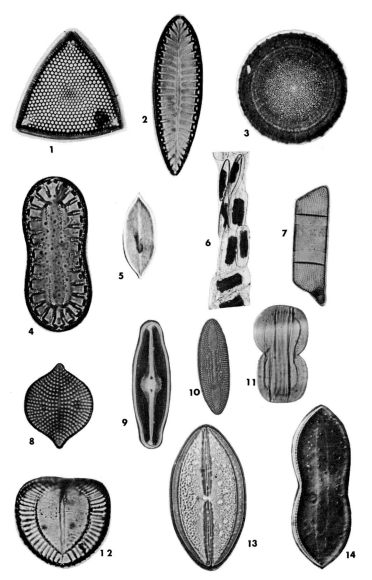

Plate V. Benthic diatoms. *1. Triceratium, 2. Surirella, 3. Actinocyclus, 4. Surirella, 5. Mastogloia, 6, 13. Navicula, 7. Isthmia, 8, 10. Rhaphoneis, 9. Caloneis, 11. Amphiprora, 12. Campylodiscus, 14. Nitzschia.*

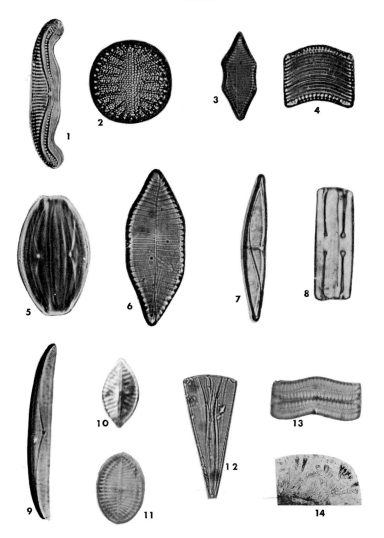

Plate VI. Epontic diatoms. *1, 7, 9. Amphora, 2. Campyloneis, 3, 6, 10, 13. Achnanthes, 11. Cocconeis, 8. Grammatophora, 12, 14. Licmophora.*

The basis of classification of the diatoms is the shape and structure of the siliceous exoskeleton, except in the genus *Chaetoceros*, where the number and distribution of chloroplasts is also important. The fact that diatoms are important in the geological record and the siliceous skeleton *(test* or *frustule)* is the only part preserved, makes it necessary to continue the present classification, even if it can later be shown that it is not phylogenetic. I have shown, as stated previously (WOOD, 1959c), that a single frustule can exhibit characters belonging to two species, two genera or even two so-called families. It is obvious from this that the whole classification of certain groups should be reviewed very critically. If a hybrid is possible between *Coscinodiscus* and *Asteromphalus*, they must at least be placed in the same family and possibly in the same genus. The frequency of cells with valves belonging to different "species" of *Coscinodiscus*, means that such species are to be regarded as varieties; the frequent absence of the pseudocellus in cells of *Actinocyclus* makes this distinction between that genus and *Coscinodiscus* invalid. In one phytoplankton sample, it is possible to find *Actinocyclus* frustules with pseudocelli on each valve, others with none, though the valves are otherwise identical. I have frequently observed this in Antarctic material. If we assume from the evidence we possess that *Coscinodiscus* is a variable form, many of the "species" must disappear. This reduces the unwieldy number of "species" in the genus and removes this objection to lumping genera where considered necessary. One of the big difficulties in lumping species is that many identifications are based on drawings, some of which, e.g., those of Karsten (1906–1907) are very pretty but hardly sufficient for identification. Moreover, on occasions when I have asked my colleagues to draw the same organism, the differences in the resulting illustrations would warrant specific rank. Because of the lapse of time since so many drawings of types were made, it is almost if not quite impossible to show their identity. Thus we would seem to be stuck with a number of "species" which it is impossible to abolish and which must clog the literature in perpetuity.

The difficulty raised by the existence of the *Coscinodiscus–Asteromphalus* cross is that discoid diatoms, which have a truly radial or regular symmetry, must be rather closely related to some which have an irregular radial pattern. The two genera involved appear to be structurally farther apart than *Coscinodiscus*, *Actinocyclus*, *Asterolampra*, *Schimperiella*, *Arachnoidiscus* or *Stictodiscus*. Just what then should be the status of these genera: do they now become species of a super-genus?

The planktonic and benthic genera of the centric diatoms apart from those mentioned do not present so many difficulties. The primary separation is by the mode of attachment of the cells as in *Melosira*, *Skeletonema*, *Stephanopyxis*, *Thalassiosira* and *Coscinosira*, or by the irregularity of the valve surface as in *Actinoptychus* and *Cyclotella*. In the biddulphoid group, the shape, number and position of the processes and spines seems adequate for discrimination, though variation in *Biddulphia anthropomorpha* does suggest that it is probably identical with *B. aurita*. A difficulty arises in species such as *Corethron criophilum*, essentially Antarctic in distribution, but with a monotypic form endemic in tropical waters and geographically distinct from the Antarctic occurence. Should these be regarded as forms or as eco-species?

Rhizosolenia presents difficulties in that such species as *R. alata* have a number of forms, some of which are eco-forms (e.g., *R. alata, f. inermis*) and restricted in distribution but occur with other, more cosmopolitan forms of the same species. *Chaetoceros* presents the difficulty that a number of "species" which differ but little occur in the same phytoplankton sample. It seems safe to conclude that a number of these so-called species are merely forms. The presence of chloroplasts in the setae of the Phaeoceros group seems characteristic, but the separation of *Ch. vanheurckii* from *Ch. lorenzianum* by the number of chloroplasts in the cell may not be valid. In the Phaeoceros group it is probable that *Ch. peruvianum*, *Ch. pendulum* and *Ch. concavicorne* are merely varieties of forms and the same applies to *Ch. dichaeta* and *Ch. atlanticum* which have intergrades at times in the same sample.

Although the planktonic centric diatoms have been well studied, the illustrations by well-qualified diatomists do not always agree, and this lack of uniformity raises difficulties in studies of the ecology of the species.

The pennate diatoms are divided according to the presence or absence of a raphé which is essentially a slit-like opening in the valve. The Araphidineae have no raphé on either valve and appear as stated above to show a phylogenetic succession from the centric forms. Some genera such as *Fragilaria* show a great deal of form variation and there has been some unnecessary splitting off of genera with only one or two species such as *Thalassionema* (one species) and *Fragilariopsis* (with about three). I cannot find any use for monospecific genera unless they have undoubted phylogenetic significance. *Fragilariopsis* is now placed by HASLE (1964) close to the genus *Nitzschia*, i.e., in the Biraphidineae.

The Monoraphidineae include the genera *Cocconeis* and *Achnanthes*, which are distinctive and apparently soundly based.

The Raphidoidineae have only one genus, *Eunotia*, which has a rudimentary raphé on both valves.

The Biraphidineae is a large, rather unwieldy group having a raphé on each valve. It has several small genera, e.g., *Diploneis*, *Mastogloia*, *Trachyneis*, and *Anomoeoneis*, with a central raphé and distinctive frustule structure, the large genus *Navicula* with innumerable species many of which are not valid and many more of doubtful validity. The only way to sort out the tangled nomenclature of this genus would be a large-scale culture program, collecting strains from numerous localities and studying them under a range of conditions to note the variability patterns. Unfortunately, most taxonomists have no interest in the living forms but rely on museum specimens. A large section of the Biraphidineae have asymmetric valves or else the raphé is asymmetric. *Gomphonema* is asymmetric with respect to the transverse axis, *Cymbella*, *Epithemia* (*Rhopalodia*), and *Amphora* with respect to the longitudinal axis, and in *Nitzschia*, *Amphiprora*, *Tropidoneis*, *Surirella* and *Camylodiscus*, the raphé is carried on a keel, the genera being differentiated by the shape of the frustule and the keel structure.

Electron microscopy of the frustules has recently been used to confirm or refute taxonomic relationships. In this way, J. C. Lewin (personal communication) has shown that *Phaeodactylum tricornutum* is closely related to *Cylindrotheca* and that *Nitzschia closterium* also belongs to that genus, thus reestablishing the close relationship between *N. closterium* and what used to be known as *N. closterium* f. *minutissima*.

Phylogeny

From the fossil record we find the centric diatoms in the Jurassic and the pennates in the lower Tertiary, suggesting that the centric forms are more primitive. The Araphidineae too appear in the fossil record earlier than the Raphidineae, thus indicating that the development of a raphé is an advance in morphology.

Diatoms in common with the Chrysophyceae and Xanthophyceae (also known as Chrysophyta and Xanthophyta) have oil as a storage product and do not form starch. Diatoms have as pigments chlorophyll *a* and *c*, carotenes, diatoxanthin, diadinoxanthin, fucoxanthin and neofucoxanthin A and B and possibly lutein. The Chrysophyta have the same pigments, the Xanthophyta lack fucoxanthin and diadinoxanthin, while the Phaeophyta have lutein and violaxanthin in addition. The male gametes of the centric diatoms have only one flagellum, while the Chrysophyta are usually biflagellate. The reproductive cells of the Phaeophyceae are biflagellate except for the mono-flagellate genus *Dictyota*. It would seem that the diatoms have a phylogenic history related to that of these other groups, but derived from a common ancestor rather than from one of them.

Reproduction

The vegetative cells of diatoms are diploid and there is no alternation of generations. Centric forms are oogamous, oogonia being formed by elongation of the cell and nucleus. There reduction divisions are followed by the degeneration of one nucleus, leaving a single nucleus for each oogonium, except in cases such as *Biddulphia mobiliensis* where each oogonium has two egg cells. Normally the eggs remain in the oogonium, but in a few cases they become free.

The spermatogonia may be derived directly from a vegetative cell, or smaller spermatogonia may be formed by mitotic division. They may remain within the sperm mother cell until meiosis occurs, or be released into the medium prior to meiosis. There are four spermatozoa per spermatogonium; in some cases the cytoplasm and plastids are distributed among the sperms, in others the sperms do not contain plastids. The sperms have a single flagellum.

Rhabdonema adriaticum is regarded as a pennate diatom having other characters peculiar to many Araphidineae, such as septa. On the other hand it is oogamous, each oogonium producing a single egg cell. The male cells are released as spermatogonia, attach by pads of mucilage to the oogonium and produce amoeboid, non-flagellate sperm. Only the nucleus penetrates the egg. The related

Grammatophora is isogamous, so *Rhabdonema* probably represents a transition.

The pennates have isogamous, amoeboid gametes. Mature diploid cells meet, meiosis occurs, resulting in four haploid nuclei, of which one or two develop into gametes while the rest disintegrate. The gametes fuse within the parental walls of the cells. The production of gametes varies considerably. Some species are autogamous, others allogamous.

The zygote begins to grow immediately, becoming an auxospore which is much larger than the mother cell. Two mitotic divisions occur, a new cell wall being formed each time, so that the final cell represents the maximum cell size of the species. Thus diatom cells tend to diminish in size after sexual reproduction, and in most species cell size steadily diminishes from then on. The sexual process therefore is confined to the small (mature) and not the large (immature) cells. Some species however do not noticeably decrease in size.

Motility

Until recently it has been held that only the Raphidineae are motile, but it is now known that many centrales and some Araphidineae can move. *Coscinodiscus* moves by sudden jerks suggesting that liquid is squirted out through pores in the valve. *Rhizosolenia delicatula* and *R. alata* have been seen to move in a nutatory way, and *Fragilaria* and *Synedra* have also been seen to move in the direction of the long axis.

Velocities of pennate diatoms on glass range from 0.2 to 25 μ/sec and some can move if either girdle or valve surface are in contact with the substrate. On the other hand, I observed a *Navicula* cell which had a larger sand grain on the upper valve surface. It seemed that the organism could either move bodily along the dish in either direction of the longitudinal axis or could move the sand grain likewise in either direction longitudinally, but could not effect motion on both valve surfaces simultaneously. The cell tried all available combinations without much success until it managed to get the sand grain right to one end. It then moved bodily in the other direction, trailing the sand grain which was obviously attached to the cell. At last, the friction between the sand and the glass of the vessel exceeded the adhesion of the grain to the cell and the cell contents visibly snapped back within the raphé. This indicates that, in this type of motion in pennate diatoms, the raphé is related to such motion. Where there is motion without a raphé, another mechanism must be adduced to explain this. No adequate explanation has yet been made for such locomotion in the diatoms or other groups without obvious organs of motility (e.g., blue-green algae).

The frequency of motion among centric diatoms of the Araphidineae has not been determined. Reports of motion in *Coscinodiscus* are infrequent, and I have observed motility in this genus only on rare occasions. On the other hand, even when motile cells are seen, the motion is not continuous and it may well be that lack of records is due to ineffective observation. In routine phytoplankton studies, workers other than myself have almost universally relied on pickled specimens, and when living organisms are used, motion tends to remain unobserved unless one were looking for it.

Rhythmic migrations

Diatoms associated with benthos or periphyton may migrate through vertical distances of several millimeters. C. N. d'Asaro (unpublished) had found that *Nitzschia closterium (Cylindrotheca)* attached to glass slides and other surfaces migrates upward in daylight and downward at night. Some other species follow this pattern but others do not.

Hantzschia amphioxys at Barnstable, Massachusetts, and Sapelo Island, Georgia, among other places, appears on the surface of the sediments after the tidal flats are uncovered and disappears below the surface ahead of the rising tide. This rhythm and that recorded by CALLAME and DEBYSER (1954) is linked to tidal rhythm and is intrinsic, as it is maintained in the laboratory for some days in the absence of tides and could be reversed by training to a different tidal rhythm. If a false tidal rhythm were induced or ebb tide artificially delayed, the organisms adapted, appearing only after the water had left the sediment. The diatoms disappeared below the surface about 10 min before the water covered the flats. This rhythm would seem partly phototactic and partly tidal. At Whitstable, in turbid water conditions, ALEEM (1950) found that diatoms migrated vertically in light if the flats were dry. This was a phototactic rhythm, but the flats were dry before migration commenced. In the R. Eden estuary in Fifeshire, Scotland, the response of the diatoms was phototactic only, the diatoms rising in the morning and disappearing at dusk whether water covered the surface of the flats or not. Tube-dwelling diatoms can withdraw below the surface with a thigmotactic response at a rate between 44 and 500 μ/sec.

It is assumed that the phototactic cum tidal rhythm enables the diatoms to photosynthesize without being subject to washing away with the tide, as they are protected by the sediment whenever the flats are covered by water.

The migration of epiphytic diatoms could have survival value in that they would move above the non-migrating species during the daylight hours and withdraw to their protection at night when grazing animals are most active.

Physiology

The physiology of diatoms has been studied mainly in culture, and one faces the difficulty that culture results without confirmation from the natural environment are guides rather than records of actual behaviour. The information in diatom physiology is largely taken from LEWIN and GUILLARD's paper (1963). Most field results have been obtained in fresh water lakes and ponds, because the study of algae in marine environments presents great difficulty. Further, it is necessary to use axenic cultures if the physiological effects of an experiment are to be attributed to the organism under test. So many organisms have alternate metabolic pathways which may be controlled by external influences, i.e., growth factors or extracellular products of other organisms, that their behavior in axenic culture may vary from their behavior in natural environments.

Temperature and light

Nitzschia ovalis grew between 16 and 18° C at 1,500 lux, at two intervals, i.e., between 14–18° C and 27–29° C at 2,500 lux, and 25–30° C at 6,500 lux. At low intensities it can live only at low temperatures. Temperature and light intensity optima are also dependent to certain levels on nutrient concentration.

Growth rate of *Asterionella formosa* doubled for a 10° rise between 4 and 18° C. *Cyclotella nana* increased from 0.5 divisions/day at 4° C to 2.75 at 27° C. Rapid rates of cell division may correlate with high rates of photosynthesis per unit biomass. Variation of sulfate-chloride ratios caused maximum growth rates to occur at different salinities. Estuarine clones of *Cyclotella nana* were unaffected by salinity, but shelf clones were affected by dilution.

Inorganic nutrients

HARVEY (1934) calculated that, assuming all ions impinging on the cell surface are absorbed, the concentration of ionic iron in sea water is insufficient to account for observed growth rates of diatoms.

Rate limitation by phosphate should not occur above 10^{-10} g/l.

Nitrogen. All diatoms tested can use nitrate, nitrite and ammonia as nitrogen sources. Limit of tolerance of NH_4Cl is close to 0.1 mM for some marine species. Some diatom species liberate nitrite into the medium from nitrate under certain circumstances, others deaminate amino-acids and liberate free ammonia. Organic nitrogen seems unavailable to diatoms according to LEWIN and GUILLARD (1963, p.390). This statement seems strange as Guillard grew *Coscinodiscus* and other forms on glutamate and glycine (p.394). Most species could use urea.

Rate of assimilation of nitrate and phosphate increased with increasing phosphorus concentration but was relatively independent of nitrogen.

Phosphorus. Diatoms can use orthophosphate readily in light or dark, pyrophosphate more slowly and organic phosphate at varying rates. Colloidal phosphate from clay-loams can also be used where dissolved phosphate was undetectable. *Phaeodactylum* can get adequate phosphorus from 10^{-8} g atom/l. It cannot divide if the concentration falls below 6×10^{-14} g/cell but can accumulate more than 30 times this in excess phosphate, and can divide using this when there is no external source of phosphate. Phosphate assimilation is easier in natural than artificial media. Silica assimilation is also increased by added phosphate, but this depends on light and temperature. Diatom growth is not inhibited by excess phosphate, though some other algae appear to be sensitive to this.

Iron and trace metals. Diatoms obtain iron from colloidal particles but not from soluble organic complexes. The amount required for nutrition is probably larger than can be supplied by diffusion of dissolved iron. It may be that presence of colloidal particles is necessary, rather than the amount of iron involved. Oceanic species seem to require less iron than coastal species. Aluminum may replace iron to an extent. Gallium and cerium may also spare iron.

Manganese requirement is of the order of 10^{-9} g atom/l.

Copper, cobalt and nickel were not deficient at concentrations as low as 10^{-11} to 10^{-13} g atom/l. Boron inhibits growth and reproduction at concentrations above 10^{-4} M.

Silicon is essential. In *Bacillaria paxillifer* log growth rate was independent of silica concentration down to 10^{-6} g atom/l. Growth rate limitation probably occurs at or below natural concentrations. Intensity and duration of illumination affects silica uptake. Silicon absorption requires energy-yielding aerobic reactions.

Sulfur. Sulfur assimilation as sulfate probably reflects total cation, total anion concentration, and favorable sulfate levels. SH$^-$ ion is necessary for silicon assimilation.

Calcium ion stimulates growth, and seems more important than Ca/Mg ratios, and monovalent/bivalent cation ratios seem also important. Sodium may be critical for estuarine neritic and oceanic species.

Vitamins. 46% of diatoms tested required one or more vitamins, 14% needed thiamine, 25% B_{12} and 7% both.

Autotrophy and heterotrophy. Most species have improved growth with small amounts of organics such as glycine or other amino-acids. Organic nitrogen compounds may replace inorganic nitrogen. Bottom-dwelling forms used glutamate or glutamine, organisms from polluted estuarine waters used uric acid. Organic phosphorus compounds can replace inorganics for some planktonic species. Of marine littoral pennates 60% could grow heterotrophically. Osmotic pressure is 4–8 atm above that of the surrounding (surface) water. Diatoms can exclude heavy-metal ions, presumably by chelation.

Sinking rates were estimated to vary from a few mm/day to 30 m/day; sinking or rising increases exposure to nutrients, and thus may increase the rate of nutrient assimilation. Nutrient-deficient diatoms sink more rapidly than growing cells, and sinking rates decrease as nutrients are restored.

Respiration rates are stated to be a linear function of temperature, but this is not true for *Fragilaria sublinearis*. The respiration rates of phytoplankton should be re-evaluated by modern methods; Q_{10} values for a number of species is around 2, but others have lower values. According to LEWIN (1963) capsular material cannot support heterotrophic growth, for, as it is a polyuronide, it would raise the RQ above 1. However, RQs well above 1 are possible, so Lewin's conclusions may not be valid. Lactic acid probably plays a role in the metabolism of diatoms as a supplement to CO_2 as a carbon source.

Photosynthesis

Pigments are mainly chlorophyll *a* and *c*, β-carotene, diatoxanthin, diadinoxanthin, and fucoxanthin, this last being the principal accessory. Chlorophylls *a* and *c* and fucoxanthin are about equally effective in light absorption in photosynthesis, at least eight quanta being required for each molecule of oxygen. The other carotenoids are believed to have little or no activity. According to G. C. McLeod and J. Kanwisher, as quoted by LEWIN and GUILLARD (1963), damage to their photosynthetic mechanism occurred below 290 mμ. Chlorophyll fluorescence was as efficient with fucoxanthin as with chlorophyll, indicating energy transfer by fucoxanthin.

Photosynthesis of all species studied in culture increased with light intensity up to about 10 kilolux, further intensity reducing photosynthetic rate. There are, however, diatoms which have much lower maxima and one wonders whether the high rates recorded from cultures are entirely artificial and due to undue selection. Rate of photosynthesis was thought to be independent of temperature at low light intensities, but higher at higher temperature with light saturation. Photosynthetic quotients (Pq) estimated by Warburg respirometer varied from 1.013–1.19, but these results are from strains adapted to somewhat artificial culture conditions. First products of photosynthesis are thought to be labile, and followed by fatty acids, proteins and polysaccharides. Leucosin is common to diatoms and chrysomonads, and is closely allied to laminarin; this is one reason why the diatoms have been regarded as phylogenetically close to the brown algae. Extracellular polysaccharides may be polyuronids (glycuronic acid) or may yield xylose and mannose without glucosamine.

THE FLAGELLATES

Although the diatoms were long known as "the grass of the sea", owing to the fact that they were the most frequent microorganisms to be caught in the nets formerly used for sampling phytoplankton, it is now known that the flagellates as a group rival them in importance, and, in some waters, are, both numerically and in mass, of far greater significance. A study of SILVA's (1962) and PARKE and DIXON's (1964) lists of families show that a number of groups of colored flagellates are represented; the colorless flagellates have been sadly neglected in work on marine protoplankton. Until very recently, most of the work on flagellate taxonomy had been done on freshwater organisms and we knew little of the marine ones, except in regard to the dinoflagellates. Even these were regarded as being numerically far less important than the diatoms and the naked forms were not studied in the oceanic environment. The lack of concern for such organisms was due in part to the fact that they break up easily, and often change their form with the addition of any preservative. Thus they went unrecognized in preserved material. It is because of these organisms that, in my writings, I have stressed the necessity for phytoplanktologists to do a great deal of their microscopic work at sea on living material.

Even now, the taxonomy of many flagellate groups is in a state of flux and probably many forms of oceanic flagellates are still unrecognized. BUTCHER's work (1959, 1961) is of limited value, as he spent little time in the field and relied largely on cultures. However, PARKE (1961), BRAARUD (1951, 1958, 1960), GAARDER (1962), HASLE (1960a), HOLLANDE (1952a,b), DEFLANDRE (1950, 1952a,b), SCAGEL and STEIN (1961) among others have made exceedingly useful contributions to an understanding of these groups.

The dinoflagellates, however, have been studied in great detail from the taxonomic point of view, and, apart from some splitting in one or two groups, the classification is exceedingly useful, and enables us to use this group of organisms to provide "indicator species" of water masses and other important hydrological phenomena. We shall therefore discuss the dinoflagellates first.

The dinoflagellates (Plate VII)

Taxonomy

Once again, we have a choice of several schemes for dividing this group into orders and families, and will follow that used by PARKE and DIXON (1964) as I consider it superior to that of SILVA (1962). The Dinophyceae consist of a number of orders, all of which occur in marine environments. The Prorocentrales resemble the Dinophyseales in having two lateral plates joined by a third, dorso-ventral plate which has two flagellar pores, in this case at the apex of the cell. From these pores extend two flagella, and there is frequently a spur or spine, sometimes two, beside the flagellar area. The number of genera in this order varies (there is only one family, the Prorocentraceae) with the taxonomist; the two important ones being *Exuviaella* and *Prorocentrum*. The former occurs in the plankton and as an epiphyte, the latter in the plankton, sometimes being abundant enough to form a red tide.

The Dinophyceales differ from the Prorocentrales in having the flagellar pores on the ventral surface, and a transverse girdle flanged by two ridges or lists which may be greatly extended. The portion of the cell above the girdle is known as the *epitheca* and that below is the *hypotheca*. The flagellar area is more or less depressed and is known as the *sulcus*. This is bordered by two flanges known as the *sulcal lists*, and one of the flagella is transverse between the girdle lists, the other extends posteriorly between the sulcal lists. The combined effect of these flagella is to give the cells a rotary forward, or corkscrew motion.

The family Dinophysaceae includes the genera *Phalacroma*, which has an epitheca higher than the anterior girdle list and which may even be median as in *P. argus*; *Dinophysis* which has a simple anterior girdle list which is higher than the very low epitheca; *Citharistes* which has a C-shaped body, Dinophysis-like lists and a spore-containing pouch between the arms of the C. *Ornithocercus* has a rotund body, a very low epitheca, high flaring girdle lists which may be much larger than the body and a sulcal list which is produced into a sail which extends ventrally and more or less antapically. *Histioneis* which Kofoid separated from the simpler *Parahistioneis*, is the most beautiful and complex of the dinoflagellates. These organisms have a small rotund, or sausage-shaped body, the girdle lists have been

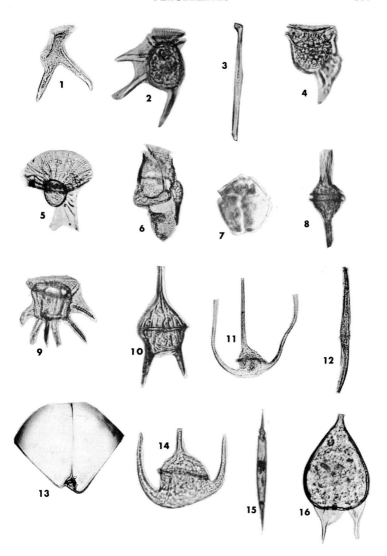

Plate VII. Planktonic dinoflagellates. *1, 2. Dinophysis, 3. Amphisolenia,
4. Parahistioneis, 5. Ornithocercus, 6. Histioneis, 7. Gymnodinium, 8. Goniaulax,
9. Ceratocorys, 10–14. Ceratium, 15. Oxytoxum, 16. Podolampas.*

elongated into tubes, the anterior being funnel-shaped, the posterior cylindrical or gibbous, often ribbed; the left sulcal list is extended until, at times it is much longer than the body and is fluted and ribbed to reticulate; at the sides are two spore-carrying pouches, often as large as the posterior girdle list.

The family Amphisoleniaceae represents another development in which the body is extended in one or two processes. In *Amphisolenia* the organism is rod-shaped with a swollen middle, a neck and "head" on which is the girdle, with two small lists, from which narrow sulcal lists extend to the base of the neck. The antapex is frequently curved and may bear two to four small spinelets. *Triposolenia* is a very rare form in which the processes extend sideways from the rotund mid-body, and then curve posteriorly with curved ends and spines as in *Amphisolenia:* the head and neck are similar to those of *Amphisolenia.* KOFOID and SKOGSBERG (1928) list several species but these should almost certainly be united.

The Dinophyceales seem to represent a genetic experiment which has had difficulty in survival, the more primitive forms having fared slightly better than the two ends of this branch, *Histioneis* and *Triposolenia.*

The Peridineales are a larger and more successful group which are frequently dominant or sub-dominant, especially in tropical and sub-tropical waters. Parke and Dixon follow other taxonomists in listing a number of monogeneric families such as the Glenodiniaceae and Glenodiniopsaceae which must be discarded, as PRAGER (1963) points out from his studies on axenic cultures of *G. foliaceum.* It is, in my opinion, preferable to put the Warnowiaceae with the Gymnodiniaceae, and *Polykrikos* could also be included in this group since *Goniaulax* also tends to show the longitudinal union of partially differentiated cells as in *G. series. Pronoctiluca* and *Noctiluca* are phagotrophic, colorless organisms, with probosces, and are naked. The latter genus is large but has dinoflagellate-like spores, really the only evidence of its relationship with the group. The Gymnodiniaceae are the most important group and represent large oceanic and estuarine populations at times. They differ much in the degree of morphological variation which they exhibit. The strain of *Gymnodinium simplex* from my laboratory is very constant in its morphology in the natural environment or in culture, but another form which we provisionally call *G. mirabile*, because this was the original designation we gave it on isolation, varies through the morphology of several *Gymnodinium* and one *Gyrodinium* species (KIMBALL and WOOD, 1965). The genera are divided according to the complexity of the girdle and sulcus. In *Gyrodinium*, the girdle is considerably offset and the sulcus straight or slightly sigmoid, with increasing length and twisting of both girdle and sulcus in *Cochlodinium*, *Warnowia* and *Nematodinium*, and the development of a pod in *Protoerythropsis*.

Of the thecate dinoflagellates, it seems preferable to retain the Peridiniaceae, including in this group the monogeneric families Amphilothaceae, Ptychodiscaceae (Glenodiniopsaceae, Glenodiniaceae), Peridiniaceae, Goniaulacaceae and Protocerataceae of Park and Dixon, the difference lying mainly in the plate formulae and spore shape (where it is known). The Heterodiniaceae might be retained, lying close to the Ceratiaceae which include two genera, *Ceratium* and *Centrodinium*. The Goniodomatacae include the symmetrical *Goniodoma* and the asymmetrical *Ceratocorys* and maybe the Cladopyxaceae *(Cladopyxis)* should be included here. The Oxytoxaceae *(Oxytoxum)* and Podolampaceae *(Podolampas* and *Blepharocysta)* are unique developments phylogenetically, while the remaining families of Parke and Dixon are either epiphytic or parisitic.

To show the confusion which appears to exist in formulating a phylogenetic classification of the flagellates, the nuclear division of *Goniaulax* has some characteristics of other dinoflagellates, and others of the euglenids according to DODGE (1964).

Nutrition of dinoflagellates

Most dinoflagellates contain chlorophyll and may therefore be regarded as primarily photosynthetic. Many of them are also able to ingest particulate matter including other dinoflagellates, and they must therefore be regarded as potential or actual phagotrophs. *Gymnodinium simplex* and other species which were tested by HUTNER and PROVASOLI (1951, 1954) or PROVASOLI and McLAUGHLIN (1963) could not be grown in the dark, though many were auxotrophic. The naked dinoflagellates often produce large quantities of extracellular substances and many of them can be observed inside a large blob of gelatinous material. They may thus be responsible for a large amount of the particulate organic matter associated with dinoflagellate blooms.

The Cryptophyceae

These are a small group of naked monads with a furrow which may lead to a "gullet". The flagella arise at the upper end of the furrow and may be lateral or terminal; the reserve material is starch or lipid. There are two or three families, Cryptomonadaceae (may include the Senniaceae) and the Cyanthomonadaceae.

These organisms are phototrophic if they contain chlorophyll and also phagotrophic. They have a thick, elastic cuticle, are flattened laterally, two slightly unequal flagella and their pigments include chlorophyll *a* and *c* and biliproteins. Marine genera include *Cryptomonas*, *Chilomonas*, *Rhodomonas*, *Chroomonas*, *Cryptochrysis*, *Hillea*, *Hemiselmis* and *Cyathomonas*. They divide longitudinally and may have a palmella stage as in *Cryptomonas*. *Chilomonas* and *Cryptella* are colorless genera. The cryptomonads are frequent in oceanic and estuarine waters within the photic zone, especially in warmer waters, but their importance in the phytoplankton has not been determined. *Nephroselmis gilva* has characters of the Cryptophyceae and Chlorophyceae bridging the gap between *Micromonas* and *Pyramimonas* (PARKE and RAYNS, 1964).

The Chrysophyceae

The Chrysophyceae, on account of their pigments and other attributes, are believed to be phylogenetically close to the Bacillarophyceae which have on occasion been united with them, taxonomically. The relationship is probably that of a common origin rather than a direct affinity. The silicoflagellates are now often included in this group, and so were many of the groups now placed by CHRISTENSEN (1964) and PARKE (1961) in Haptophyceae. Among the Chrysophyceae as amended by Parke and Dixon are the families Phaeothaminaceae (one genus), Phaeosaccionaceae (one genus), Ochromonadaceae (four genera), Dinobryaceae (two genera), Synuraceae (three genera), Ruttneraceae (one genus), Chromulinaceae (three genera), Chrysapsidaceae (one genus), Pedinellaceae (two genera), Chrysococcaceae (two genera), Sarcinochrysidaceae (one genus), Thallochrysidaceae (one genus), Chrysomeridaceae (one genus), Dictyochaceae (one genus—silicoflagellates).

The chrysomonads have an elastic cuticle naked or with uncalcified or lightly silicified plates, similar in shape to those of the coccolitho-phores and of similar origin (see PARKE et al., 1955, 1956, 1959, 1962). The majority contain chlorophyll and are phototrophs, heterotrophs or phagotrophs as opportunity offers, i.e., are myxotrophic. They have flagellate and pseudopodial forms, and may be free-swimming or attached. The phototrophic forms contain chlorophyll a and c, fucoxanthin and β-carotene; *Prymnesium parvum* also contains dia-toxanthin and produces a toxin. The storage product of photo-synthesis is leucosin, which is contained in vacuoles. The silico-flagellates have a siliceous endoskeleton which supports the organism. The Chrysomonads are motile by one to three unequal flagella which are terminal. They contain one or two contractile vacuoles, have an isogamous sexual phase, and may divide by fission or budding. They are widely distributed in marine environments, but do not appear to be of major importance except in certain areas close to shore.

The Haptophyceae (including the coccolithophores)

This group of organisms, apart from the coccolithophores (Fig.12), was separated from the Chrysophyceae by PARKE in 1961. It contains the same pigments as the Chrysophyceae and the same general charac-ters of the flagellation and storage products, as well as having the same nutrition. Marine families recorded by Park are: Isochrysidaceae *(Dicrateria* and *Isochrysis*, both important marine genera in certain localities), Prymnesiaceae *(Chrysochromulina*—marine; *Platychrisis* and *Prymnesium*—sometimes marine), Phaeocystaceae *(Phaeocystis*, some-times dominant in marine environments, especially in the Antarctic), Chrysotilaceae *(Apistonema)* and the coccolithophorid families Syracosphaeraceae with a number of genera, some obviously, others less obviously identical, Coccolithaceae, and the doubtful Braarudo-sphaeraceae, Thoracosphaeraceae and Ochrosphaeraceae. Some of the Coccolithophores are the sporophytes of filamentous gametophytes belonging to the Chrysotilaceae; other forms are motile phases of other cyst forms listed as Coccolithineae and possibly Braarudo-sphaeraceae and Thoracosphaeraceae. Parke's work on this group, as far as it has gone, suggests that the sporophyte-gametophyte relation-ship may exist in more of these forms so we may expect still more revision of both the Chrysophyceae and the Haptophyceae in the future.

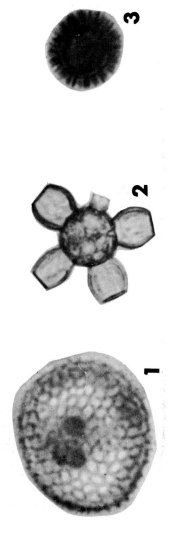

Fig.12. Coccolithophores. *1. Coccolithus, 2. Scyphosphaera, 3. Rhabdosphaera.*

Some forms, e.g., *Coccolithus fragilis* have palmelloid stages which may remain in the plankton up to 60 days and from between 5,000 and 50,000 cells. These palmelloid stages can, according to BERNARD (1963) sink at the rate of 4–260 m/h when suspended in tubes. Bernard believes that they carry with them vitamins and other organic materials.

PARKE (1961) has shown that the classification of the Chrysophyceae and the Haptophyceae is complicated by the fact that many of them have a life history including two or more phases. The coccolithophore *Coccolithus pelagicus* has a *Crystallolithus* motile phase, which is distinguished from the genus *Chrysochromulina* when the scales have become calcified. Even with the scaly exoskeleton, both forms are phagotrophic. The type of life history in which there are two coccolithophore phases is apparently quite common. There is, however, another type of life history in which the coccolithophore stage alternates with a non-motile or attached *Apistonema* stage. In this case, a number of stages occur which have in the past been given generic names. Parke lists the stages of *Syracosphaera carteri* and two other coccolithophores as an *Ochrosphaera* stage, non-motile and possibly attached by a haptonema, possibly a *Chryosphaera* stage, followed by *Nematochrysis* or *Thallochrysis* stages and *Apistonema* and *Chrysonema* and later a *Chrysotila* stage. The problem then becomes one of relating the coccolithophores with the Apistonema and other stages.

Coccolithus huxleyi has been shown by BRAARUD (1963) to have a non-motile stage with coccoliths, a motile, non-flagellate amoeboid stage, non-motile, naked cells, and biflagellate, naked cells which may have coccoliths. The number of coccoliths varied from one to several layers.

Parke comments that it will probably be found that life history studies will supersede the present method of classification by means of the coccoliths. She does not suggest that all marine benthic Chrysophyceae or Haptophyceae are stages of coccolithophores. The haptophycean *Phaeocystis* has a motile *Prymnesium* form. The work of Parke is still continuing and the problems of this group of microorganisms are being steadily elucidated. At the same time, it is exceedingly difficult for the student to know the exact relationships of the orgaisms he is finding in the plankton or benthos.

The coccolithophores are numerically an exceedingly important group in many tropical waters such as those of the Atlantic and parts of the Indian Ocean, so a knowledge of their life-histories becomes very important to the ecologist. They are also important as food of a number of marine invertebrates, as their numbers may drop overnight by up to an order of magnitude, due presumably to grazing. This makes it important for us to know, not only their life histories but also their nutrition and the relative importance to them of phototrophy, heterotrophy and phagotrophy. The fact that they have been recorded from depths to 5,000 m by BERNARD (1963), WOOD (1966), and others suggests that aphotic means of nutrition may be very important in this group in the oceans, and this in turn is important in productivity equations.

PAASCHE (1964), in a detailed study of the inorganic carbon uptake during coccolith formation, concluded that this formation is independent of carbon assimilation, but is light-dependent probably due to its association with cyclic phosphorylation; that it is derived from bicarbonate ion and not from carbon dioxide. On the other hand, if coccolith formation occurs outside the cell membrane, as in the *Crystallolithus* stage of *Coccolithus pelagicus* (MANTON and LEEDALE, 1963), the conditions of calcification will be very different. Incidentally, with such different mechanisms for forming coccoliths, one is led to wonder whether the inclusion in one genus of the two species mentioned is tenable.

The Xanthophyceae (Heterokontae)

This group of microorganisms is a mixed one and includes some motile algal spores; it is also a dumping ground for other species of unknown relationships. As an example, *Vaucheria* was placed here by Parke as recently as 1964 (PARKE and RAYNS, 1964), but it has also been suggested on good grounds that this genus be transferred to the Chrysophyceae. The cells are markedly dorsoventral with two (occasionally one) unequal flagella and have only chlorophyll *a* as a photosynthetic pigment. The families include the Heterochloridaceae, Rhizochloridaceae, Heterogloeaceae, Pleurochloridaceae, Characiopsodaceae and Tribonemataceae. They are present in marine environments, but their importance relative to other groups is unknown. SCAGEL and STEIN (1961) recently described several of these from the northwest Pacific. I have found them rarely in oceanic phytoplankton and believe they are important only in local inshore situations.

The Prasinophyceae

This group, separated by PARKE and RAYNS (1964), includes green forms some of which were included in the Volvocales such as *Pyramimonas*. The genera included here by Parke are important in marine environments, e.g., *Heteromastix, Micromonas, Asteromonas, Pyramimonas, Stephanoptera, Tetraselmis, Prasinocladus, Hexasterias, Hemiselmis, Pachysphaeria, Pterosperma, Sphaeropsis, Hyalophysa* and the spherical *Halosphaera* which has *Pyramimonas*-like spores, or which may be regarded as a cystose stage of a *Pyramimonas*. *Micromonas pusilla* is the *Chromulina pusilla* of BUTCHER (1961), which on account of its pigments should never have been placed in the Chrysomonads.

The Chlorophyceae

Only the microscopic flagellates of this group will be treated here. We must remember nevertheless that many of the filamentous forms such as *Ulva* and *Enteromorpha* have unicellular, flagellate spores.

Of the Volvocales, *Dunaliella* is important in estuarine environments and sometimes in the sea; *Collodictyon, Brachiomonas, Chlamydonephrys, Pyramichlamys* and *Pseudoraciborskia* are unimportant as far as is known, *Chlorella, Nannochloris* and *Oocystis* are frequent in estuaries, while *Sphenochloris, Chlorococcum, Trebouxia, Characium, Codiolum, Sykidion, Chlorochytrium, Gomontia* and *Ostreobium* are also unimportant.

The Euglenaceae

These are important in the surface sediments, particularly the colorless ones such as *Astasia*, though *Euglena, Phacus* and *Eutreptia* may occur in the phytoplankton, as well as in the sediments of the estuaries. Forms such as *Trachelomonas, Leptocinclis* are rare and possibly adventitious in marine environments. *Eutreptiella* is probably synonymous with *Eutreptia* as PRINGSHEIM (1948) suggested. These organisms have a more or less elastic integument, an eye spot, a gullet with a narrow canal, and one, or more usually two flagella.

They contain chlorophylls *a* and *b* and store paramylum. They are phagotrophic or osmotrophic, and those with chlorophyll are photo-trophic.

CHAPTER IV

MARINE MICROORGANISMS

(colorless Protozoa)

Formerly, the chlorophyll-containing and colorless flagellates were classed together among the Protozoa, and some authors still maintain this classification. The pigmented flagellates were known as the Phytomastigina and the colorless as Zoomastigina. PRINGSHEIM (1948) raised the question of the relationship between the two groups in his discussion of the euglenids and showed that it was possible to cause *Euglena* to lose its pigment more or less permanently, thus making it identical, morphologically and physiologically with the colorless *Astasia*. Such relationships are not confined to the Euglenaceae so the distinction between Zoomastigina and Phytomastigina becomes academic. For this reason, the flagellates (colored and colorless) have been discussed with the algae.

It should also be remembered that some of the amoebae have flagellate stages or vice versa, and that no hard and fast line can be drawn between plants and animals at this stage.

THE SARCODINA

Foraminifera (Plate VIII)

The importance of the Foraminifera is largely due to their abundance in the fossil record. At the present time, they are rarely abundant in the plankton, and I can only remember one or two stations in the many thousand that I have examined to which Foraminifera were dominant or even abundant, and these were close to antarctic upwelling water north of Bass Strait in the Southern Hemisphere. In routine sampling for these organisms, a 30 l sample does not give sufficient individuals for either quantitative or qualitative study; this will give some idea of their present-day distribution in warmer seas.

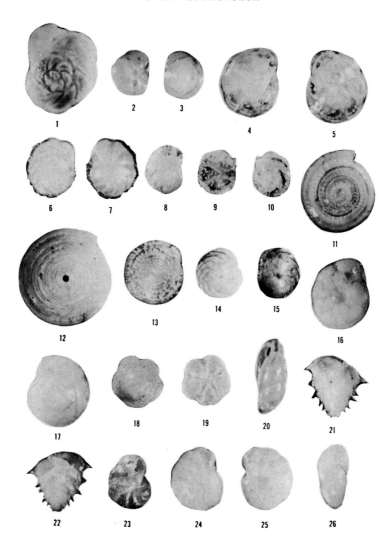

Plate VIII. Planktonic Foraminifera. (Photo by W. Bock.)

They occur, not only in the plankton, but as epontic organisms attached to algae such as *Ecklonia*.

Classification

The classification, as with so many of the unicellular organisms, is very subjective and tends to be complicated, as is usual when it is not possible to study variation in culture, except of course with the living species. Most of the taxonomists of this group are palaeontologists, and not interested in living forms, though this is now changing.

GLAESSNER (1948) gives the following super-families:

(*1*) Astrorhizideae with arenaceous shells, unilocular, tests tubular, stellate or sub-spherical and aperture simple, terminal or absent.

(*2*) Lituloidea with arenaceous, simple shells, straight, uniserial, biserial or complex and variable apertures.

(*3*) Endothyridea with arenaceous, composite or calcareous, complex shells, planospiral, apertures basal or absent.

(*4*) Miliolidea with imperforate, calcareous simple shells coiled in varying planes, apertures simple, dentate or cribrate.

(*5*) Lagenidea, Bulimidea and Rotaliidea are calcareous, perforate usually simple forms, the first being uniserial, the other normally trochospiral to biserial, the last mentioned usually complex.

Biology of Foraminifera

The shells may be composed of tectin (sand grains embedded in an organic matrix) or crystalline calcite. The organisms possess a pseudopodial network of fine protoplasmic extensions, which move about and are filled with granules which seem to stream actively in opposite directions at the same time. The mechanism of this intracellular motility has not been determined. In the tectin-shelled Foraminifera, a particular grain-size is selected by the organism, e.g., sponge spicules, sand grains of limited size.

The animals feed on bacteria, Protozoa and algae, including diatoms, digesting their food in food-vacuoles. At times they will stockpile their phytoplanktonic food giving a green halo and fluorescing bright red with violet light, appearing as red globes. Some are specific in their feeding, being restricted to one species, e.g., of *Nitzschia* and being repelled by another species of the same genus. They may even attract certain species of algae, e.g., *Dunaliella parva*, according to LEE and FREUDENTHAL (1963) and LEE et al. (1963). Many species contain zooxanthellae.

Reproduction

There is an alternation of generations, meiosis taking place in the asexual generation and resembling plant rather than animal reproduction. *Agamont* or *schizont* is larger than the *gamont* but the initial chamber of the test is smaller (microsphaeric) than that of the gamont (macrosphaeric). The gamonts are uninucleate, haploid and in *Rosalina* coil clockwise, whereas the agamonts are diploid, multinucleate and coil counter-clockwise. Schizogony produces multiple gamonts which grow for one or two years and release flagellate or amoeboid gametes which pair to form a zygote which secretes the first chamber.

Distribution

Living Foraminifera occur in salt marshes, in shallow or deep water, in benthic, epontic and planktonic communities. Some are confined to Arctic and Antarctic waters, some to warm or tropical seas. We may get alternation of species in a region, due to temperature changes in the case of stenothermal species; the winter-spring forms may sink into, and remain in colder water in the summer; some species change the direction of coiling in different seasons. Planktonic foraminifera have been studied by BÉ (1959) who listed nineteen species from the north Atlantic, belonging to the genera *Globorotalia*, *Globigerina*, *Globigerinita*, *Globigerinoides*, *Orbulina*, *Pulleniatina*, *Candeina*, *Hastigerina*, *Globigerinella* and *Hastigerinella*. Bé noted that most species were found in the three water masses studied by him, the Sargasso Sea, Gulf Stream and continental slope area. He divided the species into warm and cold water forms on account of their temperature preferences.

Heliozoa

This group of protozoa is amoeboid in character with a hyaline ectoplasm and a granular endoplasm, contractile and pulsating vacuoles, one or more nuclei and pseudopods, typically strengthened by axial rods, but others may be thread-like or reticulate. They have no firmly knit skeleton, and may be naked or may have a protective covering of siliceous spines or plates or both. A few Heliozoa are marine but the majority are confined to fresh water.

Radiolaria

These amoeboid organisms form huge fossil beds from past ages, but still occur in saline environments, though not in their former quantities. They have a capsule which separates two protoplasmic regions, the inner one containing the nucleus, the outer with contractile threads, which give rise to the pseudopodia. The hard parts consist of siliceous tests which have varying relations to the protoplasm of the cell. In some it is internal, in some external; and in others partly internal, partly external. The life cycle is unknown though sexual reproduction has been postulated. The Radiolaria contain zooxanthellae and are stated to be able to live without particulate food in the light; those living below the photic zone are reported to be phagotrophic, although many of them contain chlorophyll-bearing zooxanthellae. It is apparent that a detailed study of the reproduction and physiology of this group is urgently needed.

Taxonomy

There is a large number of divisions of the Radiolaria which it is not proposed to give here. The two generally recognized orders are Porulosida and Osculosida with four sub-orders, totalling 901 genera. The reader is referred to MOORE's treatise (1954) for further details.

THE CILIATA

This group of organisms contains a number of genera which are to be found in the marine environment. The most important planktonic group are the Tintinnids which were dealt with monographically by KOFOID and CAMPBELL (1939).

The Tintinnina (Fig.13)

The Tintinnina are characterised by a conical or trumpet-shaped extensile body inside a test or *lorica*, which consists of a clear organic material which may be impregnated with particles such as sand grains. The organism is attached to the lorica only at the base, and expands and contracts within it. At the broad end of the body are a series of membranelles surrounding a peristome. A ciliary membrane exists

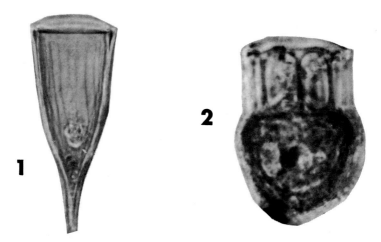

Fig. 13. Tintinnid loricae. *1. Rhabdonella, 2. Dictyocysta.*

below the membranelles, and body cilia extend backwards on the outside of the animal. Zooxanthellae occur in some species, and the host organism is frequently green owing to chlorophyll released from the plant food according to CAMPBELL (1942). The cell contains macro- and micro-nuclei. Reproduction is by conjugation and by binary fission.

The lorica, which is used as a taxonomic feature, is very characteristic and makes these organisms very useful as indicators of water masses. It is tapered from a closed end to an open one, the animals being attached at the former, with the membranelles at the latter. The test wall may be laminar, prismatic, alveolar or hyaline, may have particles of various materials impregnated with it, and may be of different shape with various bands or rings all having diagnostic value.

The Tintinnids feed on phytoplankton and bacteria, according to Campbell; whether they use particulate but not living organic matter or can use dissolved organics has not been stated.

Taxonomy

Family Tintinnidiidae. The lorica is tubular or saccate with or without a suboral spiral structure, the wall is gelatinous, frequently with aggregated particles.

Family Codonellopsidae has a top-shaped hyaline collar, often spiral and a dense, rotund bowl, the base round or pointed or with a horn.

Family Dictyocystidae has a dense bowl and collar formed of arched frames and windows, no aboral horn, and the wall is wholly reticulate.

Family Coxiellidae has a tubular or goblet-shaped lorica, open or closed aborally, wall smooth or with spiral lamina.

Family Cytharocyclididae has a bell-shaped lorica with a flared collar; wall has a coarse structure.

Family Ptychocyclididae has a bell-shaped lorica with a denticulate or lipped rim; may have a pilar lamina and an aboral horn.

Family Epiplocyclididae has a short acorn-shaped lorica with an entire oral rim, blunt base with or without horn; reticulate.

Family Petalotrichidae has cup-shaped lorica with wide, smooth or dentate oral rim and one or more collars, wall hyaline with faint primary structure.

Family Rhabdonellidae has chalice-shaped or conical lorica, smooth mouth, aboral end with a horn, may be pedicillate; wall with raised, maybe spiral ribs.

Family Cystonellidae has an elongate chalice-shaped lorica with a long, narrow pedicel, not ribbed but with primary and secondary structure.

Family Undellidae has a goblet-shaped lorica, a close aboral end and trilaminate wall, intermediate region without secondary structure.

Family Tintinnidae has a variable lorica with flared oral region and a hyaline wall.

Other ciliates

Other ciliates are numerous in the estuarine environment where they occur in the plankton, the epiphyton and in the sediments, even under anaerobiosis. The marine ciliates have been greatly neglected both as regards taxonomy and ecology. HAMBURGER and Von BRUD-DENBROCK-HEIDELBERG (1907) list five orders: Holotricha, Heterotricha, Oligotricha, Hypotricha and Peritricha, and about 180 species. The reader is referred to this work for taxonomy.

The ciliate *Euplotes* was found by BAAS BECKING and WOOD (1955) growing in and feeding on a culture of *Desulfovibrio* at a redox potential of -270 mV at pH 7.5. The medium consisted of sea water ammonium chloride and di-potassium phosphate, with steel wool added to produce hydrogen. The ciliates were observed to ingest the bacteria. They are usually present in small numbers in protoplankton catches, but become obvious only in ageing primary cultures of phytoplankton. As the redox potential of ocean water is of the order of $+450$ mV, the Eh range is at least 730 mV, i.e., through the whole of the oceanic and estuarine ecosystems. Their pH limits are not known, but they appear to have no difficulty in occurring throughout the whole marine habitat. I have not observed them in deep water samples or in the deep sediments but they may well be there. When they are numerous in phytoplankton cultures, they decimate the phytoplankton, and one can imagine that they would play a decisive part in the degradation of large blooms such as red tides. However, this is mere speculation.

Ciliates have been seen in some quantity in sea-ice habitats in the Antarctic by J. S. Bunt (personal communication).

CHAPTER V

MICROBIAL SYMBIOSES

Symbiosis may be defined as the living together in close association of two or more organisms, for mutual benefit. This does not necessarily mean that each of the two derives an equal benefit from the association, but does require that neither will cause the death of the other either directly or indirectly. Often the dividing line between symbiosis and parasitism is very fine, and a symbiont, particularly a bacterial symbiont, may become parasitic by a slight change in the environment, depressing the activity of one participant relatively to the other. For example, although *Escherichia coli* is a normal inhabitant of the human intestinal tract, it can, at times, cause malaise if not definite disease. The benefits to the partners in symbioses may be and usually are, or are believed to be nutritional, but one may provide the other with transportation (e.g., algae contained in ciliates), or protection as in the case of the algae within *Hydra* with its nematocysts.

BACTERIAL SYMBIOSES

One of the most startling cases of symbiosis is that of certain fishes with the luminous bacterium *Pseudomonas (Photobacterium)*. In this case the bacteria live in certain glands of the fish where they obtain their nutrients for heterotrophic growth and in return provide light which the fish use to attract their prey. In one case, the gland is reversible and in another a membrane is present, which can be used as a blind and in either case the fish is able to turn the light on and off at will.

Symbiotic associations between bacteria and other marine organisms have not been well documented, and there is no record of anything to correspond with the *Rhizobium* association. Bacteria do occur in the intracellular spaces of algae such as *Penecillus* and other

Siphonales, and are active in the precipitation of calcium carbonate. Whether they are merely adventitious there or have a symbiotic association with the plant is not known. The dependence of many marine micro-algae on vitamin B_{12} produced by bacteria and other algae is well known, but, as there is no definite spatial relation between bacteria and algae, this can hardly be called symbiosis; it is rather a case of metabiosis. JOHANNES (1964b) suggested that bacteria in the gut of certain amphipods and other crustacea alter the nature of undigested phosphorus compounds so that these newly formed compounds were available to the same or other zooplankters which reingested the fecal pellets.

ALGAL SYMBIOSES

DROOP (1963a) has recently published a very good review of algal and invertebrate symbioses, and gives a long list of the species and groups known to be involved. We are interested only in the species which belong in the marine environment, so our list will be somewhat shorter. It will include both bacterial and algal symbioses.

In the tropics, many, probably most, of the reef-occurring animals have algal symbionts and these extend through most of the invertebrate animal phyla. There are also a few algal symbionts in other algae, and these again are mostly confined to tropical and sub-tropical waters. Quantitatively, it is probably true that the symbiotic algae are more important than the phytoplankton and free benthic algae in coral reefs and other shallow waters with calcareous sediments, and that the productivity of such waters is essentially due to such symbionts which are more usually known as zooxanthellae.

Very recent work by DiSALVO (1965) suggests that the algal symbionts of the corals exceed the biomass of the animal components by as much as five to one, and that they produce a large excess of oxygen. It would seem that these zooxanthellae are as important in the coral reef environment of the tropics and sub-tropics as are the benthic micro-algae of the salt marshes and estuarine flats.

DROOP (1963a) points out that the symbionts are known as *Cyanellae* if they belong to the Cyanophyceae, as *Zoochlorellae* if they belong to the Chlorophyceae and as *Zooxanthellae* if they are yellow in color, i.e., belong to the Dinophyceae. Nearly all the marine symbionts are zooxanthellae, so this term has come to be specific for marine symbionts.

The symbiotic relationship between two plants or between plant and animal may be such that both members benefit equally, or one may benefit greatly and the other hardly at all. In symbioses between plants, such as *Richelia* and the diatoms *Rhizosolenia* and *Pleurosigma*, the blue-green *Richelia* would appear to gain physical protection by living within the siliceous test of the diatom, and the diatoms frequently lose much or all of their chlorophyll, so we may presume that the blue-green does most of the photosynthesis. *Rhizosolenia* is a planktonic diatom and there seems little advantage in its having another photosynthont as a partner, except that *Richelia* is a member of the Nostocaceae and this family has the ability to fix atmospheric or dissolved nitrogen. Several species of *Rhizosolenia* are known to contain *Richelia,* though not every cell in a given population will necessarily do so. I do not know of another record than my own of the benthic *Pleurosigma* containing *Richelia;* that record was from the north Australian coast inside the Great Barrier Reef where there was considerable turbulence. *Pleurosigma* is actively motile and the cells contained chlorophyll; in this case the advantage to the blue-green may have been mobility and protection, that to the diatom nitrogen. It may also be that *Pleurosigma* is a facultative heterotroph which could be of use to *Richelia* in turbid waters.

ZOOXANTHELLAE

In the algal-animal relationships we have basic physiological differences in the two partners, one being phytotrophic and the other zootrophic. As I have stated, the marine algae associated with zooxanthellae are almost exclusively dinoflagellates and these in the free-living state are usually facultatively phagotrophic, though the Miami strains of the free-living *Gymnodinium simplex* cannot be grown in darkness. It would be interesting to know whether the symbiotic strains of dinoflagellates have any power of phagotrophic nutrition. It is known that many dinoflagellate species require vitamin B_{12} and possibly other growth substances. They may well gain these substances by their association with the animals, most if not all of which can and probably do ingest and digest bacteria which in turn are believed to provide cyanocobalamin for most auxotrophic marine algae. It is assumed that the algae pass organic materials to the animal, and this has been proven in some cases, e.g., T. F. Goreau and N. I. Goreau (personal communication) for *Tridacna*. It is also possible that the animal is not necessarily able to assimilate all this material. Zooxanthellae of Gorgonian corals produce terpenes (D. W. Anderson, personal communication) and these substances are quite refractory and do not seem to be digested or used by the coral. The quantity of external metabolites produced by micro-algae may amount to 50% of the total photo-assimilate, and dinoflagellates investigated have been shown to be prolific in these substances. Some of these, e.g., the terpenes mentioned above, have been shown to be bacteriostatic or even inhibitory, and some to accelerate bacterial growth in limited quantities. If such substances were produced by the zooxanthellae, they could be of indirect use to their hosts in encouraging the growth of digestable bacteria or in repelling deleterious organisms. It would be interesting to see whether such low molecular weight organics as glycollate are retained quantitatively by the animals, or are partly or wholly excreted into the environment. It would also be interesting to know whether such substances can be taken up by either the animal or the zooxanthellae. If particulate matter excreted by the algae, either directly or by accretion, is also excreted through the animal tissues, this might again be ingested by the animal in ordinary digestive processes. Peptides and organic acids which have been shown to be excreted by algae may well be assimilated directly by the animals. That this is true is suggested by the fact that some adult Radiolaria containing zooxanthellae do not feed. *Paramecium bursaria* with *Chlorella*, a fresh water zoochlorella, does feed and is stimulated by glucose in the light.

Some animals, e.g., madrepore corals, expel their algal symbionts when solid food is unavailable to the coral; apparently the alga takes nutrient from the coral, and we suppose supplies in return some product which is unavailable to the animal, but desirable if not necessary, though T. F. Goreau (personal communication) could not demonstrate this. If the animals are kept in the dark, the algae frequently use animal products as carbon sources, but do not seem to be completely heterotrophic, thus conforming to the general pattern of dinoflagellate metabolism. Many of the animals associated with zooxanthellae excrete the algae in times of stress, e.g., Gorgonian corals (E. J. F. Wood and F. M. Bayer, unpublished) and frequently devour them. Others do so regularly at certain stages of their life history. Thus, the degree of interdependence and of reciprocity varies from one species to another, and also in different stages of the animal's life history.

It is assumed that the animals utilize to some extent the oxygen produced by the plants in photosynthesis, but whether this oxygen is necessary for the respiration of the animals is not known. It has been suggested that the oxygen available from phytoplankton photosynthesis should be sufficient for the animals without that from the zooxanthellae, but the most active symbiosis takes place in tropical coral reefs where the calcium carbonate–bicarbonate content of the water is high, precipitation is continuous and nutrients poor, due possibly to co-precipitation. In such cases, e.g., in the Straits of Florida, the phytoplankton is far from numerous and possibly insignificant in the oxygenation of the water, so the zooxanthellae may be necessary for the respiration of reef animals. Carbon dioxide produced by the animals may well be required by the plants for maximum photosynthesis, as the availability of bicarbonate and carbon dioxide decreases rapidly with increasing pH, and carbonate precipitation is heavy in shallow reef waters. In bright sunshine on shallow reefs, the respired carbon dioxide would be available to the zooxanthellae with minimum diffusion. Nitrogen compounds, mostly organic, are assimilated directly from the animals by the algae, and it is possible also that the algae may scavenge nitrogen and phosphorus from the water and store them when they are in excess of the plant requirements, as GOLDBERG et al. (1951) have shown for diatoms. The flow of these nutrients would be controlled by diffusion gradients and membrane selectivity.

The mechanisms of symbioses of the plant–animal kind differ from one group of organisms to another. In some cases, each generation of animal does not contain the algae after division and must be reinfected, often by phagocytosis, the degree of infection depending on the abundance of free-living algae at the time. Some animal species which are carnivorous may obtain their algae after digesting the animals that previously contained them. In many Protozoa, the algae are divided between the two daughter cells at division, and thus quantitative continuity is maintained. In most coelenterates, the unfertilized egg contains algal cells and thus continuity of infection is assured. The degree of certainty of transmission is apparently not paralleled by the necessity of the symbiosis to the animal. The adjustment of the number of cells in each host may be obtained by chemoregulatory means (supply and demand of nutrients exchanged) or by digestion by the animal of surplus cells; in some cases, divisions of the alga and host synchronize to some extent, and if they get out of phase, colorless hosts are common. One of the most difficult questions is how the algae resist digestion if they are taken into the host by phagocytosis.

The existence of chlorophyll-containing zooxanthellae in a number of Radiolaria at depths to 4,000 m in the eastern Mediterranean is very difficult to explain. These cells were found in September, some six months after the sinking of the surface water in that area. Moreover, the zooxanthellae were found at all depths, and there seems no doubt that they were autochthonous. They were accompanied by chlorophyll-containing ceratia which were in chains and obviously still dividing.

It seems strange that the Radiolaria should continue to support plant cells which, in the absence of light (other than that of bioluminescence), must, it would seem, be entirely supported by their animal counterparts. One would expect that such animals would be at a disadvantage in competing with other unicellular animals without zooxanthellae, and would therefore be outgrown in the struggle for existence. The discovery of these symbionts raises questions which must be answered if we are to understand the nutrition of plant-animal symbioses.

It is interesting to note that plant-animal symbiosis in the marine world is far more common in warm than in cold waters. DROOP (1963a) suggests that it is due to the more rapid metabolism in warm waters requiring more rapid removal of waste products and that the symbionts assist one another in this. The relationship of the algae to the carbon dioxide equilibria is probably more important in tropical waters where the sediments consist largely of calcium carbonate. The algae, of course, are assured of remaining in a relatively constant light intensity range, and there is no chance of desiccation. Further, the high production of primary energy from sunlight makes the ecosystem much more efficient. Tropical and sub-tropical waters are normally much more transparent than cooler waters and this may well account for the greater growth of these symbiotic algae;

we have yet to learn their light requirements however. The productivity of these reef areas is much higher than that of the open oceans nearby, but this is to be expected. It is, however, of the same order as that of algal beds in cooler areas. The larger algae disappear as we approach warmer waters, maximum growth of the Laminarias and *Macrocystis* occurring in higher latitudes, on the colder sides of the sub-tropical convergences. In the tropics, algal beds are restricted to the smaller browns, greens and especially the reds, mostly corallines, and the algae of the zooxanthellae. These last then, play a very important part in the productivity of tropical waters, especially in the vast reef areas.

An interesting experiment was recently made with the sponge *Tethya* which contains a number of green spherical bodies and has been stated in the literature to have zooxanthellae or more probably cyanellae. Portions of the sponge containing the green bodies were examined under the fluorescence microscope using light at 450 mμ but showed no red chlorophyll fluorescence. Acetone extracts were studied in the spectrophotometer and gave no chlorophyll peak, but showed an almost pure β-carotene absorption curve. The green coloration is apparently due to a carotin-protein complex. Because the bodies in *Tethya* look so like algal cells, one begins to wonder whether some at least of the records of zooxanthellae are due to the same cause.

Fig.14. *Coscinodiscus excentricus* with rays of a pectinoid substance.

Brenneckella was regarded as a case of symbiosis, but GAARDER and HASLE (1962) believe that this is really *Coscinodiscus excentricus* which has produced a gelatinous envelope to which coccolithophores have attached, rather than a case of symbiotic growth. In the tropics, cells of *C. excentricus* frequently have a gelatinous envelope, often with four to six spoke-like gelatinous rays (Fig.14).

In addition to algal symbionts of animals and other plants, certain symbioses exist between algae and fungi resembling more or less, and perhaps homologous, with the lichens. These include:

Blodgettia confervoides

        with fungus *Blodgettiomyces* and algae *Cladophora,*
        with fungus *Mycosphaerella* and algae *Pelvetia,*
        with fungus *Mycosphaerella* and algae *Ascophyllum;*
        with fungus *Guignardia*   and algae *Prasiola;*
        with fungus *Guignardia*   and algae *Ulva.*

CHAPTER VI

THE ROLE OF MICROORGANISMS IN THE WATER

THE MARINE ENVIRONMENT

If we are to understand the role of microorganisms in a given environment, we must first consider the peculiarities of the environment, and the niches which the organisms have to fill. The oceanic environment is controlled primarily by physical factors, the earth's rotation, insolation, temperature, water density (which brings in a chemical factor, chlorinity or salinity), wind and the effects of land masses. The earth's rotation, wind, and the land masses control and are responsible for the existence and direction of surface currents in the oceans. The surface currents often move at different directions from other layers of water below them. The lower currents are known as *Intermediate* and *Deep* currents.

The sub-surface currents are influenced in direction by the earth's rotation, convection, and the surface of the ocean bottom. For example, the deep Antarctic water is derived from the surface Antarctic water by the winter freeze removing water and leaving the salts in solution thus increasing density. This cold, highly saline water sinks around the lower salinity water of the sub-Antarctic and moves centrifugally northeast beneath it, being channelled by the continents and the bottom topography. The Intermediate water moves by convection generally in a direction roughly opposite the surface water. Each water mass tends by inertia to retain its identity for long distances and times, diffusion of salts and migration of organisms from one water mass to another being slow. There is thus a boundary between each water mass which can be usually defined by a sharp change in density (σ t) represented by differences in salinity and temperature, usually referred to as a thermocline, or less frequently a halocline. Temperature is preferred to salinity as a criterion because it is easier to measure, particularly since the development of the bathythermograph which can be used from a moving vessel and thus increase the number of measurements that can be taken. The boundary, however, creates friction and this causes turbulence resulting in eddy diffusion and thus some mixing.

Vertical movement of water can be caused by the bottom contour, changes in density due to insolation, evaporation or precipitation, or to winds, especially off-shore winds close to the land. As an example of bottom contour affecting upwelling, the southern Tasman Sea is almost flat at about 5,000 m, and the Antarctic bottom water is moving north between Tasmania and New Zealand. A shelf extends off the west coast of New Zealand for about 400 miles and a series of ridges running northwest arises in the Central Tasman Sea. These confine the Antarctic bottom water and divert it towards the west. A series of underwater canyons along the southeast coast of New South Wales completes the process, and water of Antarctic origin upwells at places along that coast.

Changes in density by insolation cause the heating of surface waters and consequent decrease of density; heavy precipitation of rain water produces the same effect by decreasing the salinity. This causes such waters to rise and, if moving, to flow over water which was previously of the same density or even lighter. Thus we may find a surface water mass flowing under another mass with the same primary characteristics, but now lighter, and maybe reappearing on the far side. The East Australian Current flowing south along the coast of New South Wales often encounters water of lower salinity in the vicinity of Bass Strait, passes under it and emerges on the northeast coast of Tasmania. Land drainage from New Guinea and the Moluccas causes the Arafura Sea to have a very low salinity and insolation causes a high temperature, so this water, as it flows through and south from Torres Strait, passes over the tropical high chlorinity water moving in from the equatorial Pacific in the northern Coral Sea. The latter water owes its high chlorinity to evaporation of water particles from the surface, another effect of insolation. Slow mixing occurs through eddy diffusion as the water mass moves south, and the East Australian current is the result, although complete mixing rarely occurs until the water mass turns east from Tasmania across to New Zealand. These phenomena are detectable by physico-chemical methods, but can also be followed by a study of the protoplankton communities as has been discussed in a series of papers by Wood (1964).

Upwelling and upward vertical movements generally introduce nutrients to the surrounding water and tend to increase phytoplankton production along the area affected by eddy diffusion. Movements in which the net transport of water is upward are known as *divergences*, as the upwelling water moves away from the divergence, those in which the net transport is downward are called *convergences* as the surface water moves towards the actual convergence zone. A thermocline is often a strong barrier to exchange of salts and organisms, as the rapid change of temperature requires more energy to provide mixing, so the vertical component of eddy diffusion is reduced and the water masses tend to slide over each other with a minimum of mixing. This also induces a continued difference in salinity at the boundary, and the change in density serves as a mechanical barrier to the microorganisms, which tend to concentrate either above or below the thermocline depending on nutrient concentrations or on the origin of the population. In the tropics, where insolation is high, nutrients tend to become rapidly used up at the surface so the phytoplankton maximum tends to be below the thermocline where nutrients can be reinforced from the intermediate water. In colder waters, where insolation is less and growth rates of organisms slower, the phytoplankton tends to mass above the thermocline, i.e., in the warmer regions especially in areas such as the ill-marked sub-tropical convergence of the Southern Hemisphere, the thermocline is ill-defined owing to mixing by wind and heavy seas, to upwelling, and to shallow density gradients; in parts of the Indian Ocean where there is much upwelling and influence of turbidity currents, there is no thermocline, and phytoplankton is more or less constant in numbers from the surface to a considerable depth. We shall discuss the detailed effect of current and other water movements on marine microorganisms later in this chapter.

Temperature

Temperature of sea water ranges from about $-2\,°C$ to over $30\,°C$ in the ocean waters and to over $40\,°C$ in shallow estuaries. In point of fact, a large majority of ocean waters is below $12\,°C$, so we might expect many microorganisms to have optima in this region or slightly higher, i.e., between 12 and 15 °C and recent work on bacteria and micro-algae by MORITA and HAIGHT (1964) and BUNT (1964) suggests that this is the case ("extreme psychrophils" of SCHOLES and SHEWAN, 1964), though most workers have chosen 22–25 °C as an incubation temperature. Changes in the physico-chemical aggregation of water occur at certain temperatures according to DROST-HANSEN (1956) and this may account for certain optimum temperatures among microorganisms. Microorganisms are much more tolerant of gradual changes over a wide temperature range than of sudden changes over a narrow range; this is probably why microbial populations in adjacent water masses may be very different, though the temperature difference is less than that through which the organisms continue to live in the same water mass. For example, waters from the Coral Sea and from the West Central South Pacific water masses often run parallel to each other off the Australian coast; the temperature of adjacent water may differ by about 2 °C but the water masses may lose 8–10 °C slowly during their southward movement, yet the two waters will have considerably different flora.

Salinity

The density of water depends on its temperature (the higher the temperature the lower the density) and total dissolved salts (salinity); the more salts the greater the density. These dissolved salts consist largely of sodium chloride so we frequently speak of the chlorinity (which includes only chlorine and other halide ions) rather than salinity (which includes total ions.) These can be equated by the following formula:

$$S\% = 0.030 + 1.8050 \ Cl\%$$

where S = salinity, and Cl = chlorinity, which is correct for the Baltic Sea but not for the fringe-ice area in the Antarctic where ice is melting into the surface water. Salinity is now usually determined by salinometers which measure electric conductivity of the water. The specific gravity of sea water can be determined accurately from salinity and temperature measurements with the aid of KNUDSEN's hydrographic tables (1901).

The salts present in ocean water have the following composition:

Na^+ 30.4%; Mg^{2+} 3.7%; Ca^{2+} 1.16%; K^+ 1.1%; Sr^{2+} 0.04%; HBO_3^- 0.07%; Cl^- 55.2%; SO_4^{2-} 7.7%; Br^- 0.19%; CO_3^{2+} + HCO_3^- 0.35%

The boric acid is mainly undissociated and the carbon dioxide mainly as bicarbonate.

It will be noticed that nitrogen and phosphorus compounds are not among the major components of seawater, but these, with practically every element, are present in sufficient quantity to promote biological growth, except in certain cases where one or another of them may prove limiting.

Two important processes control the availability of these minor constituents, chelation and adsorption. Hydrogen ion concentration, which so often controls availability in terrestrial environments, is usually between 6.5 and 8.3 and rarely, except in shallow estuaries, reaches 9.4. These pH ranges do not affect appreciably the availability of minor constituents with the exception of carbonates and bicarbonates. The effects of chelation and adsorption are similar in that they can remove toxic substances or provide nutrients by concentration.

Dissolved gases

Dissolved gases are exceedingly important in the sea for the maintenance of plant and animal life. In surface waters, especially those in which there is considerable wave action, the water is usually supersaturated with oxygen. In waters which have little motion over a long period, the rate of entry of oxygen will be much less, and biological, including microbial activity, may cause an actual reduction with consequent undersaturation. In shallow waters, oxygen values will show a diurnal variation dependent on the amount of photosynthesis during the day, and respiration during the night. In photosynthesis, water is the hydrogen donor for the reduction of carbon dioxide and so oxygen is released. In respiration, oxygen is used as the oxidant of carbon compounds to carbon dioxide, so the oxygen content of the water decreases. As respiration continues in plants during photosynthesis, the oxygen produced by them is diminished by the amount required for respiration, i.e., is *net oxygen*. It has been assumed that respiration was independent of photosynthesis so that oxygen consumption in the dark measured true respiration, and this could be added to the oxygen produced in the light to give a figure for total photosynthesis. It has long been suspected and recently shown that this assumption is invalid for the most part, and that a great deal of further work is necessary to allow us to determine a factor for respiration by photosynthesizing plants. In waters below the photic zone, for example, the Intermediate water, oxygen will become depleted by continuing animal and plant respiration, and if studies are made along a moving water mass it is possible to follow the biological use of oxygen and get an estimate, however crude, of the importance of this utilization of oxygen. In heavy plankton blooms, as in the shallow waters of the Gulf of Mexico and the continental shelf of Walvis Bay in South Africa, biological phenomena may completely use up all oxygen, and thus cause a mortality of all organisms which cannot live anaerobically. The same phenomenon may be sometimes observed in landlocked bays and estuaries. GRINDLEY and TAYLOR (1964) record such a mortality caused by deoxygenation during a red tide of *Goniaulax polygramma* and *Prorocentrum micans*.

Nitrogen is also dissolved in sea water, and because it is little used in life processes, it has been regarded as a conservative property of a water mass. The solubility of nitrogen, like that of oxygen, is controlled by salinity and temperature. It has recently been suggested that a number of marine microbes, i.e., all those containing an hydrogenase and certain blue-green algae in aerobic environments, may be able to fix quite considerable amounts of dissolved nitrogen; the extent to which this would affect the nitrogen content of a water mass is still unknown. Electric storms are also believed to contribute combined nitrogen to the oceans.

Together with nitrogen are the inert gases found in air such as argon, neon, krypton and xenon. In estuaries, traces of hydrogen and hydrocarbons such as methane have been detected, due no doubt to the activity of hydrogen- and methane-producing bacteria. Hydrogen sulfide is found in shallow waters where microbial sulfate reduction occurs in the sediments.

The carbon dioxide system

Plant life in the sea, and to an extent animal life also, is controlled by the carbon dioxide system. This consists of equilibria between carbon dioxide dissolved in the water, bicarbonate ion and carbonate ion. Plants depend mainly on bicarbonate ion as the source of their carbon, but can probably use some carbon dioxide. It appears however that carbonate ion is unavailable to them. The availability of bicarbonate is dependent on the hydrogen ion concentration of water and is greatest on the acid side of neutrality, i.e., at pH values below 7. As water gets more alkaline, the availability of bicarbonate decreases while the percentage of carbonate ion in the water increases. At pH 9.4 in sea water the bicarbonate becomes unavailable, as there is sufficient calcium in sea water to precipitate all the available carbonate ion as calcium carbonate. It is found in practice therefore that photosynthesis ceases even in bright sunlight at pH 9.4. This is only reached in heavily grassed estuarine flats with a heavy periphyton. In fresh water, where calcium is low, the pH can reach 10.1. At this pH, bicarbonate ion is almost quantatively converted to carbonate ion. It can be seen from this discussion, that the carbonate equilibria can and do control photosynthesis, and thence the amount of plant material that can be formed. Respiration replenishes the bicarbonate (via carbon dioxide) available for photosynthesis, and more carbon dioxide is added by solution from the air in surface water and from dissolving carbonate where the sediment is calcareous, as in many tropical waters and in reef areas, where corals and other lime-secreting organisms predominate. The equilibria here are biological, and are quite complicated. As the pH increases, carbon dioxide diminishes, and carbonate increases, and this liberates some "excess base" which sets free borate ions from undissociated boric acid. Thus we have both carbonate and borate equilibria available to buffer sea water, and this buffering action is of great importance for biology.

Pressure

In the oceans, the hydrostatic pressure increases approximately 1 atm for every 10 m depth, so that in the deepest parts of the ocean, it will exceed 1,000 atm. This increase of pressure will affect a number of chemical equilibria, although, water being only slightly compressible, it will not have much effect on the density. It will tend to lower the pH, and increase the solubility of carbon dioxide and bicarbonate, decreasing that of carbonate ion. The solubility of other gases will also be affected, and the net effect on chemical equilibria is complicated and, with respect to biological processes, little known.

The main contribution to the study of pressure effects on marine bacteria are those of ZoBell and his colleagues (ZoBell and Johnson, 1949; ZoBell and Oppenheimer, 1950; ZoBell and Morita, 1957; Morita, 1957). This has already been discussed at greater length in Chapter II.

Hannan's work (1964) on the effect of pressures on oxygen production by *Chlorella pyrenoidosa* is significant. He showed that even small increases in pressure cause increased oxygen production, if the water is not saturated with carbon dioxide, and that there is a small decrease in respiration rate with pressure. This confirms some preliminary findings of my own. If the carbon dioxide pressure was saturated, oxygen production diminished. In the ocean, however, it is most likely that the water would not be saturated with carbon dioxide and therefore that pressure would increase the efficiency of oxygen production, i.e., tend to increase photosynthesis. Unfortunately, Hannan only investigated pressures up to 50 p.s.i. and we cannot extrapolate to really high pressures. His results do suggest however an additional reason for the usual presence of the maximum phytoplankton population at depths of 20 m or more.

THE RELATION OF MICROORGANISMS TO THE OCEANIC ENVIRONMENTS

The bacteria

In the oceanic environment, the bacteria play important parts in several aspects, but not at the first or plant trophic level. It has been said that their major role is in the "regeneration" of nutrients, i.e., in the conversion of organic materials to inorganic so that these would be available to the autotrophic plants which were believed to require such inorganics for their nutrition. It is true that we can grow some of the microscopic plants of the marine world on defined media consisting entirely of inorganics, but many of them will not grow at all on such media, or will grow only until the adsorbed organics are used up. Apart from growth factors which are required by so many microorganisms, many of the plants can use organic nitrogen and phosphate as well as organic sulfur and other micro-nutrients. We can then no longer assert that bacteria are *required* for the regeneration of nutrients. What then do they contribute? We know that they produce such substances as lactic and pyruvic acid from carbohydrates, they hydrolyse starches and other polysaccharides, converting them into soluble and more easily assimilable compounds, that they attack nucleic acids and other phosphate containing compounds converting these also into forms of lower molecular weight, and that they also hydrolyse and deaminate proteins, etc., so that simple depolymerized soluble compounds are produced; we know also that just these compounds are very often used by the plants without completing the cycle from organic to inorganic. JOHANNES (1964a) has shown that this is one of the roles of bacteria in the gut of crustaceans and other animals. These animals use all the available nutrients from their food, but the bacteria act upon the useless residues, and produce further nutrients therein. Coprophily therefore becomes understandable. An animal eating its own feces is taking advantage of this bacterial activity. This means that the decomposition of organic matter by bacteria in the sea is a step-wise process, not confined to any particular microbial process or any definite katabolic product. Johannes could not confirm the total degradation of such organic matter by bacteria, and believes that, instead they tend to use this material in their own metabolism and it is other organisms using bacteria and detritus as food that complete the decomposition in the oceans. This is an interesting idea.

Some heterotrophic bacteria do, however, have side reactions that produce inorganic compounds or elements. Several pseudomonads deaminate proteins with the release of nitrogen, others produce ammonia. GARVEL and GILMOUR (1965) state that anaerobic cultures produced up to 2,000 μg of nitrogen at 15 °C, 1,150 μg at 28 °C. The microbial oxidation of ammonia to nitrite and nitrate is known as nitrification and this process can be due to bacteria as we have stated previously (p.47). HAMILTON (1964) could not demonstrate photochemical oxidation of ammonia in the Straits of Florida. However, it was long believed that nitrifying bacteria did not occur in open water, and were confined to the sediments. Recent evidence by SPENCER (1963) and others suggests that these organisms are frequent in the oceans, but they grow very slowly in culture and it is difficult to see how they could be a major factor in oceanic nitrification. This may be due to limitations in experimental techniques. Many marine bacteria reduce nitrates to nitrites but this is unimportant, as most marine algae are able to use either with more or less equal facility. The reduction of nitrite to nitrogen can be performed by only a few bacteria and by photochemical means (HAMILTON, 1964) and there is no evidence that this is an important process in the sea. Bacterial denitrification in the water was regarded by DREW (1914) as responsible for a large amount of calcium carbonate in coral reef areas. GREENFIELD (1963) found that marine pseudomonads require calcium or magnesium for growth on nitrogenous media. The organisms, he believes, adsorb considerable quantities of calcium and magnesium, produce ammonia during their metabolism, and calcium carbonate is precipitated, presumably according to the equation:

$$Ca(HCO_3)_2 + 2\ NH_3 \rightarrow CaCO_3 + (NH_4)_2CO_3$$

or:

$$(NH_4)_2CO_3 + CaSO_4 \rightarrow CaCO_3 + (NH_4)_2SO_4$$

The carbonate is precipitated on the bacterial bodies. The importance of this reaction in the formation of marls and reef limestones is not known. The validity of these equations has been questioned.

ZoBELL (1946b) suggested that the reason for the apparent paucity of bacteria in the open ocean is that they are grazed very rapidly, and the populations found are residual to such grazing. Recent workers using direct methods believe that there are many more bacteria than ZoBell or Wood found by viable counts and both these authors have stated that direct counts exceed viable counts by one or more orders of magnitude. The slide-attachment technique of HENRICI (1933) used extensively by the Russians, however, cannot be classed as quantitative, as there is a time factor involved in exposing the slide and because the organisms attaching are not all bacteria. For example, it is now believed that most of the Krassilnikoviae of Kriss are really ctenophores, and others of his attached organisms may, from the appearance in his drawings, be yeasts or small flagellates.

Bacterial activity in the phosphorus cycle has been recently studied by JOHANNES (1964a,b) and his conclusions are extremely interesting. He found for example that the turn-over time for phosphorus by a marine amphipod is 41 h, but that there is a higher uptake in non-sterile than in sterile animals. He attributes this to the bacterial flora breaking down the ingested material to a degree that facilitated uptake. The amphipod released 30% of the ingested phosphorus in an organic form and 80% of this was utilized by bacteria. In sterile media, 30% of the fecal phosphate was hydrolysed, presumably by alkaline phosphatase released by the amphipods. This means that hydrolysis by exo-enzymes may well be more important than bacteria in "regenerating" phosphate. Bacteria-free diatoms released little dissolved organic phosphate during growth, but 20% after growth had ceased. Fresh cultures of growing diatoms could use 40% of this, marine bacteria 92%. Such bacteria did not regenerate inorganic phosphate, and released little organic phosphate either from living or dead cells. This indicates that alkaline phosphatases from marine animals and not bacteria are the principal producers of regenerated inorganic phosphate. KUENTZLER et al. (1963) found that the diatom *Phaeodactylum* produces extracellular phosphatases.

The role of bacteria

The main role of the bacteria in the oceans would seem to be the conversion of dissolved organic matter into particulate in the form of the bacteria themselves, and the breaking down of complex organic substances into simpler ones. Such complex substances would include plant polysaccharides such as cellulose, agar, alginates, and chitin as well as proteins, nucleic acids and other substances. I was surprised to find, in my work on bacterial processes in Lake Macquarie, that I could not isolate cellulose digesters from this environment, though I had done so in Port Hacking. More recently, J. Reynolds (personal communication) failed to isolate cellulose digesting bacteria, either aerobic or anaerobic from seawater in the Straits of Florida or the tropical Atlantic Ocean between Nigeria and Florida and found only limited numbers in the Virginia Key area near Miami. SEKI and TAGA (1963) found that chitinoclastic bacteria made up less than 0.4% of the bacterial population of plankton in seawater, that most occurred in the suspended matter though many were on living copepods. These authors found that the rate of decomposition of chitin was about 30 mg/day 10^{10} bacteria, that chitin digestion was inhibited at 20°C by 200 atm pressure (i.e., equal to a depth of 2,000 m) but that the bacteria were not killed by 600 atm. They concluded that, from the numbers of chitin digesters in the stomachs of squid, fish and other crustacean-eaters, the activity of these bacteria in releasing nutrients from chitin in the intestinal tract is negligible.

Some idea of the extent of the problem of particulate organic matter in the oceans is afforded by some experiments of LASKER (1964) on the moulting of *Euphausia pacifica,* a crustacean of a type which abounds in the oceans. He found that these euphausids discard their own weight of particulate matter every 50 days, or seven times their own weight a year. It is probable that the moulting of other crustaceans such as copepods would provide a similar order of magnitude of particulate organics. If this quantity of material (mainly refractory) reached the bottom of the oceans it would completely alter the nature of the sediments and rapidly deplete the organic matter of the seas. From the figures given by bacteriologists, e.g., V. Cviic, C. E. ZoBell, E. J. F. Wood (quoted in: WOOD, 1965), the bacteria in the sea would be quite insufficient to cope with such quantities of material. Lasker's work raises the important question: "What does happen to this material?" I think we must assume, in the absence of further evidence, that organisms other than the bacteria are responsible for its disappearance from ocean waters. It is possible that crustaceans and other marine animals have enzymes such as chitinase which can attack these refractory organics. The colorless Protozoa no doubt play their part, but I rather doubt whether they are sufficiently numerous to cope with the amounts which are produced, assuming that Lasker's figures can be extrapolated to other marine organisms.

Proteolytic bacteria have been regarded as of the greatest importance in the regeneration of simple nutrients from decomposing plant and animal material and it is probable that they do produce some such materials. Cultures show that they can break down proteins to simple amino-acids and many can also deaminate. MERKEL (1965) found, as one might expect, that proteolytic bacteria are more numerous inshore than offshore and that in the offshore waters they occur largely at the surface and in the vicinity of the thermocline. We now know that many simple substances can be and are produced directly by algae as by-products of photosynthesis and a reappraisal of the role of bacteria in protein degradation in the oceans is necessary. It may be that the major role of bacteria is in the assimilation rather than the decomposition of proteinaceous matter, and their subsequent ingestion by other organisms.

I found in Lake Macquarie that agar-digesting bacteria were unexpectedly rare, even on red algae, although in Botany Bay, New South Wales, large quantities of *Gracilaria confervoides* were completely decomposed in a few days; this red seaweed is used for the manufacture of agar, which constitutes up to 3% of the net weight. As we do not find quantities of these materials on the sea floor, or even in estuarine sediments, their digestion must be reasonably rapid, despite evidence to the contrary from bacterial assessments. The bacteria and fungi are then available as food to most of the zooplankton and other marine animals.

Bacteria do not seem to play an important part as plant or animal pathogens in the seas. Some pseudomonads appear to become toxic to certain organisms under definite conditions, but otherwise to remain as saprophytes or benign parasites. It is probable that the production of antibiotics by algae, sponges and other forms is responsible for the paucity of bacterial parasites in the marine environment.

ANTIA et al. (1963) consider from their plastic bag experiments, in which phytoplankton was held in a large plastic bag so as to minimize surface effects, that vitamin B_{12} consumed by the algae was released by bacteria, and BURKHOLDER (1963) also believes that bacteria are responsible for the production of B_{12} (cyanocobalamin) in the sea. DROOP (1957a) maintained and DAISLEY (1957) questioned that there is always sufficient B_{12} in most oceanic environments for maximum algal growth. As biotin and possibly other vitamins appear to be produced rather than consumed by phytoplankton in the plastic bag experiments, it would seem unlikely that B_{12} or other vitamins could ever be limiting to phytoplankton production under natural conditions. The heavy blooms such as red tides of the Gulf of Mexico have been related to an excess production of vitamin B_{12} derived from terrestrial sources, presumably by bacteria in the soil and in the rivers, but this has not been confirmed.

Quantitative aspects of bacteria in the sea

It is very difficult to estimate the quantitative importance of bacteria in the seas. Three methods of enumeration are available: direct counts, slide counts and "viable" counts. Direct counts are made by putting a concentrated or unconcentrated sample of water or sediment on an area of a slide and counting the organisms under the microscope, with or without staining. There are a number of procedures for this, but only certain staining methods can even begin to distinguish live from dead bacteria (e.g., the acridine orange fluorescence method). The technique tells us nothing of the function of the organisms. The slide technique consists of setting slides in the water for a certain time, removing them and counting all organisms which have attached. This does not account for the bacteria which do not attach or which attach and then move away from the slide; it also gave us the Krassilnikoviae and other forms which are probably not bacteria at all. It may give us some information on whether bacteria are abundant or scarce, and may even give settlement proportional to the number of bacteria in a given area, but we have no confirmation of this. Again it tells us nothing of function. The "viable" count method requires a culture medium, and only counts the organisms which will grow on the material selected. If we use a number of media aimed at culturing organisms which have different functions, we have a number of difficulties. Firstly, a single organism and its progeny may perform one or many of the functions which are being tested, and thus may or may not appear on several or all of the media used. Secondly, an organism may perform a given function (say agar digestion) in the sea and may not perform it on the selected medium. Thirdly, an organism may grow very slowly (e.g., nitrifying bacteria) and be overgrown by other organisms.

If one rejects these methods as being merely relative, and most bacteriologists seem to reject them at this time, one must have recourse to the study of products of the bacteria. These are probably what most of us are interested in, and bacteriologists are tending more and more to look to the end product of microbial activity as likely to give us a real picture of bacterial communities. This is a realistic attitude, but is fraught with as many difficulties as the counting methods. It requires isolating the organisms, even in mixed cultures, from their natural habitat and making a simulated environment. This introduces some subjective factors, which can only be determined by going back to the natural environment with its complications. The chief difficulty here is the ingenuity of the student. As more thought is being given to this method of attack, which in its more primitive form was put forward by Winogradsky, it is becoming more useful.

It does not differentiate between the activity of bacteria and heterotrophic algae or fungi, but that is probably not important. It is the overall picture that we want rather than the knowledge of the contribution of a given organism or group of organisms. Maybe, when we get the overall picture, we can analyse the contribution of individual organisms or groups from a somewhat simplified system.

The fungi

It has already been stated that we do not know the significance of filamentous fungi in marine environments. Because of their oxygen relations, they could theoretically be present in the oceans and could play an important part in the disintegration of marine animals and plants. We know that certain fungi occur on and in many species, and that some of them do not die with the death of the "host". The intracellular and intercellular penetration of fungal hyphae would assist in the mechanical breakdown of other organisms, and this would be expected to be important in transformations in plankton at any rate. It is strange that we have no information on this, and stranger still that so obvious a theory should not have been tested. Let us say that such penetration is not obvious, and has not led to studies of oceanic fungi.

Yeasts. Recent work by FELL (1965; Fig.10) shows that the yeasts are probably ubiquitous in the oceans and are numerous in the productive intermediate water. Here, they probably replace to some extent the algae of the photic zone as food for the filter-feeding crustaceans, and may indeed be important in the food web of this ecosystem. They require short-chain compounds as their carbon source, and no doubt compete with the bacteria and micro-algal heterotrophs for the dissolved organic matter in Intermediate waters. Their importance in the oceans is only now being recognized.

The algae

The most important role of marine algae, especially the micro-algae is in photosynthesis. We do not know just what proportion of the total marine productivity is due to micro-algae, but it has been estimated that only 2% of the ocean surface covers the larger marine algae, though their biomass represents far more than this fraction. We do not even know the comparative rates of carbon assimilation or gross or net photosynthesis or respiration of the larger and microscopic algae in the seas.

Photosynthesis and production

As has been stated elsewhere, photosynthesis is the only biological transformation by which energy is added to that available to living forms on earth. It represents the harnessing of an external source of energy (solar energy) to carry out a chemical reaction against an energy gradient; the reduction of carbon dioxide aerobically with water as the hydrogen donor is overall an endothermic reaction. For this reason, it is important for us to be able to estimate the amount of this transformation which is occurring annually on this planet, on the land as well as in the water. At present we do not even know, whether the land or the seas have the higher primary production, and because of the complexity of the problem, are a long way from finding out. I have previously criticised the methods adopted for estimating production and productivity and have defined these terms. Here, I shall merely try to point out some biological implications of recent work in this area, particularly of physiological studies. Fogg (1964, see above) has shown that photosynthesis can take several pathways, from the high energy-yielding carbon dioxide reduction to lower energy-yielding reductions involving organic carbon compounds. The partial heterotrophy of some protoplankters and the suggestion of Bunt (1965) and others that in some cases photosynthetic rates are enhanced by a partially heterotrophic nutrition, raises the question of the validity of estimates of photosynthetic rates based on assimilation of ^{14}C from carbonate. Quantitative relations between autotrophic and heterotrophic assimilation by potentially photosynthetic microbes have not been studied to any extent. It would seem that many microorganisms can slip from phototrophic to heterotrophic nutrition or maintain an equilibrium between these depending on the organism and the total environment, and this makes quantitative studies by any means, either dynamic or standing crop (e.g., chlorophyll measurement) very difficult to interpret.

In a recent review in which Anderson and Banse (1963) tried to relate phytoplankton production to hydrological conditions, the authors have been forced to follow some rather doubtful precedents. They used such concepts as compensation depth and critical depth which are based on tests made from samples kept in small vessels and thus subject to extensive adsorption effects or to culture studies from which it is dangerous to extrapolate to natural conditions.

Most studies of the effect of chemical and physical factors on productivity have been made, as the authors point out, in temperate and sub-arctic regions. What they failed to point out is that these studies were made in such places as Long Island Sound, Georges Bank, the North Sea, which are shallow waters with high turbidity and considerable mixing. In warmer waters, most work has been done in the Sargasso Sea, a gyral with peculiar properties, not representative of sub-tropical waters as a whole. It would be fallacious to consider results from these areas as applicable to the open sea in the mid-Atlantic, Indian and Pacific Oceans, as has frequently been done in the past.

STEELE (1964) in a study of production in the Gulf of Mexico, basing his conclusions on chlorophyll data which are probably accurate enough for his purpose, discusses the assumption made by RILEY et al. (1949) and STEELE (1956). He lists these as: (1) that chlorophyll *a* concentration is proportional to plant carbon, i.e., the chlorophyll maximum corresponds to the maximum phytoplankton population; (2) that photosynthesis is proportional to light except at high light intensities; and this puts the maximum growth rate of phytoplankton near the surface; (3) that the grazing rate of herbivores is independent of depth; (4) the plants sink at a constant rate. These four assumptions are almost certainly invalid.

Steele gives theoretical reasons why the sinking theory of Riley et al. is untenable, and I can confirm this from observation. In a period of 24–48 h, the phytoplankton maximum is usually at the same mean depth, though the total vertical distribution may extend further up or down at different times of day. There is no evidence that the phytoplankton maximum sinks below the photic zone at any time. Grazing would appear to be related to plant concentration, and this would be expected, as the greater the distance between phytoplankton organisms the longer would be the time required for capture by the zooplankton, until at length further capture would prove unprofitable. The fact that the phytoplankton decreases rapidly in association with the rise of the deep scattering layer (Fig.5) and then remains almost constant until the layer descends again is confirmation of the theory of unprofitable feeding.

WOOD and CORCORAN (1966) give evidence that chlorophyll must not be assumed to be proportional to plant carbon even in a population in which species composition does not vary appreciably.

Light

Postulate 2, that photosynthesis is proportional to light, except at high intensity is naive, as observation shows that phytoplankton maxima in warm waters are usually below the thermocline and the level of 1% surface illumination and are often bimodal, which would require more complex conditions than a mere light requirement. Further, the nature and nutrition of the organism rather than light intensity will govern the relation between the organism and illumination. The chlorophyll maximum found by Steele below 50 m in the Mediterranean and off Bermuda is typical of the tropics and certainly does not represent sinking as would be required by the theories of Riley et al. STEELE's (1964) theory that the supply of nutrients to the plants comes mainly from in situ "regeneration" is in accord with our knowledge of diurnal phytoplankton distribution in a number of areas. It is also supported by recent evidence that such "regeneration" does not mean production of nitrate and phosphate but merely the formation by microbial or enzyme activity of simple organic phosphates and nitrogen derivatives which the phytoplankton can assimilate. This, accompanied by adsorption tends to keep the nutrients in the general area of their immediate use. Diminutions of phytoplankton populations, formerly referred to sinking, are, on the evidence, largely or chiefly due to grazing, and their replacement due to reproduction and not to upward mixing.

CLARKE and DENTON (1962) made some very important observations with regard to the ecological aspects of light in the oceans. They point out that these include intensity, length of day, light energy per 24 h, cyclic changes, spectral composition, angular distribution and polarization. These are controlled by climatological factors and by physical factors within the water, such as selective absorption of wave lengths, turbidity and wave action. These authors give as the depth to which surface light is reduced to 1% as 10–30 m in coastal waters, 100 m for clear oceanic waters (it was about 70 m in the eastern Mediterranean Sea in September 1965) and less than 3 m in turbid estuaries and harbors. The maximum penetration in clear ocean waters is in the region of 400–500 mμ wave length. The transparency of deep ocean waters was found to be as great as that of the clearest waters in the upper region. Detectable light from the surface has been recorded to depths of 800 m in the Mediterranean Sea, 950 m in the Caribbean Sea, and 1300 m in the Indian Ocean (CLARKE and KELLY, 1964).

At night, or in deeper waters during the day, bioluminescence was found to contribute a significant part of the light present. Further, bioluminescence has been shown to be practically universal in the oceans, though at decreasing intensity as the depth increases. The authors compare bioluminescence with solar radiation and record up to $10^{-3}\sigma W/cm^2$ which is 10^{-7} the value of surface light, with bright sun. They further suggest that in the Mediterranean, most of the flashing of bioluminescence is produced by unicellular forms. Bioluminescence providing continuous light in the oceans has been recorded at all depths to 3,750 m, and such bioluminescence probably has great ecological significance in the deep seas.

My own evidence concerning the movement of parts of the deep scattering layer in the Gulf of Guinea tends to confirm the statement of CLARKE and BACKUS (1964) that the diurnal migration of these organisms is controlled principally by changes in light intensity at the rising and setting of the sun. These authors pointed out that the luminescent flashes of organisms in the water may be of the same overall intensity as the daylight at the depth of the deep scattering layer, prior to migration.

It is interesting to note that Clarke and Backus record that the vertical migration of the organisms from the deep scattering layer stopped at 80–95 m in the Virgin Islands area where the phytoplankton maximum may be assumed to be close to those depths by analogy with my own data for the Amazon region (80–100 m). In our recent work in the eastern Mediterranean, B. Kimor and E. J. F. Wood (unpublished) found that the maximum numbers of zooplankton occurred at night (19.00h) at 100 m, in contact with the maximum phytoplankton population, and that the guts of the zooplankton (copepods, ostracods and cladocerans) were full of phytoplankton elements in a large number of the specimens.

It would seem then, on present evidence, that part of the vertical migration is a feeding one, and, while it may be light-induced, could also be due in part at least to a feeding rhythm.

It has been assumed on rather slender evidence that the spring diatom bloom in cooler waters is due to an increase of available light, that the deep mixed layer keeps the phytoplankton below the

compensation depth (the depth at which photosynthesis and respiration are believed to balance and below which the plant must lose
energy and ultimately die), and that a bloom can only occur when
the mixed layer becomes shallower than the *critical depth*. If light is
the controlling factor, it seems strange that psychrophilic phytoplankton, which is able to grow at a low light intensity (e.g., the
organisms studied by BUNT, 1965) of < 5 to 20 foot-candles and grows
abundantly in the Antarctic at 2 °C, does not bloom in the cooler
waters below the 1% surface light level. Although Bunt's organisms
were found in felts up to 2 mm thick within Antarctic ice, they
included such species as *Rhizosolenia alata* vars., *Coscinodiscus*, *Actinocyclus*, *Asteromphalus* spp., and *Fragilariopsis antarctica* (BUNT and
WOOD, 1963), all of which are capable of forming blooms in Antarctic and sub-Antarctic waters. J. S. Bunt (personal communication) states that his algae were too heavy to remain afloat, though
this may be a function of their position beneath the ice. Conditions approximating these occur below the thermocline in many
temperate waters, yet I have not found evidence of such blooms in
my Tasman Sea and Indian Ocean studies, although the waters were
not poor in nutrients. It might be profitable to study the effect of
increased temperature, or the rate of temperature increase on phytoplankton blooms in cooler waters, since temperature as well as light
will change more rapidly in waters that are not turbulent. Because
of the versatility of most protoplankters, especially with regard to
light, it seems doubtful whether the paucity of light could limit
reproduction rates near the surface, even of the most turbid water,
and from my own observations there are always sufficient cells to
start a bloom if the right conditions are present. I have found that
a bloom, once started (WOOD, 1959a) will continue to increase even
in the dark, though not quite at the same rate. In Arctic and Antarctic
waters, the spring bloom of phytoplankton is associated with melting
ice and it is possible that the trigger is the incidence of fresh water,
coupled with the release of cells trapped in or growing on top of
the ice, some of them associated with the under-ice flora (BUNT and
WOOD, 1963). This would account for the appearance of Antarctic
blooms immediately the thaw begins. ANTIA et al. (1963) found in
their experiments at Nanaimo that mean cell-division rates were
constant and relatively independent of temperature and light, and
that the rate of photosynthesis per unit chlorophyll was remarkably

constant and not proportional to light intensity. This is difficult to explain and requires further experimentation.

Species distribution

BRAARUD (1962) discusses species distribution in phytoplankton, and this is probably a key to the productivity problem. If we assume that there is always a seed population appropriate to the region, and one never finds an area totally devoid of phytoplankton, we must also believe that, given the required nutrients and illumination, a bloom will occur in that area. That this does not always happen, that we can find areas in which nutrients are apparently sufficient and conditions seem otherwise to suit a bloom, means that there are other factors which prevent bloom formation. Braarud lists some of the possibilities:

The background lies in the initial populations, the flotation capacity of the organisms to keep them within the photic zone, and the rate or comparative rates of reproduction. More immediate factors which affect the initiation and maintenance of populations of protoplankton include temperature tolerance and temperature growth curves, salinity tolerance, light growth curves, nutrient requirements including organics, inorganics and trace elements, mechanisms for flotation and motility, life cycles and form and production of resting spores, growth rates, the production of external metabolites, including auto- and hetero-toxic and auto- and hetero-stimulatory substances. These are the autecological factors. The environmental factors which interact with these include temperature range, rate of change, seasonal changes of temperature, salinity range and rate of change, water density, light, nutrient supplies, horizontal currents, vertical mixing, transport and nutrient distribution by water movements, pressure, environmental barriers such as thermoclines and current barriers, and selective grazing.

VAN LANDINGHAM (1964) adds predation grazing and parasitism as well as migration as biotic factors affecting bloom formation.

Bound up with species distribution are the problems of succession (Fig.15) and species diversity (Fig.16). BURSA (1963) discusses the problems of succession in high Arctic latitudes. The annual cycle is unimodal in the highest latitudes because of the short vegetative period, whereas in lower latitudes the cycle is bimodal. The phytoplankton maxima occur over a period of a few days, suggesting a

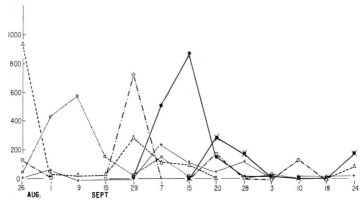

Fig.15. Species succession of diatoms in a neritic area; note that there is usually a second, small peak about 4 weeks after the main bloom of each species. (After Wood, 1964.)

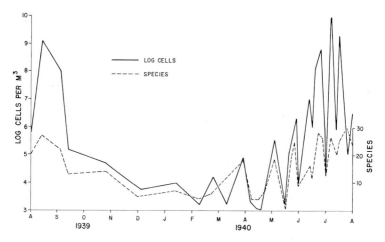

Fig.16. Graph showing the relation between diversity of species and numbers of individuals in an estuarine situation. Such relationships are much less constant in the oceans.

very rapid reproduction rate in this environment. Sudden change in the water conditions, such as re-freezing, together with selective grazing can alter and obscure the picture of succession. In these waters, the spring maximum consists of pennate diatoms, the summer maximum of centric, mainly *Chaetoceros*, followed by a lesser peak of green flagellates or coccolithophores and dinoflagellates about 20 days later. In the Antarctic, the maxima consist of a mixture of pennate and centric diatoms, and, close to the ice, in some areas the flagellate *Phaeocystis* in vast quantities. As the studies in the Antarctic were made using nets, the extent of the nanoplankton is not known. Very recent work by J. Walsh (personal communication) at the University of Miami suggests that the flagellates, except for the ubiquitous *Phaeocystis*, are relatively unimportant in the Antarctic areas sampled during the summer. In the Arctic, the flagellates consist of *Chlamydomonas*, *Euglena*, *Polyblepharis* and *Chlorella* in the fresh water region close to the melting ice and the Chrysomonads *Mallomonas* and *Ochromonas* in the brackish and saline waters. At the end of summer, large numbers of holophytic Gymnodiniaceae occur and are entensively grazed. Cyanophyceae are absent from the Arctic waters, and are absent or unimportant in the Antarctic. Bursa comments on the absence of pennate diatoms in seas with no ice, but this is not true in the Antarctic where *Fragilariopsis antarctica F. linearis*, and *Synedra reinboldii* and *Thalassiothrix* occur in sub-Antarctic waters as far north as the sub-tropical convergence.

In the cool-temperate waters of the Northern Hemisphere, there is a marked spring diatom peak followed by a lesser autumn one. In similar waters of the Southern Hemisphere the two peaks are much less regular and there is a series of fluctuations usually accompanied by a succession of seven or eight species rather than a single peak (Fig.16). In the tropics, the seasonal picture is much less clear as one would expect from the more equable climate. My own belief, based on observations made at sea, but unsupported by laboratory evidence, is that phytoplankton blooms are triggered mainly by changes of temperature, or, perhaps of salinity and that possibly biological rhythms play a part. There is evidence from field and laboratory studies such as those of CALLAME and DEBYSER (1954) that diurnal biological rhythms are tied to physical or chemical factors such as tidal rhythms, but can be reversed to an extent by slowly changing the external rhythm.

In a study of the distribution of protoplankton in the Indian and South Pacific Oceans, I found that one can trace a number of populations in tropical waters, related to certain water masses (Fig.17), but the Antarctic populations appear to be homogeneous. This is due to the fact that there is no land barrier to the rotation of the Antarctic Current, so the population right around the Antarctic continent is derived from the same elements. Local populations develop in areas richer in nutrients, such as the Bellingshausen Sea, but it would be difficult for a phytoplanktologist to decide, just from an inspection of the population, where in the Antarctic the sample came from. In the tropics, such decisions are possible. For example, the dinoflagellate *Dinophysis miles* is peculiar to the Indonesian-New Guinea region, *Ceratium dens* is an Indian Ocean species which does not normally occur in the southwestern Pacific, and the same applies to the diatom *Chaetoceros messanense*. Coccolithophores are rare in the southwestern

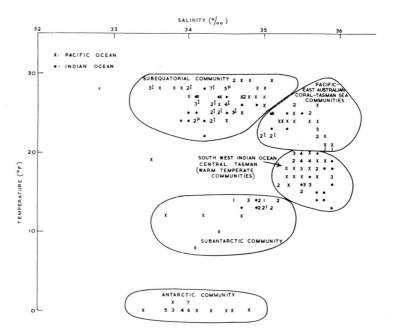

Fig.17. The relationship of a diatom population *(Thalassiothrix nitzschioides)* to phytoplankton communities as defined by salinity–temperature relations. (After WOOD, 1954.)

Pacific also. There are few warm or cool temperate species in oceanic waters, the water masses being characterised by the gradual disappearance of truly tropical species as the water moves away from the equator. Certain peculiarities in the species distribution are of great interest to the ecologist. I can quote the distribution of *Corethron criophilum*, which has a circum-tropical occurrence in all the oceans, and an Antarctic clone or clones which is spatially separated from its tropical counterpart by thousands of miles. According to BRAARUD (1951) *Biddulphia aurita* has a cultural temperature optimum of 5 °C and a field optimum of 1 °C. This would account for the occurrence of this species in Antarctic waters especially close to and below the ice, but does not account for the same species occurring in Hauraki Gulf, New Zealand, or on the east coast of Australia, where the temperature is of the order of 18–25 °C. We have here two or more obviously different populations. *Biddulphia chinensis* in culture grew at 16 ° and in the sea at 13 °C, which agrees with the occurrence of this species on the south coast of Australia and on the east coast of the North and South Islands of New Zealand. It does not however account for the northern strain of this diatom which occurs in the Arafura, Timor and Coral Seas, at temperatures of 26–30 °C, but not south of them for about 1,000 miles. Braarud also recorded *Asterionella japonica* at 20–25 °C in the laboratory and the same strain as living at 8 °C in the water; GRØNTVED (1960, 1962) recorded it from Denmark in inshore waters at 20–25 °C and this is approximately the temperature range of this species in Australian waters (15.1–26.3 °C).

Succession and diversity. In estuarine waters, it would seem that salinity rather than temperature is the controlling factor in succession, oceanic, neritic and estuarine species being reasonably easily separated by these criteria (WOOD, 1964). The seasonal peaks and maxima are essentially similar to the oceanic ones, but the main difference is in the species diversity.

Much is now being made of species diversity in relation to phytoplankton populations and Margalef has applied information theory to this. HULBURT (1963, 1964) working in the western North Atlantic, found that the distribution of species in the Bermuda area conformed with Fisher's diversity index only when growth conditions were poor. In further studies, he found that this applied generally, except in estuarine waters in the northwestern region of the United States. In the Florida area, there is usually a large number of species present at any time in Bear Cut and the Fowey Rocks region, and in the water influenced by the continental shelf or *Edge* water of the southern Straits of Florida. This is roughly independent of the phytoplankton population. From previous experience in Australia, where the situation is analogous to that in Florida waters (i.e., warm estuarine and neritic water), greater diversity is usually to be expected in warm than in cool water. Monospecific phytoplankton blooms are confined to certain species and are not associated with preconceived formulae. This is probably due to antibiotic production or to auto-accelerators which preclude the development of other organisms. Apart from these monospecific blooms, large tropical and sub-tropical blooms tend to have an increasing diversity with total numbers of phytoplankton. The factors associated with blooms are probably too diverse to be accounted for by any formula based on terrestrial population dynamics.

There seems from field evidence to be a relation between diversity and succession. In cases where there are normally monospecific blooms such as those of *Trichodesmium*, I have not observed a sequence of other species following the bloom, which appears to exhaust temporarily the available nutrients. In areas where a considerable diversity is found one usually finds a succession of dominant species which follow one another maintaining a moderately high population, which fluctuates slightly as each species reaches its peak and diminishes. The overall bloom time is much longer, lasting weeks rather than days as in the first case. An interesting facet of the multi-species bloom is that there is usually a secondary but small peak of each population about 4 weeks later. This was found also in a monospecific *Goniaulax* bloom in Port Jackson (WOOD, 1964). There is more than a suggestion of lunar rhythm in these pulses, and one wonders how much part biological rhythms do play in plankton succession.

BRAARUD (1962) mentions as one of the factors influencing species distribution the life cycles and form and production of resting spores. Because of the difficulty of cultivating most of the true oceanic phytoplankters, life histories are known of only a few, and the form and distribution of spores is still less known. *Goniaulax* species form spores regularly and so does the diatom *Skeletonema costatum*. There is evidence that in both these cases, the spores settle on the bottom of estuaries and continental shelves, and germinate there. Sporulation occurs in a population simultaneously, and so apparently does germination thus giving rise to an apparent rhythm. Whether lunar rhythms in protoplankton are due to physico-chemical, or to intrinsic factors or to a combination of both, we cannot say. We have observed the form of spores of a number of organisms such as *Ceratium tripos*, most *Chaetoceros* species and some coccolithophores, though it has recently been found that these organisms have a rather complicated life history involving sporophyte and gametophyte phases, and in some cases, free-swimming and attached phases. I can find no record of observations on the fate of *Chaetoceros* spores or of those of *Rhizosolenia*, *Peridinium* or *Ceratium*. One factor which Braarud has not considered directly is pigments, though he does mention the importance of light. We know that some organisms require bright light, others are shade forms, those of Bunt (requiring < 5 foot-candles) being extremes in the latter category. Most, however, can adapt within wide limits, and this renders many of the culture studies of little value. We know too that the blue-green algae as a group contain

TABLE IV

TABLE OF PRINCIPAL PHYTOPLANKTON PIGMENTS

Organism	Chlorophyll				Accessory pigments
	a	b	c	d	
Cryptomonas (Crypto)*	×	—	×	—	α-carotene, diatoxanthin
Hemiselmis (Crypto)	×	—	×	—	β-carotene, diatoxanthin
Vaucheria (Xantho)	×	—	—	—	β-carotene, 3 xanthophylls
Nemalion (Rhodo)	×	—	—	×	β-carotene, neoxanthin, lutein
Polysiphonia (Rhodo)	×	—	—	×	β-carotene, zeaxanthin
Hemiselmis†	×	—	×	—	biliprotein (phycoerythrin, phycocyanin)
Cyanophyceae	×	—	—	—	biliproteins
Chrysophyceae	×	—	×	—	fucoxanthin, β-carotene
Prymnesium (Chryso)	×	—	×	—	diatoxanthin
Bacillariophyceae	×	—	×	—	fucoxanthin, diatoxanthin
Chloromonadaceae	×	?	?	?	?
Chlorophyceae	×	×	—	—	lutein
Euglenophyceae	×	×	—	—	
Phaeophyceae	×	—	×	—	fucoxanthin

* Allen et al., 1964.
† Oheocha and Raftery, 1959.

certain accessory pigments which tend to filter out excess light and thus fit this group for their role as surface organisms. *Trichodesmium* grows in blooms right at the surface of the water and we have the tapetic forms such as *Oscillatoria*, *Microcoleus* and *Lyngbya* which can stand up to high insolation and even drying (see Table IV).

Nutrients

Nitrogen compounds. We have already mentioned that marine micro-algae have, as a group, ability to use organic as well as inorganic nitrogen compounds. SYRETT (1962) states that all algae containing chlorophyll, with one or two exceptions, can use either ammonium or nitrate nitrogen if these are at a suitable concentration; if the energy available is limited the plants prefer ammonium as aerobic nitrate reduction is endothermic and the plants use their nitrogen largely in the amino form. Nitrite is also used by many species if it is in low concentration, but higher concentrations of nitrite and ammonia are often toxic, the latter inhibiting nitrate reduction. Ammonia seems to be incorporated during the reduction in the plant of α-ketaro-glutaric to glutamic acid. The reduction of nitrates seems to be linked with photosynthesis in plants, but in colorless micro-organisms another source of energy must be used. Organic sources of nitrogen which algae can use include urea (presumably regenerating ornithine directly from arginine), asparagine, glutamine, glycine, glutamic acid, purines, pyrimidine, casein and other protein hydrolysates, and amides such as acetamide and succinamide. Some of these organic sources of nitrogen may act as chelating agents also.

Nitrogen fixation among marine algae is largely confined to the Cyanophyceae. W. D. P. STEWART (1964a,b) found that two estuarine species, *Calothrix scopulorum* and *Nostoc entophytum* vigorously fixed nitrogen in natural seawater, liberating some of the fixed nitrogen into the medium. Fixation was highest in the winter, lowest in the summer. *Trichodesmium* has been correlated with nitrogen fixation by DUGDALE et al. (1964), but the rate is variable. This may be explained by autotoxification which also inhibits photosynthesis. Fixation is stimulated by phosphates or trace elements, and more so by both, according to Stewart, and ammonium nitrogen did not completely inhibit nitrogen fixation; FOGG (1962a) states with regard to the algae studied by him that ammonium salts do completely suppress fixation, urea suppresses it by breaking down to ammonia, and nitrate partially inhibits it. Fogg also points out that nitrogen fixation in the algae depends on photosynthesis for hydrogen donors and carbon skeletons, hence inhibition of photosynthesis must inhibit nitrogen fixation. As nitrogen-fixing algae produce extracellular substances, these have to be accounted for in the nitrogen budget. This raises the interesting possibility that nitrogen-fixing organisms may produce excess nitrogenous compounds which, as we have seen, can be used by a number of algae, and thus may contribute directly to the nitrogen supply of organisms which cannot fix nitrogen. The nitrogen budget in the ocean appears to be taken care of by the blue-green algae restoring that which is lost to the atmosphere as a result of denitrification to nitrogen. It would appear that there is a steady state with regard to nitrogen, and this would probably exist if there were no contributions from terrestrial sources. Marine microbes have it in their power to maintain this balance, an important conclusion to a humanity which is looking increasingly to the oceans for its food.

Phosphate cycle. The phosphate cycle is less complex because no valence changes are involved. Moreover, the quantity of phosphate required by each individual microorganism is minute, as GOLDBERG et al. (1951), MACKERETH (1953) and others have shown. Phosphate, however, is essential for the photosynthetic reactions, as the high-energy phosphate bonds such as those of ATP and the reduction of pyridin-nucleotides supply both energy and "hydrogen" for the reduction of carbon dioxide. This can and does occur in the dark with previous photoillumination or from certain other energy sources. It has recently been shown that phosphate ions in small quantities are inhibitory to certain micro-algae, thus setting an upper limit to phosphate concentration in the promotion of growth in algae.

We have discussed the assimilation of carbon from the point of view of the plant. Carbon, however, occurs in the oceans in a variety of forms, and the form of its occurrence is of outstanding importance in oceanic ecology. There are in the oceans, even at the greatest depths, large quantities of dissolved and particulate carbon. We know that these can be utilized by a number of organisms as alternatives to, or instead of, photosynthesis. Further, some of the soluble organics may act as growth accelerators or depressors (antibiotics). Let us first discuss the origin of some of these substances.

Particulate organics. WOOD (1964) has shown that the number of particles in ocean waters in some areas may be one to several orders of magnitude larger than that of the protoplankton; some of these are obviously inorganic but a variable but considerable proportion are organic, and may consist of thread-like or plate-like particles from 50 to several hundred microns long. They appear to be derived from organic (possibly hemicellulose or cellulose) filaments, fragments of chitin or similar material which is refractory to microbial digestion. RILEY et al. (1964) and BAYLOR and SUTCLIFFE (1963) claim to have produced organic aggregates by bubbling air through filtered sea-water. These, according to RILEY (1963) are smaller than natural aggregates from Long Island Sound, but on standing they coalesce into particles similar to natural aggregates. These particles were fed to *Artemia* which grew faster than starved animals but less fast than those fed on dried yeast. Riley et al. believe that dissolved organic matter is extensively converted into particulate by adsorption on near surface bubbles and state that the aggregates have a carbon content far in excess of living phytoplankton. They believe that these aggregates are a very important source of food to microscopic and macroscopic phagotrophs. The highest numbers of particles were found in the Guinea Current, lowest in the Sargasso Sea and North Equatorial Current. The numbers of these aggregates in Long Island Sound were of the order of 3 to $100 \times 10^4/l$; in the Sargasso Sea, $1,000/l$; and off the west coast of Africa, $2.5 \times 10^4/l$. In their assessment of the importance of particles, the various authors have ignored *Trichodesmium* cells when these were present, and also forgotten the fact that in tropical and sub-tropical waters, the phytoplankton is one to two orders of magnitude greater at 50–150 m than at the surface, which would make the phytoplankton and particles through the photic zone of the same order. This is in accord with the findings of Wyrtki and myself (see WOOD, 1964) in the Coral and North Tasman Seas, where the extinction coefficient was controlled at the surface by such aggregates, and at 60–100 m by the phytoplankton. Moreover, J. Vallentyne(unpublished, 1965) could not confirm the formation of such particles by bubbling in the Guinea Current, in an area rich in both phyto- and zooplankton. In short, while the air bubble theory is interesting, and may apply in limited areas near the surface, or may even be important in Long Island Sound, it seems doubtful if it is important in the open ocean or through the photic zone.

As well as serving as food for other organisms, the particles also act as adsorbents of dissolved organics, and they may have been serving this purpose in the *Artemia* experiments. They also adsorb bacteria as JONES and JANNASCH (1956) and I have observed, and fluorescence microscopy shows that they can also adsorb chlorophyll- and non-chlorophyll-containing microorganisms; they can also adsorb nutrients and toxic substances. It is significant that these organic particles are numerous in ocean waters, and if, as we believe, they represent nutrient material, one wonders why they are never quantitatively removed by plankton swarms or blooms. We must remember that, as with the protoplankton, the material we find in the oceans is that left after grazing. Probably a significant, though little-regarded source of particulate organic matter is the external capsular material produced by many algae. The threads could easily be the tubes of blue-green algae and the plates and scales those of dinoflagellates, Chrysophyceae and diatoms. One does not know for example what becomes of the siliceous scales of *Rhizosolenia* or whether these could act as nuclei for organic particles.

Dissolved organics. We have recently learned a great deal about dissolved organic substances in the sea, and their relation to life therein. Produced by marine organisms both plant and animal, they stimulate, feed and inhibit other organisms and even regulate the growth of the organisms which produce them. DUURSMA (1960) questioned whether such substances were produced from healthy cells, believing that they were mainly if not solely degradation products. FOGG (1962b) quotes evidence which shows conclusively that, although some of the dissolved substances may be produced as Duursma suggests, or from the hydrolysis of capsular materials, they are definitely also produced from healthy cells and may amount to from 5–60% of the total organic matter synthesised. Because of the variation in quantity produced by different organisms and under different conditions, the method used for measurement of carbon assimilation by ^{14}C does not allow for such losses. FOGG et al. (1964) makes the following points: "In the present state of our knowledge, it does not seem possible that standard corrections can be made to allow for liberation of extracellular products."

The proportion of photosynthetic products *retained* in the cell is less in light intense enough to inhibit photosynthesis. On the other hand, since the rate of photosynthesis towards the bottom of the photic zone is low, the tendency to minimal liberation of extracellular products at low light intensities is of little quantitative significance.

Release of ^{14}C-labelled materials from damaged cells is not important.

Extracellular products may sustain the growth of phytoplankton under unfavorable light conditions and may thus be regarded as extracellular storage products.

In a discussion of the substances produced, Fogg lists the following:

l-lactic, succinic, pyruvic, acetic acids by fermentation processes; autotrophs may produce oxalic, tartaric, succinic, glycollic, pyruvic and long-chain fatty acids, amino-acids and peptides. From the capsular materials, plants excrete carbohydrates, polysaccharides, pentoses and pentosans, glucose, xylose, glycuronic acid, galactose, rhamnose, arabinose and mannose. Carotenoids, carotenoid-protein complexes and organic sulfides such as dimethyl sulfide are derived from micro- and macro-algae. Among the vitamins and growth substances are thiamin and auxins, and antibiotics include fatty acids, chlorophyllides and acrylic acids, while some species such as certain *Goniaulax* and Gymnodiniums produce toxins which are probably alkaloids or cyclic peptides. LEFÈVRE (1964) discusses the mixed effects of certain extracellular substances which may be beneficial to some species and harmful to others. These may be thermostable or thermolabile, and auto- or heteroantagonistic. Heteroantagonism can cause inhibition of division without growth or assimilation and finally bursting or lysis of the cell of other organisms and thus ensure the supremacy of the organism producing the toxins. Final disappearance of the bloom is often caused by autoantagonism.

WHITTON (1965) found that *Anabaena cylindrica* produces extracellular polypeptides which differ from those of the bacteria and can, in fact, reduce the toxicity of polymyxin B produced by *Bacillus polymyxa*. OVERBECK (1964a,b) has demonstrated that phosphatases, amylase and saccharase may be dissolved in the water, activity being related to the standing crop of phytoplankton; the greater the standing crop, the greater the enzyme activity. There is an increase in enzyme activity in the winter which is probably related to the release of enzymes from the dying phytoplankton. I have also found some evidence of the release of urease from Corynebacteria and of sulfate reducing enzyme systems from *Desulfovibrio*.

Toxins. SCHWIMMER and SCHWIMMER (1964) discuss the importance and implications of toxins produced by algae, particularly blue-greens. The victims of these can include livestock, domestic animals and wildlife. Tumors can be produced by subcutaneous or intra-peritoneal injections of such substances as caragheenin (from red algae). Symptoms of algal toxicity include gastro-intestinal, hepatic, neuromuscular, respiratory or cardiovascular symptoms. Allergic reactions of the hay-fever and asthmatic types are produced by red-tide organisms such as *Gymnodinium* and dermatitis by *Lyngbya majuscula* in Oahu, Georgia and Florida. This cyanophyte is a major component of algal communities in Tampa Bay and Indian River according to PHILLIPS (1963), in Bermuda (BERNATOWICZ, 1952) and St. Georges Sound and Apalachee Bay (Florida) by HUMM, 1956. The Schwimmers also report that a correlation between a conch diet and immunity to polio-myelitis could be due to the algal food of the conch. It is even suggested that toxic algae acting through clams could be responsible for outbreaks of hepatitis in humans in New Jersey and Mississippi, as this disease can be caused by algae alone. It may be that the acceleration of algal growth by detergents (see for example OPPENHEIMER and WOOD, 1962) would in part account for the correlation between the use of detergents and the occurrence of hepatitis.

SIEBURTH (1962) states that the antibacterial activity of corals is due to the zooxanthellae (dinoflagellates) and many diatoms and other algae also produce antibacterials. SIEBURTH (1964a) lists the known antibacterials produced by marine algae (Table V).

Sargassum in the Sargasso Sea apparently contains antibacterials and has no bacterial flora. As it drifts northward the bacterial flora increases due, Sieburth believes, to decreased antibacterial activity of the alga.

Flotation mechanisms. BRAARUD (1962) mentions the importance of flotation mechanisms and motility in protoplankton ecology. The

TABLE V

ANTIBACTERIALS PRODUCED BY MARINE ALGAE

Main taxon	Genus	References; antibacterials
Cyanophyta	*Lyngbya*	STARR et al., 1962
Rhodophyta	*Porphyra*	KATAYAMA, 1962. Fatty acid, carbonyl, terpene
	Grateloupia	KAMIMOTO, 1955
	Callophyllis	PRATT et al., 1951
	Gloiopeltis	KAMIMOTO, 1955
	Cystoclonium	ROOS, 1957
	Gracilariopsis	ALLEN and DAWSON, 1960
	Iridophycus	PRATT et al., 1951. Acrylic acid
	Plocamium	KAMIMOTO, 1955
	Chrysymenia	KAMIMOTO, 1955
	Holosaccion	PRATT et al., 1951
	Gelidium	KAMIMOTO, 1955
	Ceramium	ROOS, 1957
	Delesseria	ROOS, 1957
	Falkenbergia	BURKHOLDER et al., 1960
	Phycodrys	ROOS, 1957
	Murrayella	ROOS, 1957
	Chondria	BURKHOLDER et al., 1960
	Wrangelia	BURKHOLDER et al., 1960
	Digenia	KATAYAMA, 1962. Fatty acid, carbonyl, terpene
	Polysiphonia	CHESTERS and STOTT, 1956. Acrylic acid ROOS, 1957; J.McN. SIEBURTH and J.T. CONOVER, unpublished data, 1962
	Rhodomela	MAUTNER et al., 1953. Brominated phenol
	Laurencia	BURKHOLDER et al., 1960
	Spyridia	ALLEN and DAWSON, 1960
Dinoflagellates, Zooxanthellae		BURKHOLDER et al., 1960. Terpenes and H/c CIERESZKO, 1962
	Amphidinium carteri	WANGERSKY and GUILLARD, 1960. Acetyl choline analogue
	Goniaulax	BURKHOLDER et al., 1960. Alkaloid?
Phaeophyta	*Ectocarpus*	ROOS, 1957
	Dictyota	ALLEN and DAWSON, 1960; STARR et al., 1962
	Pandina	ALLEN and DAWSON, 1960; STARR et al., 1962
	Dictyopteris	BURKHOLDER et al., 1960
	Desmarestia	ROOS, 1957. Sulfuric acid

TABLE V (continued)

Main taxon	Genus	References; antibacterials
	Chorda	Roos, 1957. Sulfuric acid
	Laminaria	Saito and Sameshima 1955; Roos, 1957. Acrylic, fatty acids
		Chesters and Stott, 1956; Katayama, 1962. Carbonyl, terpene
	Macrocystis	Pratt et al., 1951
	Egregia	Pratt et al., 1951
	Postelsia	Pratt et al., 1951
	Undaria	Saito and Sameshima, 1955; Kamimoto, 1955
Diatoms	Skeletonema	Sieburth and Pratt, 1962
	Nitzschia	Steemann-Nielsen, 1955
Fucales	Ascophyllum	Vacca and Walsh, 1954
	Fucus	Roos, 1957
	Pelvetia	Chesters and Stott, 1956; Challenger et al., 1957. Acrylic acid
	Halidrys	Chesters and Stott, 1956; Challenger et al., 1957. Acrylic acid
	Sargassum	Katayama, 1962; J. McN. Sieburth and J.T. Conover, unpublished data, 1962
		Kamimoto, 1955. Fatty acids, carbonyl, terpenes
Chrysophyta	Phaeocystis	Sieburth, 1960. Acrylic acid
Chlorophyta	Codium	Katayama, 1962; Kamimoto, 1955. Fatty acids, carbonyl, terpenes
	Derbesia	Allen and Dawson, 1960
	Enteromorpha	Roos, 1957; Allen and Dawson, 1960. Fatty acids, acrylic
		Starr et al., 1962; Katayama, 1962; Challenger et al., 1957
	Ulva	Roos, 1957; Pratt et al., 1951; Challenger et al., 1957;
		Katayama 1962; Kamimoto, 1955. Acrylic, fatty acids, carbonyl
	Cladophora	Starr et al., 1962
	Cladophoropsis	Allen and Dawson, 1960
Chlorophyta	Spongomorpha	Roos, 1957; Challenger et al., 1957. Acrylic acid
	Chlamydomonas	Jørgensen, 1962. Chlorophyllides

TABLE V (continued)

Main taxon	Genus	References; antibacterials
	Chlorella	PRATT et al., 1944; STEEMANN-NIELSEN, 1955; LEVINA, 1961; TELITCHENKO et al., 1962. Chlorophyllides
	Scenedesmus	LEVINA, 1961; TELITCHENKO et al., 1962. Chlorophyllides
	Protosiphon	HARDER and OPPERMANN, 1953. Fatty acids
	Stichococcus	HARDER and OPPERMANN, 1953. Fatty acids

microorganisms are in themselves slightly heavier than sea water and would, under normal conditions, tend to sink slowly below the photic zone. The flagellates are motile by means of definite motile organs or flagella which, though not capable of allowing the organisms to move over long distances, are able to orientate them and to keep them in a favorable location, i.e., in the photic zone or close to a food source. Pennate diatoms possessing a raphé are also motile by a means which has never been satisfactorily explained but which is due to the extrusion of protoplasm through the raphé. It has been frequently stated that the centric diatoms are non-motile, but this is not true for such forms as *Coscinodiscus*, of which several motile forms have been observed, and *Rhizosolenia*. Some of my students and I recently found motile cells of *R. delicatula* in a class sample taken fresh from Bear Cut, near Miami; it had a nutatory type of motion, distinct from the intermittent jet-like motion of *Coscinodiscus* and *Thalassiosira*. Strickland at Nanaimo and Wilson at Tallahassee have also found motile cells of *Coscinodiscus* in culture. My own example was in a live sample of phytoplankton from the Gulf of Guinea. The Oscillatoriaceae are named from either nutatory motion, but they have another, more rapid type of motion, parallel with the axis of the filaments, a motion which can be rapidly reversed. As has been mentioned, the mechanism of this motility is not known. The ciliates, of course, have very rapid and strong motility by their cilia. The observations on motility in diatoms are very limited, due to the rarity of occasion in which living specimens of phytoplankton are studied. It is possible that such motility is universal and this would be a major factor in keeping the organisms in a suitable environment. Asymmetry is an important factor spread through a number of groups; the ceratia and peridinia have asymmetric horns, and the cell itself is often concavo-convex; the Dinophysidae have one girdle list larger than the other, and the horns and lists themselves act as flotation membranes. *Rhizosolenia* has asymmetric valves and *Chaetoceros* usually asymmetric spines. Chain and ribbon-forming species, especially the planktonic forms, tend to adopt a spiral arrangement. Within the cell itself, flotation can be affected by a differential between the internal and external cations, and by the presence of oil instead of starches and starch-like substances as a carbohydrate storage product.

Luminosity of microorganisms. Luminescence is very frequently observed in the seas, both at the surface and in the depths, in fact, it has been recorded from the greatest depths tested (CLARKE and DENTON, 1962). It is not, however, a purely marine phenomenon, occurring also in fungi, fire-flies, glow-worms, etc., on land. In the marine world it functions in fishes and other larger animals to attract prey, and perhaps to illuminate an area. On the other hand, the luminescence of bacteria, dinoflagellates, and other Protozoa would not appear to serve any useful purpose, unless related to the chlorophyll-containing algae occurring below the photic zone. SCHOLES and SHEWAN (1964) make the interesting suggestion that in the anaerobic environment of the Weltschlamm (see Chapter I), oxygen would have been toxic to the obligate anaerobes, and that luminescence, which requires oxygen, would allow the anaerobes to survive. Luminescence, then, would have been a buffer mechanism between anaerobiosis and aerobiosis, in the days of the transition from one environment to the other. That it occurs so largely in primitive groups of micro-organisms such as the bacteria and flagellates is in accord with Scholes and Shewan's view.

Among the bacteria, luminescence seems confined to the pseudo-monads especially to those which are moderate or extreme halophils, i.e., grow in sea water or brines, though fresh water forms are known. The luminous pseudomonads may be isolated from water, especially near shore, from fish, especially salt fish.

Luminescent micro-algae include the dinoflagellates *Noctiluca miliaris,* various species of *Gymnodinium* and *Goniaulax,* which fre-quently form large masses known as "red tides", *Pyrodinium, Ceratium fusus*, *C. furca*, and certain species of *Peridinium* as recorded by GOLD (1965). Most of these are warm water species. Other luminescent Protozoa include some Foraminifera and radiolarians.

The flashing, microbial type of luminescence is caused by what is known as the luciferin-luciferase reaction, and requires two components which vary to some extent in chemical structure, together with oxygen. In still water, the oxygen is supplied by turbulence, e.g., the movement of a ship's hull or of paddles through the water. These organisms are often used in bioassay of small quantities of oxygen in biological systems.

Growth rates. The growth rate of an organism will have a large effect on its ability to gain dominance in a population. It is generally believed from culture experiments that most phytoplankters have a generation time between about 8 h and several days, but my own observations, based on actual populations, are that organisms which do become dominant may have a generation time of 3–4 h. I have calculated such times for *Skeletonema costatum*, *Asterionella japonica*,

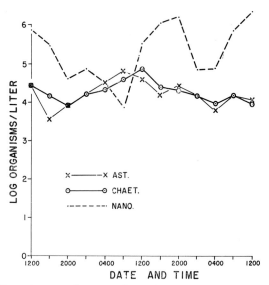

Fig.18. Growth-rates of a natural population of two diatoms, *Asterionella japonica* and *Chaetoceros secundum*, and a nanoplankton organism (broken line) during a moderate bloom in an estuary (Port Hacking).

Chaetoceros secundum (Fig.18) and *Coccolithus huxleyi*. Such generation times are more logical in populations which increase rapidly, becoming dominant and replacing other species in the course of a few days or a week. One must remember in estimating generation times that it is only the logarithmic growth phase that counts, and estimates must be strictly confined to organisms in this phase.

Water movements. We have considered the reasons why protoplankton populations tend to remain in the same water mass, even though it slowly gains or loses heat according as it moves from cold to warm regions or vice versa. Upwellings are usually associated with enrichment, as the lower strata of water have less life in them or at any rate, metabolism is slower and there will not be the demand on available nutrients. Convergences on the other hand, tend to carry down into lower layers a number of the protoplankton population, which is thus deprived of light. It is now known that many potentially photosynthetic microorganisms retain this potentiality under these circumstances and are able to take up phototrophy as soon as light energy is available. So we have vertical movement of the ocean currents transporting nutrients and organisms. An example of this, which I have quoted elsewhere, is that of Antarctic diatoms occurring in surface phytoplankton on the east coast of Australia accompanied by blooms of local species, no doubt fertilized by the nutrients available from the Antarctic bottom water. OVERBECK (1962b) observed that the coenobia of *Scenedesmus quadricauda* although non-motile, sink during the day and rise at night due to convection currents resulting from decreasing night temperatures.

Pressure. ZoBell and his school have shown some of the effects of pressure on microorganisms in the ocean and on their distribution. Many of the organisms which grow naturally at great depths cannot survive the release of pressure involved in bringing them to the surface. The rate of survival appears to depend inversely on the size of the organisms. The bacteria occurring at great depths ZOBELL and JOHNSON (1949) have called *barophilic* organisms. However, if they are staged up, many more of the deep-water organisms can grow at surface pressures. On the other hand, surface organisms have difficulty in acclimating themselves to great pressures, though this can be facilitated by gradual increase in pressure. The net effect of pressure on the population is, it would seem, to reduce the numbers of organisms occurring in deep waters, to reduce the number of species found there, and their rate of metabolism. Whether barophils use metabolic pathways different from their surface cousins we do not know, but this is possible. So far we have not separated pressure from low temperature effects in many of these organisms.

Grazing. It does not seem to be generally realized that the micro-organisms which we count or estimate in the oceans are, as I have already mentioned, the residue from grazing. This was brought home in a recent series of 24-hour studies of phytoplankton which I made in various parts of the tropical and sub-tropical Atlantic. The numbers of organisms decreased in the evening, and regained their former level during the next day (Fig.19). As the ship stayed over the same plant community, and the whole photic zone was sampled, the changes must have been due to grazing and reproduction. The main changes in numbers occurred in the coccolithophores, and the diatom *Coscinodiscus*, whereas the *Rhizosolenia* population changed little, so that while on the first day *Coscinodiscus* was the dominant diatom, on the second day *Rhizosolenia* had displaced it. The coccolithophores, however, maintained their abundance despite grazing, and on one

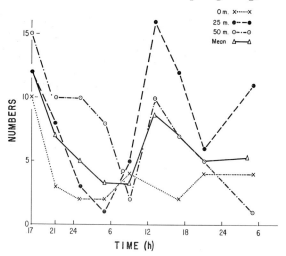

Fig.19. Graph showing diurnal periodicity throughout the photic zone for a phytoplankton population in sub-tropical waters.

occasion the rate of replenishment was greater than that of grazing. The persistence of a plant population will depend, therefore, among other things, on its ratio of reproduction to grazing. Such estimates can only be made on living phytoplankton populations and grazing tests on cultures, while they may tell us the maximum number or types of organisms which an animal may graze, do not tell us anything about its behaviour under natural conditions. It was hoped that the plastic bag type of experiment devised by Strickland's group at Nanaimo might be useful for this type of study, but such bags can only be set up in a restricted number of areas where conditions are suitable. The Miami area for instance has only about 10 ft. of water in Biscayne Bay and most of Florida Bay and its offshoots, while the Straits of Florida have strong currents, so such experiments cannot be tried in South Florida or anywhere in areas of frequent storms. In discussing the control of diatom populations by grazing, FLEMING in 1939 showed the changes in a population of 1×10^6 cells/l dividing once a day with grazing just balancing division. If the grazing rate is doubled, the population after 1 day will be 487,000, after 2 days 237,000, after 3 days, 106,000, after 4 days 56,000, and after 5 days 27,000. If grazing is stepped up five-fold, at the end of the first day the population will be only 62,000, on the second, 3,900, and after 5 days less than 1. The effect of selective grazing on dominance will be obvious from these figures, crude as they are. Fleming pointed out that if such calculations were refined, they could only apply to a single set of data, and that more definite knowledge of the rate of division of phytoplankton and the nature of the zooplankton grazing would be necessary to justify such exactness. He also recommended studies of the effect of physical and chemical factors on the division rate, size and cell contents of the phytoplankton, especially if the computed yield of phytoplankton is to be used as a measure of food supply; further, much more information about grazing by different zooplankton forms is needed. After 25 years, little of this information has been gathered, yet calculations of "productivity" have been carried out by expensive, refined methods. It is time we based our studies of primary and secondary productivity on Fleming's recommendations.

The importance of differential grazing is brought out by some experiments by DROOP (1963b), in which he fed a dinoflagellate *(Oxyrrhis)*, an amoeba *(Heteramoeba)*, and a rotifer *(Philodina)* on

Volvocales, Chlorococcales, Chrysophyceae, diatoms, Cryptophyceae and Rhodophyceae. The dinoflagellate thrived on all species tested, the amoeba on the Volvocales, diatoms, Cryptophyceae and Rhodophyceae but not on Chlorococcales or Chrysophyceae, while the rotifer grew only on Volvocales and Chlorococcales. *Monochrysis* and *Isochrysis* alone were not sufficient for *Heteramoeba*, but a small quantity of *Brachiomonas* proved adequate. Apparently *Brachiomonas* possesses some required nutrient factor. Selective grazing then is not due only to physical peculiarities such as the setae of *Chaetoceros* or the size of *Rhizosolenia castracanei* but also the nutritive peculiarities. Thus, the dominant species in the phytoplankton can determine the organisms that will grow best at the next trophic level. This is a most important biological discovery, and points to the necessity for combining laboratory tests with observations of the natural environment. It also demonstrates that we cannot assume that a measure of primary production, however accurate, has any bearing on the potentialities of secondary or tertiary production. Estimates of oceanic production can only have any pretense of usefulness or accuracy when the biologists can assess the value of each component of the system in the food web. This is a saddening thought for the "productivity" measurers, but a very reassuring one for the biologist, especially the ecologist.

OCEANIC SEDIMENTS

Oceanic sediments consist of two very different habitats which nevertheless have something in common, the ocean floor and the continental shelf or slope. The topography of the ocean floor affects the microbes that dwell in this biocoenosis only in the manner in which it deflects the flow of bottom waters. These move slowly and there is the possibility of considerable interchange of materials between them.

The evidence of microbial life in these ocean sediments has been provided mainly by ZoBell, and data from the "Galathea" expedition. Geological oceanographers do not appear to consider it necessary to take microbiologists with them, and until they do, the in situ transformations in bottom deposits will not be adequately explained. We know little for example about the microbiology of the red clays which form about 40% of the ocean bottom.

ZoBell (1952) showed that bacterial life in the deep sediments includes most if not all the transformations that occur in shallow water sediments, such as sulfate reduction, destruction of chitin and other refractory organic substances, as well as the usual deamination of proteins, hydrolysis of carbohydrates and fats; methane and hydrogen bacteria are there but I, despite repeated attempts, did not find sulfur-oxidizing bacteria, so we must assume that this process is due to chemical oxidation. Wood (1956) found Foraminifera and diatoms which contained protoplasm and were apparently also heterotrophic or phagotrophic in their nutrition.

In the shallow water sediments we have the same transformations with the addition of sulfide oxidization by the thiobacilli.

Studies on the microbiology of shallow sediments such as the California Basin have been made by ZoBell and Rittenberg (1948) and their associates (Rittenberg et al., 1955). ZoBell found few true anaerobes in these sediments but most of the heterotrophic bacteria he isolated were facultative anaerobes. Wood also failed to find many true anaerobes among heterotrophic bacteria from sediments of the Australian continental shelf. Prevot (1958) criticised Wood's findings without producing any evidence to the contrary, and either ignored or did not appreciate the significance of the fact that Wood recorded positive redox potentials up to $+250\,mV$ in the sediments he studied. The California Basin sediments on the other hand were in the main reducing, some at the surface, and others oxidizing at the surface and reducing below, with evidence of sulfate reduction. Kaplan et al. (1963) in their studies of sulfur isotopes from the California Basin showed that organic sulfur released from decaying detritus plays only a small part in the sulfur economy of the sediments. They estimated the average steady state concentration of sulfate-reducers as 4×10^8 cells/g of dried weight of the sediment, or 3.5×10^7 cells/cm^3. They believe that sulfate reduction is a major phenomenon in the geochemistry of sulfur and the early diagenesis of the Basin sediments. Pyrite is autogenic and most of it is formed at the sediment-water interface, deriving the iron from the sediments themselves, including the clay minerals.

One should comment here on the effect of trawl fishing on the microbiology of continental shelf sediments. The Botany Ground, east of Sydney, Australia was at one time an important fishing ground for trawl fish, and twelve trawlers were operating there. The sediment at that time was a somewhat reduced mud, but the action of warps and otter boards, with a strong southerly set from the East Australian current caused the removal of the lighter and finer sediment particles. At the present time, no trawlers work these grounds which are bare white sand with a low microbial content. In a large flat area such as the North Sea, where the sediment could redeposit itself elsewhere, the disturbance of the sediments is not such a serious matter, but, as EMERY and RITTENBERG (1952) pointed out, the sediments are important reservoirs of nitrogen, phosphate and other nutrients. They maintain an equilibrium with the waters above, according to the demands of the benthic and planktonic microorganisms, so that a disturbance of these equilibria results in upsetting the ecosystem which is centered at the sediment-water interface. Such a disturbance is reflected in the movements of demersal fish, benthic animals and finally in the whole animal population of the continental shelf. The Japanese recognize this, although largely unconsciously, in their fishing methods which are, on the whole, designed to avoid disturbing the sediments, and to maintain feeding chains.

The microbiology of shallow (to 1,000m) tropical sediments has been little studied, and the bacterial communities are unknown save for the nitrate-reducing bacteria which DREW (1914) believed were a large cause of calcium carbonate precipitation in the Dry Tortugas region. Recent work by GREENFIELD (1963) and his group at Miami tend to confirm Drew's hypothesis suggesting that precipitation is due to the formation of calcium-ammonium complexes in a water high in carbonates. In the Straits of Florida, large quantities of decaying *Thalassia* and other plant material are found in bottom trawls to 800 m and these are derived from the Bahama Banks and the Florida continental shelf, as can be shown by the diatom flora associated with the mass. The effect of this decaying organic matter on the calcareous sediments is not known, but would be expected to result in a sulfur cycle, at least in local pockets. The presence or absence of sulfate reduction in these headwaters of the Gulf Stream is important information for a study and understanding of phosphate release in the lower waters of the Gulf Stream.

In samples of sediments taken from Sahul Bank in the Timor Sea, from the Australian continental shelf, from inside the Great Barrier Reef between Cairns and Bundaberg, as well as from the Florida Straits, one almost invariably finds pennate diatoms and *Coscinodiscus* in depths well below the calculated compensation depth of the water. *Pleurosigma*, *Nitzschia*, *Navicula*, *Diploneis* and *Mastogloia* are the most frequent genera found. These potentially heterotrophic phototrophs may play an important part in the shelf ecosystem.

WOOD (1956) pointed out that the diatoms found in the "Galathea" samples from the sediments of the ocean abysses consist of species with a benthic habitat. In sediments from the Gulf of Guinea at 5,000 m, a few valves of *Rhizosolenia styliformis* were found, but this species was also taken alive in bacteriological samples from the water immediately above. KOLBE (1956) lists the most frequent diatoms in tropical cores from three oceans; these include *Coscinodiscus nodulifer*, *Ethmodiscus (Coscinodiscus) rex*, *C. excentricus*, *C. lineatus*, *C. africanus*, *Thalassiothrix*, *Hemidiscus cuneiformis*, *Nitzschia marina* in all three, *Pseudoeunotia doliolus* and *Actinocyclus subtilis* in two and *Stephanopyxis palmeriana*, *Asteromphalus elegans*, *A. hiltonianus*, *A. arachne*, *Actinocyclus elongatus*, *Rhizosolenia bergonii*, *Coscinodiscus obscurus*, *Thalassiosira decipiens* and *Roperiana tesellata* in one. Of these, only *Thalassiosira*, *Stephanopyxis* and *Rhizosolenia* are confined to the plankton, the others being also common in benthic situations. Kolbe discusses in detail the distribution of *E. rex* and points out that no reports are extant of its abundance in the plankton except for one by COLLINGWOOD (1868) who recorded "countless myriads" of this species during calms in the Bay of Bengal. Collingwood may well have been referring to *C. gazellae* which is often mistaken for *C. rex*. MCHUGH (1954) reports it with some frequency from southern California, which is not even warm temperate, and his forms may have been *C. gazellae* or may have been brought to the surface by the upwelling from submarine canyons which is frequent on the California coast especially in the vicinity of La Jolla, where McHugh was working. Other students of diatoms from tropical waters, including CLEVE (1900, 1903), KARSTEN (1905–1907), CASTRACANE (1886), HENDEY (1937), HART (1942), MERESCHOWSKY (1902), SCHRÖDER (1911), PAVILLARD (1926), either do not record it or found it infrequently. My own extensive collections from the Indian and Pacific Oceans contained this diatom (one empty frustule and several fragments) on only two occasions and then only from areas where upwelling in the region of submarine canyons was known. There is no positive evidence that this species occurs abundantly in any waters at the present time, and it may well be that it, like the silicoflagellates, is a declining form and truly rare in present-day plankton. I inclined earlier to accept KARSTEN's (1907) theory of a dysphotic habitat, and this may still be true, but I have not found *C. rex* from samples taken at various depths down to and below the compensation depth. Nor has BERNARD (1964) recorded this species from his Atlantic, Mediterranean or Indian Ocean samples taken to 4,000 m, in tropical and warm-temperate waters.

In the Antarctic, however, the situation is somewhat different. Many of the species found in Pleistocene and more recent sediments such as *Synedra reinboldii*, *Asteromphalus hookeri*, or *Fragilaria* spp. are dominant in the Antarctic phytoplankton today. Other species, no longer found, appear as badly eroded valves and not as the uneroded and frequently whole frustules of the modern forms. Here we have a process which is still continuing and in which the living cells must be carried down close to where the oozes are forming. The presence of Antarctic species such as *Rhizosolenia chunii* and *Biddulphia weissflogii* in upwelling water of Antarctic origin on the coast of New South Wales (WOOD, 1964) coupled with the evidence just adduced, makes it feasible to suppose that Antarctic diatoms frequently sink with the heavy Antarctic water mass and reach the bottom alive. The intact cells would represent this group of species. The eroded cells would represent species which have died on the way down and this may account for their disappearance from the present-day plankton. Diatoms could also descend in turbidity currents and this would account for the presence of live forms with chlorophyll below the photic zone. They probably grow and multiply slowly by means of heterotrophic nutrition at aphotic levels.

VERTICAL DISTRIBUTION OF PROTOPLANKTON

WOOD (1964, 1965, 1966) has studied the vertical distribution of protoplankton in the tropical and sub-tropical Pacific, Indian and Atlantic Oceans, the Mediterranean Sea and the Antarctic. BERNARD (1963) has recorded protoplankton to depths of 2,000 m. Wood's figures, derived from counting protoplankters by the fluorescence method (WOOD, 1962), show that the maximum numbers tend to occur at depths to 150 m but usually between 80 and 100 m. There is frequently another maximum at 40–50 m (see Fig.20–23). Most fre-

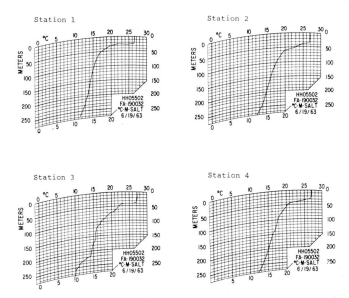

Fig.20. Bathythermograph traces from the Gulf of Guinea showing a discontinuity (thermocline), between 25 and 40 m, typical of a tropical water.

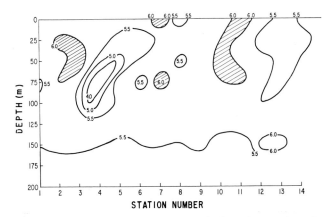

Fig.21. Quantitative distribution of phytoplankton in a region of turbulence and upwelling. (After WOOD, 1964.)

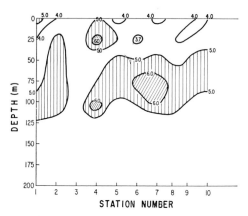

Fig.22. Quantitative distribution of phytoplankton in tropical waters with a maximum between 50 and 100 m.

quently, the maximum is below the thermocline and either in the vicinity of or below the 1% level of surface light. Where there is upwelling, the protoplankton count is more or less uniform throughout the photic zone, depending on the degree of mixing of the water masses. In shallower waters, the protoplankton maximum is found nearer the surface, e.g., between Greece and Crete, or between Cyprus and Turkey. In cooler waters, e.g., in the region of the subtropical convergence in the Tasman Sea, the maximum approaches

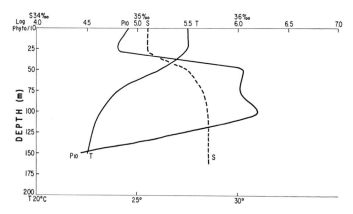

Fig.23. Tropical phytoplankton numbers (P_{10}) related to temperature (T).

the surface and is found at 25–50 m. However, in the case of oceanic and estuarine red tides, the concentration of microorganisms is from the surface to a depth of about 0.5 m.

Bernard has recorded large concentrations of protoplankton at depths between 1,500 and 2,000 m in the Atlantic and Indian Oceans and in the Mediterranean. Many of these concentrations were far larger than those found at or near the surface at the same stations. The concentrations found by both Wood and Bernard tend to be lenticular and at constant depth in a given area. It would appear from this that these concentrations are autochthonous. Moreover, Wood has found little or no evidence of strong vertical migration of protoplankton even in his diurnal studies. Where vertical movements have been observed, they tend to be irregular and are possibly due to eddy diffusion in the region of the thermocline. There seems to be a lack of correlation between the phytoplankton numbers, chlorophyll and ^{14}C assimilation except in a few instances (see Wood, 1964).

CHAPTER VII

MICROORGANISMS IN THE ESTUARIES

The dictionary definition of an estuary as a place where the sea and river meet does not satisfy the ecological implications of the term. At a recent scientific meeting on estuaries, several sessions were spent on the discussion of the term and each speaker appeared to have a different idea. Difficulties arise in the fact that an estuarine environment can maintain itself after the dictionary definition is no longer applicable. I have heard the North Sea described as an estuary, as once indeed its prehistoric equivalent undoubtedly was, with present rivers such as the Scheldt, the Elbe and the Thames flowing as tributaries into a long lost river. Biologically speaking, there is still a great deal of resemblance to an estuarine habitat throughout the North Sea in the types of phytoplankton that we find there, and in other characters as well. Thus an estuary is very much what the *author* calls an estuary and one finds considerable differences in the definitions in the literature. From the ecological point of view, an estuary should show large variations in salinity, representing the effects of salt and fresh water, and this will be represented in the type of organism which occurs there. Sometimes, the changes in salinity of most or all of the estuary will be tidal, sometimes only due to occasional phenomena such as flash floods or strong onshore currents and the invasion of the estuary by marine conditions. A neritic flora is usually regarded as occurring in the area of the continental shelf. It has a great deal in common with and may be identical with the marine-dominated estuarine flora of adjacent estuaries. It is probably derived from the estuary, though certain species may come from spores which have previously sunk to the sediment. In regions which I have studied extensively neritic waters abound in oceanic forms when there are heavy onshore winds and in neritic or marine-estuarine species when the winds are from the land. I can find no reason for postulating a neritic ecosystem.

CHARACTERISTICS OF ESTUARIES

The microbiology of estuaries is dependent on the characteristics of each individual estuary; there is no such thing as a "typical estuary". Possibly the most important factors are the origin of the estuary— (drowned valley, river delta or lagoon type with narrow, barrier islands) geological features—(situation in horizontal, anticlinal or synclinal strata, nature of rock forming the bottom and also the rock of the water-shed) and the relation of the estuary to the ocean.

Estuaries situated in drowned valleys have, as a rule, steep banks and are deep with a rocky bottom (Fig.24) unless a large river feeds into them, in which case the bottom may be silted. The river deltas are usually at the mouths of meandering rivers and consist of shallow channels separated by sandbanks which may or may not be exposed at low tide. Frequently, the mouths are silted up and one often gets large, shallow estuaries, with the channels separated by low islands which may be covered with mangrove, samfire, *Spartina* or other grass or rush (in Australia it is usually *Atriplex*), and often with tapetic growths of algae between high and low water.

The barrier island types are usually long and more or less narrow, shallow and nearly cut off from the sea. If the shallow estuaries have poor access to the sea as in Lake Illawarra, New South Wales, Lake Alexandrina, South Australia, the Texas Bays (Fig.25), or Florida Bay, the climate will have a very strong effect on their physico-chemical characters and on their microbial population. Most such estuaries have a very low intake of fresh water, and many of them are in arid climates and may be classified as evaporites. In such cases, the normal salinity may be higher than that of sea water—Lake Illawarra has reached 42‰, the Texas Bays and Florida Bay over 50‰, but in years of heavy rain, these salinities may fall well below 34‰.

In the case of the drowned valleys, even if they are cut off by barrier sand banks, the deep water holes will provide a local thermocline, and the habitat will resemble that of a lake in many characters. One of these, important for the microbes, is the presence of a hypolimnion in which seed populations of microorganisms can reside when conditions in the epilimnion are unfavorable. Thus they do not need to be able to stand up to the rigors which the shallow estuary organisms must be able to tolerate. This is probably why OPPEN-HEIMER and WOOD (1965) could not find a satisfactory correlation of

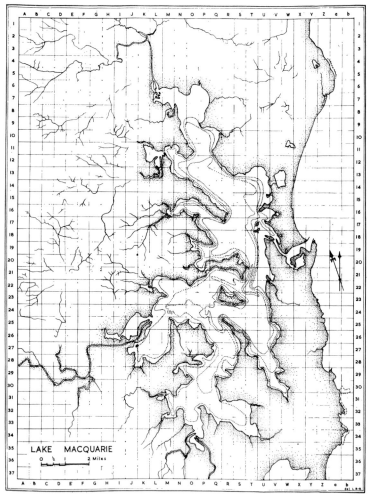

Fig.24. A drowned valley estuary (Lake Macquarie, Australia; After WOOD, 1959).

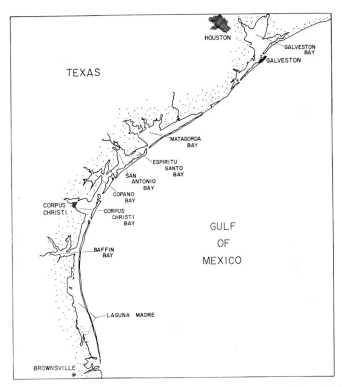

Fig.25. A barrier-island type estuary—the South Texas Bays. (After OPPENHEIMER and WOOD, 1965.)

the benthic plants of the evaporite Texas Bays with any physico-chemical parameters, finding that they tend to follow geographical patterns, and to be limited by the boundaries of the individual estuaries. The flora of the Lower differed from that of the Upper Laguna Madre, and the communities of Aransas, San Antonio, Matagorda and Galveston Bays differed from each other. Apparently, in this case, the resilience of the species in each bay was such that the microbial distribution was not appreciably influenced by depth (to 30 ft.), temperature, salinity, pH or redox potential, nor even by the nature of the substrate. Physiography governs the shape of the estuary; if the hinterland is flat, the movements of water into the estuary will be slow except in the case of flash floods, and these can occur over a wide area and cause sudden and violent changes in salinity and nutrient content. In my own experience, flash floods cause a suspension of the microbial patterns for a short time, with a diminution of phytoplankton and epiphyton blooms, a change in bacterial processes, followed by a bloom or series of blooms of different species, usually of low-salinity species. Where large rivers debouch into the sea through an estuary, floods, unless they are very extensive, have less sudden effects on the microbial flora of the estuary. Processes change more gradually and species changes are less complete. If the hinterland is mountainous, the rivers tend to flow rapidly and scour their estuaries, which then have more in common with the onshore or *neritic* environment than with the shallow estuarine environment. We may thus expect the invasion of the estuary by oceanic species when the river flow is low, and by estuarine species when it is strong. Horizontally bedded strata and glacial valleys tend to give deep estuaries with steep banks, whereas folded strata give a more varied topography with a more varied flora of microorganisms. The bedrock too, plays an important part in the microbial flora; sandstone gives siliceous sediments with a low clay content and often a low microbial content. Light penetration is considerable and at Port St. Joes on the Florida panhandle, blue-green algae were found to a depth of 2 inches. If the organic content of siliceous sediments is high, sulfate reduction may occur, and the sulfides will be rapidly oxidized in air, giving rapid changes in redox potential. This, in turn, will regulate the algal flora, which must be attuned to such conditions. In sediments derived from igneous rocks, clays or shales, the sediments will consist of montmorillonite, etc., and the redox potential will tend to be low, even if the organic content is only moderate. The colloidal organic matter will adsorb in the clay and a very mobile system will result, in which many kinds of microbes can live, including many flagellates, ciliates, and euglenids, as well as naviculoid diatom species which can live in low redox potentials. This system is much better poised than the siliceous sediment, and reduced areas will oxidize much more slowly. Gravels are very similar to the siliceous sediments, but will vary according to the interstitial material. Calcareous sediments tend to favor the blue-green algae, which are frequently to be found in a series of bands in a tapetic formation, interspersed with bands of calcite, aragonite, dolomite or magnesite, such as may be found on the Florida Keys.

The shape of the mouth of the estuary and its relation to ocean currents is often important in determining the microbial association within it. Examples of this are to be found in some east coast estuaries of Australia. Moreton Bay is a shallow estuary, really the delta of the meandering Brisbane River. It is barred by three large islands, Bribie, Moreton (a 700 ft. sand dune) and Stradbroke, with only one navigable and somewhat winding channel. Moreton Island projects well to the east of Bribie and forms a funnel directed to the northeast. The Coral Sea water mass moving southwest onto the coast tends to enter the mouth of the estuary with an oceanic planktonic flora which is seldom flushed out by the river water, and has become virtually endemic in the outer roads. In the labyrinthine channels, especially those which are sheltered from the tides, the flora is neritic or estuarine, depending on drainage from some small rivers and creeks such as the Logan and Albert Rivers and Nerang Creek. However, because of the extensive, partly-covered tidal flats the large expanse of water (about 100 by about 20 miles) and the frequent winds, there is a great deal of turbulence and mixing with the result that normally benthic organisms are usually found to be a part of the planktonic flora of the bay.

Port Hacking, a much smaller estuary with little fresh water except for flash floods, has a somewhat similar mouth, Bate Bay also facing northeast and into the East Australian current. Port Hacking is a drowned valley, highly silted to give sheltered deep holes behind shallow sand bars. In strong onshore winds, the East Australian current sweeps into Bate Bay and oceanic conditions may eventually reach the weir which holds back the fresh water some 8 miles up. At such times, oceanic species of protoplankton will ascend partly or wholly into the estuary. In such cases, the neritic forms which are common in this marine-dominated system are to be found in the hypolimnion of the deep holes. If, as frequently happens, the strong east winds are accompanied by heavy rains, the estuary is flushed out by fresh water, heavy with ferruginous sand. This seems to adsorb and precipitate the microbial flora, with the result that phytoplankton almost disappears, to be followed after a few days by a bloom of truly estuarine species.

Port Jackson, a few miles north of Port Hacking, is also a drowned valley in the Sydney Sandstone Series, larger but exactly similar in origin. The mouth of this estuary is narrow and deep with steep cliffs on either side. The micro-flora differs from that of Port Hacking in being largely neritic or estuarine in character, and, as the east Australian current cannot get far into the estuary, there is no invasion of the oceanic protoplankton. About 80 miles to the north is Lake Macquarie (Fig.24), another drowned valley originally wide open to the sea like Port Hacking, but now closed by a sand bar, except for a narrow channel about 12 ft. deep. There are several sand-flats in the lake, but most of the water is deep enough for a thermocline to develop. In easterly winds, some of the oceanic protoplankton flows through the channel and spreads over the surface of the central part of the lake, but there is also a group of endemic species which are of oceanic origin and include the diatoms *Chaetoceros peruvianum* and *Ch. lorenzianum* and the dinoflagellates *Pyrophacus horologicum* and *Peridinium depressum*. When fresh water enters the lake from the small creeks, it flows over the salt water producing a thermocline. At such times, the endemic protoplankton is to be found in the hypolimnion. In autumn, when the temperature of the epilimnion falls until the density of the surface water exceeds that of the hypolimnion, the waters will mix and this is often accompanied by an exchange of nutrients and may trigger off a bloom of protoplankton. In Lake Macquarie at this time, the lake water is less dense than ocean water, so that such ocean water coming through the channel flows down into the lake below the lake water, but the oceanic protoplankton coming in with it does not survive. It is interesting to speculate as to why the endemic oceanic species have survived in Lake Macquarie, as they do not occur in neighboring estuaries. One theory is that the sand bar was thrown up during an oceanic protoplankton bloom which was thereby imprisoned. The Old Lake water (SPENCER, 1959) has marine characteristics, and this would enable the protoplankton to retain its identity.

Biscayne Bay Florida, represents an estuary which is incompletely separated from the Straits of Florida and the Gulf Stream by barrier islands. In this estuary, which has no true river entering it, the Miami River being merely a channel in a hinterland which is only a few feet above sea level, water movements are governed by the Gulf Stream, flowing north and through the openings into the estuary. Water moves in and out according to a complicated pattern, but the truly marine environment maintains a neritic protoplankton, the origin and distribution of which has not yet been worked out. Diatom species such as *Skeletonema costatum*, *Rhizosolenia delicatula*, *R. robusta*, and dinoflagellates such as *Gymnodinium simplex* and *Amphidinium klebsi* are usually present, with, as seems to be the rule in tropical and sub-tropical estuaries, several species co-dominant. Evaporite regions are exemplified by the Texas Bays such as Aransas Bay (Fig.25). Here, as in most shallow bays, there is a great deal of turbulence and mixing, with the consequence of a close relation between benthic and planktonic forms, all having considerable tolerance to changes of temperature and salinity. There are few passes to these bays, which have developed a neritic-type flora due to the high salinity range of the area, and this flora is reinforced through the passes such as Aransas Pass by water from the Gulf of Mexico. This shallow Gulf has a rich neritic protoplankton, and this can form rich blooms in Aransas Bay, when the waters mingle through the pass.

From the examples I have given, which by no means exhaust the types of estuarine environment, it will be seen that geological and physiological factors play an important part in the kind of micro-organisms we shall find in an estuary.

Physical factors in estuaries

The most important physical property affecting the microorganisms in an estuary is temperature. While the peculiar properties of water prevent the large variations one gets in soils, diurnal temperature changes are far greater than in the oceans, especially in the shallows. Wood (1964) records that estuarine dinoflagellates and diatoms can withstand seasonal changes of up to 16 °C, from subtropical estuaries in Australia and Oppenheimer and Wood (1965) record similar tolerance from the Texas Bays. Species which are regarded as estuarine for other reasons are more tolerant of temperature differences than neritic or oceanic species.

The temperature of the sediments is far more constant than that of the water, and the benthic flora including the bacteria is not so subject to change.

Other physical factors include pH and Eh, and these are controlled by, rather than controlling, the microorganisms. Hydrogen ion concentration is as we have already learned, controlled largely by photosynthesis and respiration in the water and at the surface of the sediments, and in the latter, sulfate reduction tends to hold the pH around

7, though fermentations can reduce it to about 6.4 or maybe lower. The release of phosphate as phosphoric acid described by BAAS BECKING and MACKAY (1956) can reduce both sediments and water to 5.4 which seems to be the minimum for the estuarine environment.

Chemical factors

Chemical factors are influenced partly externally and partly by peculiarities intrinsic to the estuary. External factors include salinity, which varies with the ability of the oceanic waters to intrude into the estuary and the inflow of fresh water from rivers, and other sources. In our modern times, pollution by sewage and industrial wastes is almost a normal feature of an estuary, while, especially in rural areas, fertilizers can leach in, and insecticides are a normal hazard to the estuarine ecosystem.

Salinity depends on onshore currents, tides, configuration, winds and climate, including evaporation, inflow and flushing. The lower region of an estuary is usually *marine dominated*, and contains microorganisms usually associated with the oceanic and neritic waters. The upper region may still be marine dominated or may be river dominated, in which case fresh and brackish water species will occur. Tides and winds may control a large estuary almost entirely, and we may quote the Swan River estuary in Western Australia. In this large, shallow basin, onshore winds in the summer bring in oceanic conditions which the short, slow-flowing Swan River does little to affect. The estuary is essentially marine in character and has neritic microorganisms. In winter, the winds are offshore, rains are heavy and the estuary becomes fresh with an entirely different micro-flora. This wind system is such as practically to eliminate tides. More usually, however, estuarine conditions alternate between marine and fresh water dominated. The Laguna Madre and Florida Bay are examples of a normally hypersaline environment, due to shallowness and high evaporation rates, i.e., once again configuration and climate, as in the Swan River, but with a different result.

We often say that in the estuaries the species present are governed by the salinity (OVERBECK, 1962b), and a look at WOOD's (1964) tables appear to confirm this. However, this is an over-simplification; we have seen that our microorganisms from marine environments have different requirements for ionic concentrations, especially cation ratios. These, and the relations between salinity and trace elements, flocculation of organic matter, permeability, etc., may really be the controlling factors rather than salinity itself. Fresh water from rivers and streams often brings with it soluble and particulate organic and inorganic matter collected during its journey to the sea, and such land-effects have been blamed for the red tides which occur off the west coast of Florida and neighboring states.

Pollution is usually regarded as being uniformly deleterious to an estuary, but there are cases where it may actually be beneficial, though it will always affect the unpolluted ecosystem. Sulfite wastes and crude sewage cause devastation in the vicinity of their discharge, but microorganisms quickly work to destroy the materials and the resultant chemical entities may result in an increase in the microbial flora and a net gain in biomass over the whole estuary. Even such substances as copper and nickel are chelated or precipitated, for example, the fumes of the nickel plants in Noumea in New Caledonia devastate the countryside, but the estuarine ecosystem does not show any corresponding destruction, except in local areas.

Contamination by pathogenic microbes is also limited to the region close to sewage effluents and dock areas in which what amounts to aerobic and anaerobic sludge digestion in the water and sediments. In fact, the net result of human policy in discharging all possible wastes into rivers, estuaries and the ocean is to impoverish the terrestrial environment and enrich the marine with nutrients. Phosphate in particular is regularly discharged in sewage, and most will ultimately be converted into marine animal and plant material. Seabirds have in the past helped to restore this organic matter to the land in certain arid areas, but we are depleting this much faster than it can be replaced. It may yet be possible to effect some reclamation by utilizing the ability of marine microorganisms to collect this phosphate in our estuaries, in fact some experiments along such lines are already under way, though so far they are rather haphazard. Intelligently planned fish farms using phytophagous fish feeding on planktonic, epiphytic and benthic microorganisms may be needed to save our ever-growing human populations. The Japanese and Javanese have done more than anyone to cope with their large populations by such means, though their work so far has been ad hoc.

Insecticides and other toxic discharges affect the estuarine environment by killing the macro-fauna and sometimes the macro-flora, maybe displacing the micro-flora but essentially altering the microbial processes, e.g., increasing the activity of parts of the sulfur cycle, promoting the activity of colorless Protozoa, deoxygenating the water by the death and decomposition of the macroorganisms and thus giving the environment over to anaerobic forms. Experience teaches us that the microbes will eventually restore the balance if they are allowed to do so.

Sediments as a factor

Intrinsic factors of an estuary are controlled by the nature and constitution of the bottom, the depth of various parts, and the local flora and fauna. Interesting examples of the effect of the bottom on the microbiology are Lake Macquarie, New South Wales, and Biscayne Bay in Florida. In the former, coal mining resulted in a sediment with a high carbon content and a low redox potential but with little sulfate reduction in the deeper parts of the lake. In the latter, the calcareous bottom results in the presence of a number of organisms which can precipitate calcium carbonate, and we get a cycling of this substance resulting in the formation of marl which appears to be of microbial origin. Rocky bottom results in the growth of the macroscopic algae such as *Porphyra*, *Fucus*, *Hormosira*, *Sargassum*, many of which produce antibiotics and reduce the microbial populations to be found in association with them. As CONOVER and SIEBURTH (1963) point out, some of these algae lose their antibiotic effect with age, so the dead algae are no longer detrimental to microorganisms.

Sea grasses as a factor

The most active microbial associations of the estuaries are associated with the sea-grasses as BAAS BECKING and WOOD (1955), WOOD (1959), PHILLIPS (1963) and others have pointed out. High productivity in estuaries is invariably associated with *Zostera*, *Thalassia*, *Diplanthera*, *Posidonia* or *Ruppia*. WOOD (1959, 1964) describes the mats of *Ectocarpus*, *Enteromorpha*, *Polysiphonia*, *Ceramium*, etc., that cover the *Zostera* beds in the Australian spring, and PHILLIPS (1963) describes the floating algal communities dominated by *Lyngbya majuscula* in areas such as Tampa Bay and Indian River near St. Lucie Inlet and Florida Bay (E. J. F. Wood, unpublished) in Florida. They start as patches of scum over *Diplanthera wrightii* and *Ruppia maritima*, and the trichomes become joined by gelatinous secretions, collecting to form a mat of *Lyngbya* or *Spirulina*. As this mat decays below, nematodes, Protozoa, including flagellates and ciliates, and bacteria invade it and diatoms, crustacea and other plankton organisms become enmeshed. Frequently gastropods and other animals form part of the community. Gases are produced from the mat in such quantities that it forms large bubbles and floats off to become dispersed over the bays. The course of the process is the same in the *Zostera* beds of the Southern Hemisphere and the *Diplanthera* and *Thalassia* beds of the Northern. It is a pity that GRØNTVED, in his studies (1960, 1962) of Danish estuaries, deliberately excluded the sea-grass flats from his calculations of estuarine productivity. It would certainly have altered his figures very significantly and would have allowed a comparison of cold and warm water estuaries. It is interesting to note that WOOD (1959b, 1964) recorded that *Zostera* was host to large numbers of diatoms as epiphytes, while Phillips reported that *Diplanthera* supported mainly blue-green algae. Wood also reported blue-greens from *Ruppia* as did Phillips, while REYES-VASQUEZ (1965) found diatoms to be the chief microbial epiphytes on *Thalassia* in Biscayne Bay. We have therefore in the estuarine ecosystem, a number of plant communities which are intimately associated, because of the limited depth of the water. Let us consider these communities separately.

THE PROTOPLANKTON COMMUNITY

This consists of microorganisms, often associated with filamentous algae including the greens, *Enteromorpha*, *Chaetomorpha*, *Cladophora*, etc., the browns, chiefly *Ectocarpus*, and reds such as *Ceramium*, *Polysiphonia*, *Antithamnion*. The microorganisms consist largely of diatoms, blue-greens, dinoflagellates, and colored flagellates such as *Pyramimonas*, *Nannochloris*, *Micromonas pusilla* and a number of Xanthomonads. OVERBECK (1962b) found that in brackish water, the net phytoplankton is about 0.1–2.5% of the total phytoplankton and these figures are of the same order as those of WOOD and DAVIS (1956). The diatoms consist of neritic species in the lower, marine dominated parts, with occasional incursions of oceanic species as has been mentioned above. Centric diatoms consist of *Lauderia*, *Schroederella*, *Skeletonema*, *Rhizosolenia* spp. *Chaetoceros* spp., especially *Ch. secundum* and the probably identical *Ch. curvisetum* and *Ch. pseudocurvisetum*, *Coscinodiscus* especially *C. granii*, and the pennates *Asterionella japonica*, *Thalassiothrix nitzschioides*, *Nitzschia seriata*, *N. longissima*, and the former *Nitzschia closterium (Cylindrotheca)* and *N. closterium* v. *minutissima (Phaeodactylum)*. The dinoflagellates consist largely of species of *Peridinium*, *Gymnodinium*, *Goniaulax*, *Ceratium* (e.g., *C. buceros*, *C. tripos*, *C. symmetricum*) and *Dinophysis (caudata, tripos*, etc.). In addition, a number of normally epiphytic species such as *Climacosphenia*, or *Licmophora* and occasionally *Amphora* and *Epithemia (Rhopalodia)* are present or even dominant when there is considerable wind and current action in the estuary.

In Port Hacking, New South Wales, where tides range from 3–7 ft., channels are narrow and wind is frequent, *Licmophora* and *Climacosphenia* become the dominant species at times, and are usually present in the plankton. In Lake Macquarie, where there is no tidal action, and, because of the overall depth of the lake, wind action cannot cause strong turbulence, the epiphytic species do not appear as dominants or even sub-dominants. In a large number of examinations of stomach contents of several species of phytophagous (plant-eating) fish, truly planktonic species of microorganisms were rarely if ever found and do not form an appreciable part of the food. Various larval crustacea can ingest and digest such forms as *Skeletonema costatum*, and it is probable that the fish could be fed in controlled environments on certain planktonic species. Possibly, it is the manner of feeding that controls the species ingested, for example the mullets tend to feed on the epiphytes by sucking them off the leaves of *Thalassia* or *Zostera*. The fact that protoplankton of the estuaries is not an important source of food for the higher marine animals complicates any estimates of primary production in relation to the overall productivity of an estuary.

THE EPIPHYTIC COMMUNITY

This is the most important community in the estuarine ecosystem and is largely associated with the sea-grasses, often exceeding them considerably in biomass (see WOOD, 1959b; Fig. 26). It contains both macro- and micro-elements, the former consisting of such species as the red algae *Laurencia*, *Hypnaea*, *Gracilaria*, *Gigartina*, brown algae such as *Dictyocta* and, in Australia, *Colpomenia*, which later becomes planktonic. The filamentous species, such as *Ectocarpus*, *Polysiphonia*, *Ceramium,* often begin their growth as attached forms, breaking off later and becoming planktonic.

The micro-flora is chiefly found attached to the sea-grasses and not to the algae, presumably due to the antibiotic production of the latter. Some species such as certain Lyngbyas however do attach to such forms as *Polysiphonia* and *Ceramium*. Attached forms include diatoms, blue-green algae, and certain dinoflagellates such as *Exuviaella* and *Peridinium gatunense*. The presence of these species in the epiphyton is unexpected and *Exuviaella* even has the power of vertical migration, moving down in the day time and upward at night as C. N. d'Asaro (unpublished) has found. I had previously considered *Exuviaella* to be planktonic, but it very definitely occurs as an epiphyte in Biscayne Bay despite its possession of flagella. The finding of this form as dominant in fish (mullet) stomachs on occasion is in accord with its epiphytic character, since planktonic forms tend to become diluted during their ingestion by fish. It is probable that

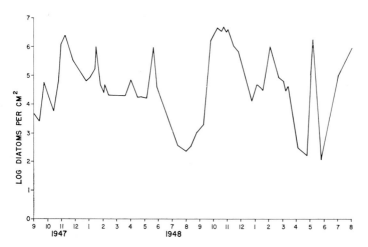

Fig.26. Seasonal fluctuation of numbers of diatoms attaching to suspended material in sea water (After WOOD, 1965.)

the Peridiniums are entrapped or planktonic guests in this epiphyton community, in fact, the epiphyton contains many such guests which may be regarded as semi-permanent members of the community. Among the blue-green algae, the dominant forms belong to the Oscillatoriaceae, mainly to *Lyngbya*, *Oscillatoria*, *Spirulina*. Diatoms include many species of *Licmophora*, *Amphora*, *Synedra*, *Fragilaria*, *Climacosphenia*, *Nitzschia*, *Cocconeis*, *Achnanthes* among the pennates, and *Melosira*, *Bellerochea* and *Biddulphia* among the centric diatoms. Together with these, we frequently find *Coscinodiscus*, *Asteromphalus* and other unattached centric and pennate forms (metaphyton). *Eunotia* and *Gomphonema* occur in brackish water close to fresh water and are epiphytic indicators of such environments.

THE BENTHIC COMMUNITY

This is composed of autochthonous forms belonging to almost all the groups we have mentioned, as well as a number of allochthonous forms derived from the planktonic but more abundantly from the epontic communities, and frequently associated with organic detritus also derived largely from above. It is in this community that the major processes which control the estuarine environment occur, apart from photosynthesis. As this process controls the pH of the water, so the sulfur cycle of the sediment controls the redox potential thereof and thus the reactions of the plants and animals. BAAS BECKING and WOOD (1955) gave a diagram in which they show the relation of the main biological processes of the estuarine environment to pH and Eh, and BAAS BECKING et al. (1957) related the chemical processes to pH and Eh, and showed how such processes could limit the biological ones. For example, the pH of the environment is limited on the alkaline side by the carbon dioxide, carbonate-bicarbonate equilibrium, and this in turn is limited by the monovalent and bivalent cations. In sea water the solubility of carbonate ion in the presence of excess calcium ion controls the pH limit at 9.4 but in fresh water with low calcium, ionic equilibrium of potassium or sodium carbonate and bicarbonate stops photosynthesis, and thus the alkalinity of the biological system at pH 10.1.

The acid extreme of the possible biological environment is controlled by the production of sulfate ion by sulfur-oxidizing organisms, chiefly *Thiobacillus thiooxidans*. Many microorganisms such as diatoms and blue-green algae can live in water of very low pH (1–2) and bacteria and fungi can endure pH of less than 0 (BAAS BECKING and WOOD, 1955; R.L. Starkey, personal communication). Redox potential is governed by the organisms of the sulfur cycle below, and by photosynthesis, and in limited areas, by the microbial oxidation of iron by the iron bacteria. Sulfate reduction and the action of anaerobic heterotrophs can bring about an Eh of −300 mV, due to the presence of SH⁻ion. This can be oxidized anaerobically in the light by the green sulfur bacteria to sulfur as long as oxygen is absent. When OH⁻ion appears in the system, the purple sulfur bacteria and *Thiobacillus denitrificans* appear, and take over the oxidation of sulfur and sulfides. Anaerobic oxidation of sulfides is also possible abiologically in the presence of light with iron as catalyst. Aerobic oxidation can proceed abiologically, but the thiobacilli make use of this reaction to obtain energy for carbon fixation.

Some recent experiments in my laboratory by Dr. Charles Willingham, suggest that anaerobic corrosion is essentially abiological with the microbes acting as depolarisers or perhaps as deanodisers of iron by removal of phosphate, presumably by release of hydrogen sulfide and formation of ferrous sulfide from the more soluble ferric phosphate. This stresses the fact that microbes merely make use of chemical reactions which release energy in order to perform their metabolic processes. They often catalyse these reactions, but do not initiate them. Thus, the activity of microbes in such areas as estuarine sediments might well be re-examined in the light of thermodynamics of some simple chemical equilibria; this could remove a number of misconceptions as to possible microbial activity. The chemistry of detritus and the relations of microbes thereto is even more complex than that of the autotrophs or quasi-autotrophs, and we are still seeking methods for the measurement of decomposition of soluble and particulate organic matter in the sediments. We do know, that, under aerobic conditions, carbon compounds are ultimately reduced, presumably by methane bacteria to methane and hydrogen, except for methionine which is reduced to dimethyl sulfide. Nitrogen compounds are reduced to ammonia, and sulfur compounds to sulfides. However, such reducing conditions in the sediments are usually quite localized, and even the cores studied by RITTENBERG et al. (1955) from the California Basin showed only pockets of strong reduction (−200 mV or less). In my own studies with Baas Becking and Kaplan, I found that in the estuaries, highly reduced areas were usually lenticular, and very often in layers where organic matter was abundant. Thus these reduced substances are usually oxidized in the sediments close to the area of formation, and the release of methane and hydrogen is most obvious in highly organic areas of shallow water from which the mysterious "will-o-the-wisp" is recorded. Such areas, fortunately for the superstitious, are rare. More usually, the break-down of organics is to carbon dioxide or even to

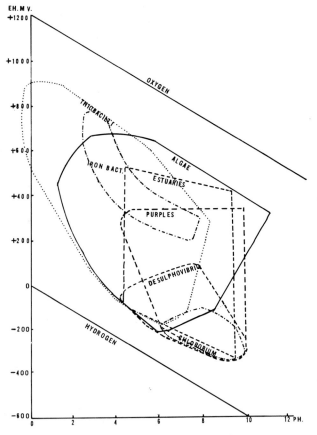

Fig.27. The pH/Eh relationships of the estuarine environment.

lactates, acetates, pyruvates, etc.; nitrogen in surface sediments and in the water tends to be in the oxidized form as nitrate, though much is used as ammonia by the microbes and larger plants to be found in the benthos. It is possible, that the sea-grasses can utilize sulfides because their root systems appear to be associated with the reduced portion of the sediments, and root hairs are frequently attached to particles of hydrotroilite.

The estuarine environment (Fig.27) only occupies a small area of the potential biological environment, and this is due to the buffering capacity of sea water with its carbonate and borate buffers (only the former is effective at the usual pH) and to the exchange of oxygen at the water-air interface, below which it tends to saturation, and if wave action or turbulence are strong, to super-saturation. The redox of the water is controlled on rare occasions in still and stagnant areas by the sulfur cycle in which case oxygen will be depleted, hydrogen sulfide and possibly colloidal hydrotroilite will be present in the water; phosphate will be liberated quantitatively, and in extreme cases, the pH will drop to 5.8, buffered by acid phosphate (BAAS BECKING and MACKAY, 1956; WOOD, 1958; OVERBECK, 1964a). Wind and consequent oxidation of the surface water followed by plant photosynthesis usually restore the system within a few days. Such a phenomenon shows the strict interrelation between chemical and physical factors and microbiological processes in the estuaries.

I have mentioned earlier that true anaerobes are rare in the marine environment, and this applies in the estuarine sediments. This is probably due to the fact I have mentioned that reduced areas are as a rule of limited extent, and the microbes have to be able to tolerate oxidized as well as reduced conditions, i.e., the environment favors the facultative anaerobes. Because the sediment contains such a hodge-podge of organic compounds, reduced and oxidized, and such a variety of inorganic salts, though usually in reasonably constant proportions, the microbes residing therein should be expected to be able to carry out a wide range of transformations and this is indeed true. Habitats which are relatively constant will have microorganisms with limited variability, while those which are subject to great changes will have strains, possibly of the same microorganisms which can tolerate such wide variations. The argument about specialization in *Desulfovibrio* in which three species were raised *(D. desulfuricans, D. aestuarii* and *D. rubentschikii)* because of their limitations of salt tolerance is a case in point. BAARS (1930) showed that his strains had the range of all three, so abolished *D. aestuarii* and *D. rubentschikii*. However, other workers who find stenohaline strains dispute Baars' findings. It fits the ecological picture much better if we accept the position that the behaviour of the strain reflects the environment, and that the creation of new species should be a last resort, when we know that no bridging forms are likely to be found.

The anaerobic environment is suited to a number of organisms including many diatoms, ciliates, nematodes and colorless flagellates. The ciliates live on the bacteria, and some of the flagellates, while the nematodes consume ciliates, bacteria, fungi, and diatoms. Larger organisms, including some of the snails can also exist in the anaerobic environment. The surface sediments are usually oxidizing and contain sulfur bacteria and other aerobic bacteria and algae. When the surface is reducing, it is usual to find black sulfide muds with *Desulfovibrio* below a layer of green sulfur bacteria; above these is a layer up to 5 mm of purple sulfur bacteria. At times when light is not too intense, these appear at the surface, but they are usually covered by a layer of blue-green algae which filter the light. It has yet to be determined whether these blue-greens can oxidize sulfides and sulfur, but, on rocks, especially those coral outcrops called nigger-heads, they are usually found directly overlying a layer of ferrous sulfide containing *Desulfovibrio*. In brackish water, in still, shallow estuarine areas, one may find films of iron bacteria, which form tubes of a pectinoid material to which adhere particles of iron oxide. BAAS BECKING et al. (1956) showed that these iron bacteria such as *Gallionella* and *Sphaerotilus* are gradient organisms, requiring a sharp change in redox potential between the two sides of the film. Similar characteristics are recorded for *Gallionella* by KUCERA and WOLFE (1957).

WOOD (1964) gave evidence that, if an estuarine sediment were shaken with sea water and allowed to settle, the finest particles thus separated contain the greatest amount of nitrogen and phosphorus (Fig.28), that is of organic matter. This detritus contains a large number of microbes, including diatoms, colored and colorless flagellates, ciliates, fungi and yeasts as well as bacteria and the non-microbial nematodes. This material serves as food for many bottom-feeding species, including (in part) the mullets, and must be considered in any study of the productivity equation of any estuary. The diatoms found in this community include *Cyclotella*, *Actino-*

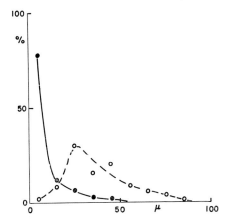

Fig.28. Relation between particle size of sediments and phosphate (continuous line) and nitrogen (broken line).

ptychus, *Coscinodiscus*, *Navicula*, *Mastogloia*, *Diploneis*, *Nitzschia*, *Surirella*, *Campyloneis* together with species from the epiphyton and the plankton. When the epiphyton is heavy, the species from this community become important members of the benthic community, in which we may also find spores of planktonic species such as *Skeletonema costatum*. The colorless flagellates include *Astasia* the colorless counterpart of *Euglena*, which is also a member of the community, *Eutreptia*, *Phacus*, and other pigmented forms, and many naked dinoflagellates including *Gymnodinium*, *Amphidinium*, *Cochlodinium*, *Warnowia*, *Gyrodinium*, and in the deeper parts, *Phalacroma* and *Dinophysis*.

ROUND (1964) divides the benthic algae into the following groups: *Epipelic* occurring on sediments, *Epilithic* occurring on rocks, *Epiphytic* on plants, while BAAS BECKING and WOOD (1955) use the term *epontic* (epi -on, ontos -being) to include all these. Round uses the term *periphyton* to apply to algae growing on artificial surfaces *(Bewuchs)* and natural surfaces *(Aufwuchs)*. The algae associated with the water plants but not attached, Round calls *metaphyton* or *pseudoperiphyton*. He points out that the large majority of species in the epipelic association are motile, the number of motile species depending largely on forces which may disturb the environment such as tidal action, or wind. Where there is little disturbance, non-motile forms are more abundant. He discounts the theory that planktonic blooms are built-up on the sediments, but there is evidence that some species such as *Skeletonema costatum* and *Goniaulax spinifera* have spores which settle on the bottom and begin to multiply there before a bloom occurs (WOOD, 1964).

Round gives some interesting comments on the factors affecting the benthic communities and divides them into spatial, temporal, internal and biotic. Among the spatial factors, latitude and longitude are important, especially the former, as exemplified by the distribution of *Dinophysis tripos* and *D. caudata* as detailed by WOOD (1964). Altitude is not important for marine forms, but depth and turbulence control the penetration of light; rate of flow governs the relation between motile and non-motile species, species with strong or weak attachment, and distribution of species in the direction of flow. Chemical factors include salinity and nutrient availability, redox potential and hydrogen ion concentration, but many of these are controlled by the plant community itself. I have already discussed the effect of the substrate in terms of microbial activity with which it is inextricably bound.

Temporal factors include cyclic, annual or seasonal and lunar rhythms which form a complicated pattern, as well as diurnal rhythms which may be intrinsic, as the vertical movement of the diatom *Hantzschia* and other forms, or due to reproduction and grazing, the former following intrinsic rhythms according to SWEENEY (1958), the latter to the behaviour of the animals associated with the plant community.

Internal factors include modes of nutrition, ability to use alternate paths such as heterotrophy and autotrophy, growth rates, reproductive cycles, movement and taxes. Organisms which are myxotrophic have a distinct advantage in the benthic environment which would account for the prevalence of facultatively heterotrophic diatoms in this environment; those with more rapid growth rates should in theory gain an ascendancy in the community, but this is tempered by the ability of so many species to produce biotic factors such as antibiotics or auto- and hetero-antagonistic substances. Movement, which is necessary for species dwelling in intertidal areas, strong tidal regions, and swift currents, is probably more widespread than is realised since it is known that several species of *Coscinodiscus* are motile and that *Lyngbya, Oscillatoria* and probably other genera from this community have the ability to move rapidly and to reverse the motion quickly. Taxes, which are associated with motion include phototaxis and chemotaxis. *Exuviaella* appears to be negatively phototactic while *Nitzschia* is positively so at moderate light intensities (C. N. d'Asaro, unpublished). Reversal of phototaxis is usual among benthic algae in strong light, and once again may be in either direction. Biotic factors include competition, which is related to the other three groups, external metabolites which have already been mentioned, parasitism, which has been little studied, and grazing.

While the sediments in the deeper parts of the estuary normally contain a mixed flora, the shallower, intertidal parts frequently have one or a few dominant species. At Barnstable, Massachusetts, one tidal flat is covered at low tide by a bright carpet of purple bacteria and another nearby by the diatom *Hantzschia*, which migrates to the surface after the water leaves the flat and disappears before it returns. The same phenomenon occurs on the tidal flats of Sapelo Island in Georgia. In clear sands of estuaries, up to and above the tidal edge close to the ocean, one frequently finds blue-green algae such as *Oscillatoria* and *Lyngbya* penetrating up to two inches into the sediment. This has been observed at Port St. Joes in Florida, Lake Conjola and Coila Lake in New South Wales. In the intertidal region of the upper estuaries, we often find blue-green algae forming a carpet which breaks up on drying and may float around in the shallows, and be piled up by the wind. These are mainly Oscillatoriaceae. At times, and in certain places, the blue-greens occur seasonally and may form beds a foot or more thick separated by layers of sand and sea-grass. One of the most outstanding examples of this occurs between the Upper and Lower Laguna Madre in Texas, but there are others in Texas Bays and in Australian estuaries. The sea-grass mats are frequently reducing owing to the high organic content, and sulfur bacteria are present. Calcareous sediments in tropical estuaries tend to have a high concentration of blue-green algae and sulfate reduction is frequent but does not seem to reach the activity that one gets in silica sands. It seems probable that the small snails which also characterise Biscayne Bay are feeding on these algae. The strange sulfur-oxidizing organisms *Beggiatoa*, *Thiothrix* and *Thiovulum* occur only in stagnant shallows and here the organic content is high. From my own observation (WOOD, 1964) and the studies of PRINGSHEIM (1964) it seems that they require organic matter, possibly organic sulfur compounds, and that sulfides are desirable but not necessary for their nutrition.

MICROBES IN THE ESTUARINE FOOD WEBS

WOOD (1964) discussed estuarine food chains at some length. From observations on Australian estuaries he found that *Mugil cephalus*, other mullets, *Mylio*, *Girella*, *Monacanthus* and *Rhabdosargus* were phytophagous, at least during part of their existence, and CHU and KUO (1959) found that some mackerels and the Peneid shrimp *Acetes chinensis* feed on diatoms. Wood listed 82 species of diatoms from fish stomachs, and these were largely epiphytic, e.g., *Achnanthes*, *Bacillaria*, *Amphipleura*, *Amphora*, *Climacosphenia*, *Cocconeis*, *Epithemia*, *Fragilaria*, *Licmophora*, *Navicula grevillei*, *Rhabdonema*, *Striatella*, *Synedra*, though predominantly benthic species were also recorded, e.g., *Navicula*, *Diploneis*, *Melosira*, *Pleurosigma*. It is significant that few if any of the species recorded from fish stomachs were truly planktonic. This means that estuarine phytoplankton is unimportant in the estuarine food web as far as fish are concerned.

Dinoflagellates were rarely found in fish stomachs; on occasion, *Exuviaella* occurred in quantity, and in the Sapelo Island region of salt marshes, a *Peridinium* has been recorded from this source. Other flagellates are occasionally seen, but it is probable that these make up a far larger part of the food of fishes, etc., than their occurrence in stomach contents would indicate. In most cases, they are fragmented before they arrive in the stomach, and are unidentifiable. I have found that such organisms can be fed to oysters and other mollusca and will keep them in good health in vitro and facilitate spawning. The work of BRUCE et al. (1940) and COLE (1936) showed that oysters and mussels can be fed indefinitely on flagellates and that these probably form a large part of their diet in the estuaries.

An important feature of estuarine and oceanic food webs is their possible connection with nuclear activity. The nuclear reactor at Windscale, England, has caused a low level contamination of the beach as far as the neighboring Seascale with radioactive material. It is known that certain animals and plants concentrate different metallic ions such as vanadium. It therefore becomes important to know what plants and animals are likely to concentrate the radio-active materials likely to escape from a nuclear source in case of an accident, so that these animals and plants can be looked at to show the biological significance of the contamination.

For example, the imminent installation of an atomic reactor on Biscayne Bay, Florida, makes it necessary for a biological study of the food web of the Florida Bay shrimp which is likely to serve as a source of human contamination in the case of a serious fault in the reactor. Similarly, the possible effect of atomic explosives in blasting a sea-level canal through the Isthmus of Panama, must be studied on the existing flora and fauna. If, let us say, bacteria con-centrate cobalt, animals consuming those bacteria will concentrate that element in excess of those that feed on other algae, and could become a greater menace to human health. The effects will be found first in the estuaries and later, and possibly much diluted, in the open ocean.

A serious change in the plant associations in shallow, and later in deeper waters can be caused by engineering structures. The flood-control and water conservation project in the Lake Okechobee region has resulted in considerable changes in the Florida Everglades, and many of these changes are irreversible. The increase in height of the Asswan Dam on the River Nile and consequent failure to release water has already prevented the phytoplankton bloom at the mouth of that river in the Fall, and hence the phytophagous sardines failed to appear in the eastern Mediterranean in 1965. This appears to have affected the tuna run as far north as Cyprus.

CHAPTER VIII

SOME ECONOMIC ASPECTS OF WATER MICROBIOLOGY

MICROBIAL FOULING OF SUBMERGED SURFACES

Microbial fouling and its effects

Fouling may be defined as the growth of marine organisms on surfaces of structures below high-tide mark. The normal flora and fauna of the littoral and sub-littoral regions attach themselves to the surfaces of the new structures, but the relative incidence of this flora and fauna varies with the peculiarities of the new environment.

Fouling occurs in fresh water, brackish and marine environments, but in fresh water is usually confined to slime formation with occasional growth of secondary organisms, mainly consisting of green algae. In brackish water, certain barnacles, mussels (e.g., *Modiolus*), tube worms (e.g., *Mercierella*), etc., may occur, but in the sea there is a wide representation of algal and invertebrate groups.

Studies on fouling have been made because of the deleterious effects of fouling organisms on submerged surfaces. The most serious effect is mechanical, but there are chemical and bio-chemical effects also. On the hulls of ships, fouling growths impede the speed and cause an increase of fuel consumption of up to 50% after 6 months under certain conditions. Another example is the mechanical constriction of ducts in water supply lines, coupled with increasing turbulence in such lines resulting in serious decreases in water flow, while further examples are the sliming of swimming pools and of the condenser tubes of steam plants.

We are not concerned here with the heavy growths which may amount to a hundred tons in the case of ships, and to several thousand tons in the case of large power-house conduits. Our concern is limited to the slimes which, according to a number of authors, are frequently the precursors of heavy fouling growths, and which may in themselves be objectionable, e.g., in swimming pools, open water channels and condenser tubes of industrial plants.

Slime films

A considerable number of papers has been written on the subject of slime and its relations with subsequent fouling, although the results do not appear to be consistent. HILEN (1923) was the first to make a microbiological analysis of slime, and he found that bacteria were important constituents. ANGST (1923) followed up Hilen's work, and found that algae play a part, while COE and ALLEN (1937) and HENDEY (1951) found that diatoms were important members. WOOD (1950a) considered that, in Australian waters, algae and diatoms were more important than bacteria in fouling slimes, and has since confirmed this (WOOD, 1953). ZOBELL (1937, 1938, 1946b) considered that bacteria were more important than photosynthetic plants in slime formation in southern California.

CVIIC (1953) found that, in Yugoslavia, bacteria attached more slowly than in California, that the rapidity of attachment depended on the quantity of organic matter in the water, and the motion of the water. Diatoms were numerically second in importance to bacteria.

SKERMAN (1956) working in New Zealand harbours found high bacterial populations in the first three days in Auckland and Wellington harbours, but low bacterial populations at Lyttelton, the bacterial populations decreasing sharply with the attachment of sessile Protozoa. Diatoms were important on all Skerman's plates, algal spores negligible. Skerman notes the sparsity of bacterial microcolonies, and even of dividing chains, and suggests, that, in the heavily polluted harbours, bacterial film is due to adventitious bacteria which become adherent, and not active slime-formation.

It is generally agreed, however, that the attachment of marine animals is usually assisted by a slime-film consisting of microscopic organisms, although barnacles and other sedentary forms can attach themselves directly to a relatively smooth surface such as glass without the formation of a primary film. I have observed the attachment of the seruplid worm *Hydroides norvegica* to slides in Sydney Harbour without the formation of such a film. WOOD (1950a) found by experiment that "live primary film promotes secondary growth, either by furthering the growth of existing organisms plus new attachments, or by a stimulation of the attachments, and early growth of other organisms by providing food material or growth factors". Films killed with mercuric chloride or chromic acid did not have a stimulating effect on subsequent growth.

ANGST (1923) found that plates from which the slime was removed weekly did not develop barnacles, while ZoBELL (1938) found that bacterial film increased the number of attaching organisms from 0.3 to 5.4/sq. inch in 24 h. D. P. WILSON (1955) believes that micro-organisms in moderate quantities assist the settlement of *Ophelia bicornis* in sand, but excess bacteria are repellent.

ZoBELL (1938, 1946b) gives five ways in which slimes may assist secondary fouling: (*1*) By mechanically assisting the attachment of other organisms. (*2*) By discoloring bright surfaces and reducing reflection, since most fouling organisms are negatively phototrophic when attaching. (*3*) By serving as a source of food. (*4*) By promoting the deposition of calcareous cements. (*5*) By increasing the concentration of plant nutrients.

ZoBELL and ALLEN (1935), WHEDON (1942) and others consider that bacteria and detritus (pelogloea) are adsorbed, the former attacking the latter, which, as the slime builds up, enmeshes diatoms, algae and other organisms. My own observations suggest that bacteria, diatoms, algal spores, and detritus will all adhere readily to submerged surfaces, and that the relative rate of attachment depends on circumstances, the detritus frequently carrying the living forms with it. Thus, the mechanical assistance to attachment begins quite early in the process of slime formation.

The discoloration of bright and light-coloured surfaces may have an effect, though my own experience suggests that considerable changes in luminosity are necessary to cause increased attachment. There are, however, critical values of light-intensity for each organism.

The use of slime organisms as a source of food by larger organisms is one of the really important factors, as a well-formed slime contains a wide assemblage of organisms fit for any marine animal's palate.

Bacteria, as GREENFIELD (1963) has shown, can precipitate calcium carbonate via ammonium complexes, producing alkaline micro-environments. At times, moreover, the micro-environment within a slime film may approximate to the meso-environment of a *Zostera* flat, and produce such a micro-pH. A film containing the algae *Enteromorpha* or *Chaetomorpha* could easily do this.

ZoBell's (1946b) fifth suggestion seems very likely, as the bacteria which are mainly heterotrophs, will produce catabolites such as carbon dioxide, phosphates, ammonia, etc., and these will be adsorbed within the slime. Renn (1940) has shown that marine muds can adsorb large quantities of nitrates, concentrating these from the water, and we have had similar experience.

A sixth possibility is that the micro-pH may facilitate or retard the attachment of secondary organisms. H. A. Cole, working at Conway, has found (personal communication) that, below critical pH values (about 8.5) oyster larvae will mature but not settle, but that, if the pH is raised, settlement will follow. This may well apply to other organisms, and it may be that the pH controls the type of organism that finally settles.

In the case of surfaces which have been treated with toxic substances such as copper and mercury paints, slimes can also act by mechanically screening other organisms from the toxin, or by concentrating the toxin and increasing or decreasing the concentration of the toxin at the water interface, thus inhibiting or accelerating the attachment of larval forms. There is some disagreement among observers on the effect of slime films on the growth of secondary fouling on toxic surfaces. Several authors have shown (Hendy, 1951; Waksman et al., 1943; Wood, 1953) that many bacteria and diatoms are tolerant to toxins and that some of these organisms can actually concentrate such toxins in their own bodies. Whedon (1942) considers that film formation is actually necessary for the efficient action of an anti-fouling paint. In this case, the copper will be concentrated in the film and discharged at the film-water interface at a higher concentration than would be yielded by the paint at its normal leaching rate. In other cases, however, the copper is adsorbed on the slime, or chelated, and so rendered non-toxic. There is some support for this theory in the results of paint trials in Sydney Harbour, where replicate trials in different places gave quite different results, and where paints with a low leaching rate gave better protection than those with a higher leaching rate. Moreover, we have observed cases in which good protective paints have a leaching rate well below the concentration at which the toxic agent per se will kill the organism under test. In such cases, it may well be that the pH and possibly the Eh governed by bacterial attack on the paint vehicle may be the controlling factor.

Research at Woods Hole suggests that slime-film may not be as important in practice as other workers believe. These workers find that copper and mercury may be concentrated to a thousand-fold the normal saturation-quantity in sea water although, in practice, the antifouling performance is more closely associated with the leaching rate. The film tends to contribute to the performance of

TABLE VI

NUMBERS OF BACTERIA, DIATOMS AND ALGAL SPORES ATTACHING TO GLASS PLATES AS RECORDED BY ZoBELL (1946b), WOOD (1950a), CVIIC (1953), AND SKERMAN (1956)

Time	Place	Bacteria	Diatoms	Algal Spores
24H	La Jolla, Cal.	278,000	140	—
	Port Hacking, N.S.W.	1,300	up to 3,000	500
	Sydney Harbour, N.S.W.	12,000	—	—
	Split Harbour, Yugoslavia	77,610		
	Split (outside)	29,500		
	Auckland, N.Z.	181,000	4,520	0
	Wellington, N.Z.	too many	2,130	0
	Lyttelton, N.Z.	45,200	355	
48H	La Jolla	1,963,000	555	—
	Port Hacking	3,900	0	3,750
	Sydney Harbour	50,000	—	—
	Split Harbour	177,400		
	Split (outside)	83,500	135?	—
	Auckland	up to 317,000	940	0
	Wellington	too many to count	1,900	0
	Lyttelton	57,500	1,890	0
96H	La Jolla	11,520,000	1,200	—
	Port Hacking	12,700	many colonial	2,500
	Sydney Harbour	300,000	930	0
	Split Harbour	381,000	244?	
	Split (outside)	226,700		
	Auckland	21,700	840	0
	Wellington	37,600	4,970	0
	Lyttelton	20,100	3,300+ filaments	0

paint resins by the action of bacterial enzymes, by altering the surface charges of the paint-slime or slime-water interfaces, or by controlling the pH and Eh of the milieu, especially at the interface between the surface and the slime. The bacteria can thus accelerate or decelerate certain chemical reactions, e.g., the oxidation or reduction of substances contained in the paints. This is important in the flaking of antifouling and anticorrosive paints, and in the corrosion of steel plates below or alongside the paint film. This effect is often a metabiotic one, wherein the slime organism creates a set of conditions suitable for another organism, for example, the decomposition of algal filaments by agar- or alginate-digesting bacteria produces redox potentials which allow of the activity of sulphate-reducing bacteria, and these in turn assist corrosion by depolarising the metal.

Table VI gives a comparison between the components per cm² of early slime films at La Jolla (ZoBell, 1946b), Port Hacking and Sydney Harbour (Wood, 1950), Split (Cviic, 1953) and in New Zealand (Skerman, 1956).

Diatoms and algal spores are very important constituents everywhere and would probably greatly exceed bacteria in proportion of film weight. In Australia, algal spores were more prominent than diatoms at Port Hacking and The Spit (Sydney Harbour), but at Shell Point (Botany Bay), diatoms on occassion completely overran test panels, and Hendey (1951) reports a similar state of affairs in Chichester Harbour. This author gives the following reasons for importance of diatoms: (*1*) They are the most numerous (apart from bacteria). (*2*) They are widely distributed throughout the world (and he might have added that the same species are liable to occur throughout the world). (*3*) They are present throughout the year. (*4*) They are oxygen-producers and provide a rich source of nutriment for the bacterial flora. (*5*) They affect the hydrogen-ion concentration of the slime. (*6*) They are, as a group, highly resistant to copper and mercury.

Bacteria in slimes

Non-toxic surfaces. Bacteria become attached to non-toxic surfaces in two ways; by adsorption of the bacteria themselves or of detrital material to which they are attached, or by actual attachment as in the case of the stalked bacteria observed by Henrici and Johnston (1935). During my own observations, stalked bacteria were observed on only two occasions on glass plates exposed in the sea. On all other occasions, the bacteria appeared to be adsorbed on the glass, although capsulate forms seemed to be attached by the capsular material. The importance of adsorption is discussed elsewhere, although the phenomenon has a special meaning in the study of fouling, where the concomitant adsorption of food material and the excretory products of bacterial metabolism may be of the greatest significance. The importance of metabiosis has already been mentioned, and this may include synergic reactions between heterotrophs, between heterotrophs and autotrophs, aerobes and anaerobes, bacteria and photosynthetic forms, etc. The majority of bacteria found in slimes appears to be heterotrophic and these are mainly catabolic in activity, breaking down organic detritus and necrotic material for the use of photosynthetic and chemoautotrophic components, and serving as food material for the flagellates, ciliates and higher forms that occur in the slime film. It is possible, however, that autotrophs may be important as it seems that no diligent search has been made for them.

Some of the bacterial forms, especially the sessile and the arborescent forms seen on glass slides immersed in the water have not yet been cultured. Some of the pleomorphic organisms found on such slides will reproduce the pleomorphism in pure cultures. This applies to spirals, rods and commas which have previously been ascribed to the genera *Spirillum*, *Vibrio* and *Pseudomonas*, but which Wood (1953) has ascribed on account of this pleomorphism to Gray and Thornton's (1928) genus *Mycoplana*. It may be that the sessile and arborescent forms change their habit when grown on liquid or semi-solid media and can grow in three dimensions.

There is now a number of bacterial genera and species recorded from fouled surfaces. Hilen (1923) recorded seven species of *Bacillus* and three of *Sarcina*, Angst (1923) recorded six species of *Bacillus*, Whedon isolated twenty species, Waksman et al. (1943) isolated chiefly gram-negative rods, while ZoBell and Upham (1944) list micrococci, gram-negative rods, commas (or spirals), corynebacteria (described as bacteria) and Wood (1953) found 87 *Mycoplana* (i.e., gram-negative, pleomorphic strains), 46 *Corynebacterium* and seven *Bacillus* strains, but no cocci, though cocci (or coccoid corynebacteria) were seen on the plates. Many if not all the strains were facultative anaerobes, capable of growing at oxidation-reduction potentials of +300 mV or higher at pH 8, but also capable of reproducing in organic media in the absence of free oxygen with potentials as low as —15 mV.

Toxic Surfaces. The poisons generally used to combat fouling are mercury, copper and arsenic, especially the two former. Some marine bacteria are particularly tolerant of both copper (SREENIVASAN, 1956) and mercury. WAKSMAN et al. (1943) found that some gram-negative rods can stand up to 500 mg of $CuSO_4$, $5H_2O/l$. HENDEY (1951) found that his bacteria, also gram-negative rods, withstood 250 p.p.m. of copper and WOOD (1953) recorded that his gram-negative rods withstood 250 p.p.m. of copper and 100 p.p.m. of mercury. STARR and JONES (1957) found that 18% of marine bacteria withstood 51 p.p.m. of copper. Waksman and his colleagues, finding that the bacteria grown on copper media became reddish-brown, suggested the possibility that the bacteria actually took up the copper from the medium. I have observed the same phenomenon. Waksman's theory seems quite probable as STANBURY (1944) has shown that diatoms can do this. I have found that *Corynebacterium globiforme* grew on control panels immersed in the sea, but not on panels coated with copper or mercury paints. *Mycoplana* and *Staphylococcus*, both non-pigmented, and a pink *Bacillus* with central spores, were isolated from low-leaching-rate copper and from mercury, but not from high-leaching-rate copper paint. These cultures were resistant to copper and mercury and there was some correlation between the resistance to the two metals. Subcultures on copper and mercury agars showed increased tolerance, suggesting that, to some extent, resistance is selective.

The tolerance of marine bacteria to copper and mercury is of great importance in assessing the effect of bacterial slimes in the efficacy of various antifouling paints.

Another effect shown by Hendey is that of slime on pH, and the effect of pH on the solubility of cuprous oxide in chlorate buffer solutions. Solubility increased almost 100% with each 10% increase in hydrogen ion concentration at 20 °C between pH 8.48 and 7.08. The leaching rate was markedly increased by a decrease of 0.05 pH. Hendey remarks that "Assuming that the pH and temperature of sea water under natural or open sea conditions remain fairly constant for reasonably long periods, antifouling efficiency of a standard batch of paint should be reasonably constant and antifouling results should be reproducible. This, however, is not always found to be so." He finds that the nature of the film governs the pH of the slime and that bacterial growth tends to lower the pH. I have studied the effect of respiration and photosynthesis on the pH of the meso-environment of *Zostera* flats, and am in accord with his findings. No one seems to have studied the effect of the microorganisms in slime on oxidation-reduction potentials, though BAAS BECKING and WOOD (1955) have found that each biological process in the meso- and micro-environments has well-defined limits of pH and Eh, and that these bear a clear-cut relationship to abiological (i.e., physcial and chemical) reactions at least in the autotrophs. This suggests that an investigation into the oxidation-reduction levels of antifouling compositions might be worth while since copper, mercury and arsenic are all capable of existing at more than one oxidation level, with concomitant differences in solubility.

STARKEY (1957) has studied the rates of decomposition of the constituents of paint matrices by microorganisms. These rates vary with constituents and time. With some components, the rate of decomposition is rapid at first and then decelerates, with others, the rate gradually increases. The ester gums and pentalyns were not decomposed by microorganisms in the sea.

Diatoms in slimes

Non-toxic surfaces. Diatoms may, as stated by HENDEY (1951) be enmeshed in the bacterial-detrital film, or, as WOOD (1950) found, attach directly to smooth surfaces such as glass. Many of them form stipes, and some like *Striatella*, *Licomphora*, *Rhabdonema*, *Climacosphenia*, etc., form colonies which grow out from the surfaces to distances of 1 cm or more. Others, such as *Navicula*, *Nitzschia*, or *Synedra* attach by one end and form a palisade. In either case, they form a tangle which causes a micro-turbulence, forming minute backwaters, which, in turn, assist other organisms to join the slime association. This tangle also harbours flagellates, ciliates and other, non-sessile diatoms such as *Coscinodiscus*, which thus takes its place in the fouling assemblage. I have also found that diatoms are frequently carried onto the fouling surfaces on particles of detritus to which they are already attached, e.g., minute fragments of *Zostera*.

The chief diatoms of the fouling association are pennate forms, but, at times, certain centric genera are strongly represented, especially *Melosira*, *Biddulphia* and *Bellerochea*, the last two being usually regarded as planktonic, the first often being found in the plankton also. *Chaetoceros* may also become enmeshed by its long processes.

A strange fact is that the pennate diatoms, except for such forms as *Nitzschia seriata* and *Thalassiothrix nitzschioides* are comparatively rare in estuarine plankton tows even in the intertidal zone, although plates at various distances above the mud surface readily become fouled in this region. However, as has been previously stated, a large number of pennate forms will be found on the water surface, held there by surface tension. This can be demonstrated by placing a plastic film on the surface. The diatoms adhere to the plastic and can be studied and counted under the microscope. Such films are made by dipping a metal ring in dissolved plastic and lowering the ring on a cotton bridle onto the water. The plastic is then brought in contact with a glass slide and examined under the microscope.

I have found that the species occurring on exposed, non-toxic plates are almost, if not completely, identical with the epontic forms found on *Zostera*, and other natural surfaces, and that this epontic flora differs considerably from that associated with the inter-tidal muds. Sometimes the differences are generic, sometimes specific. There is also a marked seasonal distribution of species as well as a regional one, though some forms are cosmopolitan. These differences are more fully discussed elsewhere. The distribution of forms is important because STANBURY (1944) and HENDEY (1951) have shown that different forms vary in their resistance to the copper and mercury used in paints (see Table VIII).

COE and ALLEN (1937) list 60 species of diatoms associated with fouling, Hendey 95 species and varieties, and I have found at Cronulla, Australia, that there are about 56 relatively common fouling forms, while the total number of species observed in the community is about 200. One would expect a greater number of species in tropical-subtropical water than in warm- or cool-temperate water.

In cool-temperate waters there are regular diatom peaks in late winter and early spring, but, in the sub-tropical eastern Australian waters, peaks are less regular, and often less abundant. These diatom peaks are very important in that they produce an abundant oxygen supply (see under corrosion) during the day and raise the pH (see above). At night, however, the pH falls to about 7.6, with re-solution of the carbonate.

Toxic surfaces. HENDEY (1951) divides diatoms into the following groups:

(*1*) Strongly resistant species

A. True slime formers

(*a*) Colonies flat, spreading over paint surface.

B. Non-slime formers

(*a*) Stalked species forming a pile on paint surface.

(2) Less resistant species

(*a*) "Flocculate" colonies over true slime formers.

(*b*) Miscellaneous free-living forms entrapped in or adhering to slime.

Hendey points out that the strongly resistant, true slime formers are usually small species which lie closely pressed to the paint surface, embedded in a mucous film in a random manner. They tend to cover any organisms already attached. The main genera concerned are *Amphora*, *Navicula*, and *Amphiprora*, and Hendey records a count of *Amphora coffaeformis* v. *perpusilla* on copper paint of 137,000 organisms/cm².

Most resistant of the stalked forms is *Achnanthes*, e.g., *A. longipes*. It forms a mucous pad at one end, and this pad elongates to form a stalk some 200–300 μ long with the cell at the distal end. The cell divides and forms a ribbon.

Frondose species, which are somewhat less resistant than *Achnanthes* are species of *Licmophora* or the sheathed *Navicula* and *Amphiprora* species, which were combined by Agardh under the genus *Schizonema*.

The less resistant species, many of which, e.g., *Nitzschia* spp. and some *Navicula* spp. form palisade colonies, include also *Pleurosigma* and some Amphoras, together with the chain-forming *Melosira*, *Rhabdonema*, *Terpsinoe* and *Grammatophora*. Forms randomly associated with these are *Diploneis*, *Surirella*, *Mastogloia*, *Cocconeis*, *Biddulphia*, etc. Hendey records *Biddulphia aurita* as entrapped in the slime, but our observations show that it can actually be attached, and at times it forms chains extending from non-toxic surfaces.

Table VII, derived from tests at Cronulla, lists the diatoms appearing on plates after 14 days.

Hendey reports that the resistance of a species is not constant but depends to some extent on the environment. STANBURY (1944) shows that the growth of "*Schizonema*", *Amphora*, and the alga *Ectocarpus*

TABLE VII

Control plates	Mercury Paint	Cold Plastic M.I. 143E	High Leaching Rate Copper Paint
Nitzschia longissima		N. longissima	N. longissima ±
N. closterium		N. closterium	
Amphora arcta	A. arcta	A. arcta	A. arcta +
Licmophora abbreviata		L. abbreviata	L. abbreviata +
Climacosphenia moniligera			
L. flabellata		L. flabellata	
Grammatophora marina		G. marina	
Gomphonema sp.		Gomphonema sp.	
Navicula sp.			Navicula sp. +
Amphora sp.			
Cocconeis sp.			
Coscinodiscus sp.		Cosc. sp.	
Melosira sp.			

± = sparse and without chromatophores

was prevented by 0.7 p.p.m. of copper between December and February, but required 1.0 p.p.m. between April and August. She ascribes the greater resistance in summer to a greater vigour of the plant, but it may well be a temperature effect.

Table VIII shows the resistance of diatoms to copper and mercury and is compiled from data given by Hendey and Stanbury.

It will at once be noticed that there are some differences between the findings of Hendey and Stanbury due possibly to differences in water temperature between Plymouth and the Solent and to the fact that Stanbury's were laboratory tests, while Hendey's were field trials. The obvious differences refer to *Cocconeis scutellum* and *Synedra tabulata*.

There is some evidence that diatoms and other algae become accustomed to gradually increasing doses of toxins, an important factor in considering the fouling of paints which are slow in reaching the maximum leaching rate. Stanbury's results suggest that there is a correlation between resistance to copper and mercury, and there is a close parallel in my Australian results between the mercury and the high leaching rate copper paint.

TABLE VIII

RESISTANCE OF DIATOMS TO COPPER AND MERCURY IN GREAT BRITAIN
COMPILED FROM DATA OF STANBURY AND HENDEY

Species	Hendey (Chichester)	Stanbury (Plymouth)	
		Copper	Mercury
Amphora turgida	very strong	—	—
A. veneta	very strong	—	—
A. exigua	very strong	1.0 p.p.m.	1.85 p.p.m.
Amphiprora hyalina	very strong	—	—
Am. paludina	—	1.0–1.3	2.2
Achnanthes longipes	strong	0.64	1.48
Navicula grevillei	medium	1.0	1.85
N. ramosissima	medium	—	—
Am. rutilans	medium	—	—
Synedra affinis	medium	—	—
S. tabulata	medium	0.26	0.54
Ach. subsessilis	medium	—	—
Licmophora gracilis	medium	—	—
Nitzschia closterium	medium	0.64	1.1
Ach. brevipes	slight	—	—
L. flabellata	slight	—	—
Cocconeis scutellum	slight	0.77	1.48
Amphora coffaeiformis	slight	—	—
Ach. microcephala	slight	—	—
Actinoptychus senarius	slight	—	—
Diploneis didyma	slight	—	—
D. bomba	slight	—	—
Nitz. sigma	slight	—	—
Nitz. apiculata	slight	—	—
Nitz. granulata	slight	—	—
Biddulphia aurita	slight	—	—
Licmophora lyngbyei = *L. abbreviata*	—	0.38	0.74
Striatella sp.	—	0.77	1.48
Fragilaria sp.	—	0.89	1.85

Stanbury also discusses the effect of light intensity, and concludes that cultures grown under strong light are less pigmented than those grown under reduced light. These facts are not new, but should be remembered when choosing sites for test panels.

Stanbury also found that speeds up to 2 km/h do little to inhibit the settlement of diatoms. I have found by means of a rotating disc that algae *(Ectocarpus* and *Cladophora)* and diatoms will form a heavy felt on the periphery which was moving at a continuous 11.2 knots, and that organisms such as the skeleton shrimps *(Caprella)* will remain on this felt and feed on it. Barnacles will not attach at speeds above 2 knots, even in the presence of the felt, nor the tube worm *Hydroides norvegica* above 1.5 knots, though the felt does seem to afford the latter organism some protection. Only on this fast-rotating disc did we get diatom felts about 1 cm deep, so it seems probable that, under normal fouling conditions, the invertebrates graze on the diatom and algal film.

Algae

Although such forms as *Ectocarpus, Ceramium, Polysiphonia, Melobesia,* and *Cladophora* border on the macroscopic, while *Enteromorpha* is definitely macroscopic, the spores and platelets of these algae bring them under the category of microorganisms at the attaching stage where they form part of the slime. WOOD (1950a) has shown that algal spores are important in initial fouling in certain Australian waters. Moreover, *Ectocarpus, Enteromorpha, Chaetomorpha* and *Ulothrix* are resistant to toxics, though *Cladophora, Ceramium* and *Antithamnion* are not. Stanbury gives the following figures (Table IX).

In the testing of antifouling paints, diatoms and algae can be used

TABLE IX

RESISTANCE OF ALGAE TO COPPER AND MERCURY
(After STANBURY, 1944)

	Copper	Mercury
Scytosiphon	0.89	1.85
Ectocarpus	1.0	2.2
Cladophora	0.74	0.38
Ulva	0.77	1.1
Ulothrix flacoa	1.0	1.48
Enteromorpha	1.0	1.48
Ceramium rubrum	0.38	0.74
Antithamnion floccosum	0.38	0.74

to confirm leaching rate studies, since the settling of susceptible forms such as *Cladophora*, *Licmophora abbreviata*, *Synedra tabulata*, etc., would suggest that the paint has little antifouling potency, while the failure of *Achnanthes longipes* suggests that the paint is adequate, at least in the critical early stages, for ships are most susceptible to fouling attack immediately after undocking.

The importance of diatoms and algae in ship fouling is greatest in the area between wind and water where the paint (known as boot-topping) is often non-toxic for the sake of appearance. In this area, *Enteromorpha* and *Chaetomorpha* often form long filaments which can exert considerable drag, and which can have a chemical effect on the paint by varying the pH, and possibly the Eh at the surface as mentioned previously.

Other microorganisms

HILEN (1923) records the presence of yeasts and fungi in fouling slimes. I have also found fungal hyphae on fouling plates but have not grown them in the cultures made from those plates. Their importance is not known.

In addition, Protozoa, including *Vorticella* and other ciliates, are common in fouling slimes, but *Vorticella* has not been found on anti-fouling paint surfaces, so is presumably susceptible to copper and mercury.

MARINE BORER AND MICROBIOLOGY

Marine borer is well known in its effect on timber structures in the sea. It riddles the wood with holes and causes serious breaks in wharf piling and in ships' planks. It is considered that the borer organisms digest the wood directly, but that they may be assisted by lignin-digesting fungi and bacteria. The question is important in connection with the effect of impregnation of timbers with creosote and other poisons.

It has been discussed by BECKER et al. (1957, 1958a,b), MEYERS and REYNOLDS (1957), REYNOLDS and MEYERS (1957, 1959), SCHAFER and LANE (1957) and KOHLMEYER (1958b), who maintain that fungi assist marine borer attack, while RAY and STUNTZ (1959a,b) maintain that there is no relation between fungal infection and *Limnoria* attack.

These opposite conclusions by very thorough and reputable workers require further evaluation.

MICROBIAL CORROSION IN AQUEOUS ENVIRONMENTS

It has been stated by VON WOLZOGEN KUHR (1923, 1939), BUTLIN and VERNON (1949), SENEZ (1953), STARKEY and WIGHT (1945), STARKEY (1953, 1956), and others that the anaerobic corrosion of iron and steel is frequently due to the agency of bacteria. Most of the work has been done in connection with pipes embedded in soil, but there is a similar problem in connection with ships, harbor structures, etc. (STARKEY, 1953). As the corrosion of pipes occurs in waterlogged soils it may be regarded as being a phenomenon of the aqeous environment. Corrosion may be aerobic or anaerobic. Aerobic corrosion has been explained by the equations:

$4H_2O \rightarrow 4H^+ + 4OH^-$ Anodic solution of iron
$2Fe + 4H^+ \rightarrow 2Fe^{2+} + 4H$ (abiological)

$O_2 + 4H \rightarrow 2H_2O$ Depolarization

$2Fe^{2+} + 4OH^- \rightarrow 2Fe(OH)_2$ Corrosion products
$2Fe(OH)_2 + O_2 \rightarrow 2FeO(OH)_2$

The oxidation of ferrous iron may be abiological or due to iron bacteria.

VON WOLZOGEN KUHR (1923) suggested that anaerobic corrosion is, in part, caused by sulfate-reducing bacteria, and proposed a possible mechanism. However, it seems probable that his equations were not adequate, and the following have been suggested:

$8H_2O \rightarrow 8H^+ + 8OH^-$ Anodic solution of
$4Fe + 8H^+ \rightarrow 4Fe^{2+} + 4H_2$ iron

$SO_4^{2-} + 10H^+ \rightarrow H_2S + 4H_2O$ Depolarization (microbial)

$Fe^{2+} + H_2S + H_2O \rightarrow Fe(SH)(OH) + 2H^+$ Corrosion products
$3Fe^{2+} + 6(OH^-) \rightarrow 3Fe(OH)_2$

STARKEY (1956) considers that the role of the sulfate-reducing bacteria *(Desulfovibrio)* is to produce hydrogen sulfide which reacts directly with iron to form corrosion cells between iron sulfide and metallic iron, and to produce strongly reducing areas of metallic iron which are anodic to other areas in contact with oxygenated sea water.

WILLINGHAM (Thesis, University of Miami, 1965) has conducted experiments to show that bacteria are not necessary for anaerobic corrosion, and that depolarization can occur through the action of such materials as sulfur or methyl viologen, and result in anaerobic corrosion in the absence of organisms. I have found the reduction of sulfate to sulfides to occur in inorganic media containing steel wool without microorganisms, but could not reproduce the conditions. It would appear then that the depolarization by bacteria is one method of corrosion, and on account of the environment, probably the commonest, but that it is not the only method. It is possible too that other anaerobic organisms than *Desulfovibrio* may contribute to corrosion, though from the work of KAPLAN et al. (1963) most sulfate reduction in marine sediments is caused by *Desulfovibrio*.

The occurrence of ferrous sulfides in iron corrosion in the sea has been recorded by IRVINE (1891), FRIEND (1922), GAINES (1910), VON WOLZOGEN KUHR (1923), COPENHAGEN (1934), VEILLON (1935). STARKEY and WIGHT (1945), STARKEY and SCHENONE (1946, 1947), STARKEY (1953) consider that bacterial corrosion plays the same part in the sea as it does in the soil. Estuarine muds (Chapter VI) have all the right conditions for the anaerobic corrosion of iron, but the position as regards ships is somewhat different.

The sea usually has a pH about 8.1, but in estuaries, the pH varies between about 7.6 and 9.0, rising in the day when photosynthesis is active. These values are within the range for the sulfate-reducers and there is always plenty of sulfate in the water as SO_4^{2-} ion. As Starkey and Wight point out, the reduction of sulfates by anaerobic bacteria requires a low redox potential. In the muds (Chapter IV) the low redox required is easily produced by heterotrophic bacteria from organic matter. On ships, reducing conditions may be produced in the slime or from the decomposition of dead barnacles, etc. Further, antifouling and anticorrosive paints used on ships' hulls frequently contain sulfates and other sulfur compounds, and also resins, which may be attacked by heterotrophic bacteria to reduce the redox potential. As many of these heterotrophs are copper-mercury tolerant, they can easily live under or in a paint coating, and colonies of these organisms may form the foci for sulfate reduction and the consequent production of corrosion cells on steel hulls (see STARKEY and SCHENONE, 1946, 1947).

SHIPLEY (1922) and VON WOLZOGEN KUHR (1939) record anaerobic corrosion of lead, while VON WOLZOGEN KUHR (1939) and ROGERS (1945) record anaerobic corrosion of copper. Baas Becking and Wood were unable to demonstrate the production of copper sulfide by *Desulfovibrio* in culture under autotrophic conditions. One would expect difficulties in direct biological production of lead and copper sulfides when one remembers the place of these metals in the electrochemical series. The evidence is that iron sulfydryl or possibly a polysulfide is formed by *Desulfovibrio* and that the iron is replaced by copper according to solubility products; alternatively, sulfides produced by heterotrophic anaerobes at very low redox potentials such as are known to occur in canned foods, etc. We have found that aluminum can be corroded by the action of *Desulfovibrio* though, of course, aluminum hydroxide or oxychloride and not sulfide is produced in sea water.

THE ROTTING OF CORDAGE AND FIXED STRUCTURES

The rotting of cordage is very important in connection with the maintenance of boats and gear, including fishing gear. In all cases, the environment is partly hydric and partly aerial, as ropes and nets are exposed in turn to water and air. Thus, contamination can and does occur from both sources. In the case of wooden structures, the greatest destruction occurs between wind and water, e.g., dry rot in boat planking, wharf piles, etc.

There are then three possibilities of infection: (*1*) By terrestrial organisms prior to submersion. Ropes may become infected with fungi (e.g., *Alternaria*) during manufacture, but the damage may only become apparent after use. Timbers with a sapwood or bark infection may also show the effects at a later date. (*2*) By "dust-borne" fungi in the water or on land during use. A large number of fungal spores are probably carried seaward by the winds, and many of these must settle on ropes, nets and timber structures. (*3*) By marine fungi, cellulose- or lignin-digesting bacteria. Wood-digesting fungi are recorded from sea water by BARGHOORN and LINDER (1944), MEYERS (1953, 1954), CRIBB and CRIBB (1955), HÖHNK (1955), MEYERS (1957), MOORE and MEYERS (1959), MEYERS and MOORE (1960), BECKER and KOHLMEYER (1958a, 1958b), KOHLMEYER (1958a,b, 1959, 1960, 1961), MEYERS and REYNOLDS (1957, 1958, 1959a,b,c, 1960a,b, 1963), MEYERS et al. (1960). These authors have shown that many of the fungi are confined to marine environments and have temperature optima between 22.5 and 27.5 °C, with distributive mechanisms adapted to aqueous environments. Cellulose and lignin digesting bacteria (ROBERTSON and WRIGHT, 1930; KADOTA, 1951; MEYERS et al., 1960; MEYERS and REYNOLDS, 1962) are also responsible for the rotting of fish nets and cordage. These and other organisms also attack cork, which is denatured, while rubber (ZOBELL and BECKWITH, 1944) is also attacked by marine bacteria.

A difficulty in the preservation of fishing nets is that colour and texture are important to fishermen. I have found that the tensile strength of cordage is least impaired by impregnation with creosote, but the cordage is less pliable and fouls more readily. With copper soaps, there is little fouling, and the texture is not impaired, but copper acts as a photocatalyst in the destruction of cellulose, and increases the rate of destruction of nets dried in the sun in the normal manner. In 6 months, the tensile strength of copper-treated ropes at Cronulla and Thursday Island (Australia) often fell by half, especially between wind and water.

Tar and creosote are used for the cod-ends of trawls and in other cases where fouling is not a factor and stiffness is an asset or at least not a liability. For flexibility, the old-fashioned bark tanning is still the treatment favoured by fishermen the world over. It has not the preserving action of copper soaps, but keeps the twine flexible and stops cutting.

The use of D.D.T. pentachlorphenates, and the acridine dyes have been considered, but no adequate substitute for "wattle bark", cutch, or mangrove tan has yet been found. This means that the preservation of cordage is still a challenge to the chemist and the microbiologist.

Timber structures are often treated with creosote or tar and this is reasonably effective in keeping out both micro- and macro-organisms. O'NEILL et al. (1961) have found a *Pseudomonas* which is tolerant to creosote and is predominant on creosoted piling in marine environments. The failure of creosote to preserve piling in certain cases may be due to the presence of such a microorganism. However, creosote leaches out in time and its replacement is always difficult. In wooden ships, "dry rot" fungi (terrestrial forms) working from within the hull at and above the waterline are the shipwright's chief bane.

A peculiar effect which I once experienced was the blackening of paint, accompanied by mephitic smells in the cabin of a fishing craft. The ballast was basalt containing pyrites, and the fish slime and gurry running into the bilge caused microbial action to produce mercaptans and hydrogen sulfide by both heterotrophic and autotrophic bacteria, with consequent blackening of the lead-containing paint. This blackening was instantaneous and the cabin soon became uninhabitable.

The microbial corrosion of concrete has also frequently been reported. Recent work on this has been carried out by PARKER and PRISK (1953). The most common cases of this phenomenon are in sewer pipes and sea water conduits, e.g., powerhouse conduits. Organic matter and sulfates are decomposed by H_2S-producing bacteria (heterotrophs and autotrophs) and H_2S and $Fe(SH)(OH)$ are produced. These are then oxidized by thiobacilli of the thiooxidans group (which includes Parker's *Th. concretivorous*) or by *Thiothrix* (which I have observed growing at pH 1.85, Eh +850 mV in a sewer vent) to produce sulfuric acid and low pH values (3.6 or less), and the acid so produced attacks the concrete. BAAS BECKING and WOOD (1955) found that thiobacilli can oxidize sulfides anaerobically as well as aerobically, i.e., by dehydrogenation as well as by oxidation. This explains the solution of sulfur in pipe-jointing compounds. In powerhouse and other industrial sea water conduits, a large growth of fouling is formed on the walls. Much of this falls to the floor and collects mud and silt, so that both organic and inorganic sulfide producers become active, to produce sufficient hydrogen sulfide to be toxic to humans. I have personally felt considerable discomfort from this gas in some conduits.

CHAPTER IX

FURTHER ECONOMIC ASPECTS

MICROBIAL FERMENTATIONS IN MARINE PRODUCTS

In European countries, fish are marketed in a limited number of ways: fresh (iced or sharp frozen), smoked, soused, salted or canned, and any microbial alteration of the flesh is considered to reduce the quality of the product (see under spoilage). For this reason, research is directed to reducing the microbial content, and not to the possibility of improving the product by microbial means. Algal products such as agar and alginates are prepared directly, by mechanical and chemical means, from the fresh weed. Carragheen, or Irish moss, is dried *Chondrus crispus*, but there has been no investigation of any possible microbiological changes in this or in dulse *(Dilsea edulis)* or laver *(Porphyra)* as prepared for food.

In India, Malaya, Thailand, Viet Nam, The Philippines and Japan however a series of degradation products of fish is extensively used as food, e.g., nuoc mam (Viet Nam), patis (Philippines), nam pla (Thailand), etc. The fish is salted with sea salt, which contains a wide assortment of bacteria, and it is said that certain Clostridia play a part in the fermentation. However, the microbiological processes in the preparation of these amino-acid containing products has not been studied in detail, the preparation being ad hoc by time-honoured methods. The essential process is the lysis of the fish in the presence of salt, and the resulting food contains 18–20 g of nitrogen/l.

Katsuobushi is prepared in Japan from tuna *(Katsuwonus pelamus)* by boiling for 40 min and drying for 24 h alternately until the fish is hard, i.e., after about 9 days. The fillets are then placed in a warm, moist chamber for about 3 days until a mold growth appears. This is scraped off and two more crops of mold are grown (KIKKAWA and KOSUGI, 1937). The product is then allowed to mature. There is obviously a microbial fermentation here, but the details are unknown.

The preparation of "soya" type sauce from fish in Hokkaido, Japan, is also in part microbiological. Fish are boiled with stirring for 30–60 min in a large vat, the solids removed in basket centrifuges and the oil separated from the "stickwater" by Sharples centrifuges. The stickwater, which contains a large part of the fish protein, is treated with 2% hydrochloric acid, and allowed to settle. It is then mixed with a little soya-bean sauce, and allowed to ferment for two to three months in large wooden vats. When I was in Hokkaido in 1946, there was no chemical control over the process.

At that time, too, a pilot plant was in action at Tateyama in Chiba prefecture for the manufacture of "shoyu" from the seaweeds *Ecklonia radiata* and *Eisenia* sp. The weed was boiled for 6 h at 100–110 °C with hydrochloric acid, neutralized with soda, sodium chloride added if necessary, and the liquor boiled again for ½ h. After this, it was stored in bulk for at least 14 days to mature, and, just before sale, pasteurized at 80 °C for 15 min. The details of the fermentation process were not known.

Whether the fermentation in the preparation of "nori" is autolytic or microbial is an open question. The seaweed *(Porphyra* or *Undaria* as a rule) is washed into thin sheets on bamboo mats, which are hung in the shade so that the "nori" dries slowly in air, and are then placed in the sun to finish the process.

The preparation in Japan of the kelp-weeds, *Laminaria* and *Ecklonia* for food also appears to be partly microbial. The harvested weed is partially dried, and then stacked in large heaps. The fronds are thatched with rice straw both top and sides, and the stipes on top only. They are left thus for about two weeks and then completely dried. The result is the growth of *Aspergillus* and *Penicillium*, and, at times, an *Alternaria*, but once again no details of the microbial process have been worked out. It may well be that the mannitol and mannuronic acid are hydrolysed and converted into substances that are more easily assimilated by human beings.

As the kelp-weeds are capable of producing hundreds of thousands of tons of food in the cooler latitudes of the world, it seems time that a full investigation of the Japanese fermentation process was made, at least as a basis for further work aimed at getting the most food value out of this source.

FISH SPOILAGE

Spoilage may be defined as the deterioration of a food product toward a point where it becomes unacceptable to the consumer. I have deliberately avoided the phrase "unfit for human consumption" which is frequently employed in British marketing acts, because much badly spoiled fish is quite fit for human consumption, in fact, most of the fish condemned in European and Australian fish markets would not cause any distress if eaten, and would be quite acceptable in Japan. In 1946, I, together with a number of fishery scientists, visited the fish-cake factory at Tokyo fish market, where fish condemned on the "fresh" market was being turned into fish-cakes. Although used to "off" odours of fish, we, Australian and American alike, were nauseated, and had to leave, passing through a queue of Japanese waiting their turn to buy the odoriferous product. The liking of Englishmen for jugged hare is another instance of one man's meat being another man's poison. I labor this point to show that, except where toxic substances are concerned, e.g., botulism, staphylococcal toxin, and Goniaulax toxin, the idea of spoilage is purely relative. The Chinese have a liking for fish which has decomposed beyond the stage of the green-fluorescent pseudomonads (the last stage of putrefaction). This means that the words "unfit for human consumption" have meaning only when toxins are present, and that a legal definition of the phrase would, in practice, be very difficult. I once asked Dr. Kintaro Kimura, then bacteriologist to the Japanese Fisheries Research Station at Tokyo, what research they had done on spoilage. He replied: "None, there are no pathogenic bacteria in fish", a statement that is generally quite true, unless pollution has occurred.

MARKOV (1939) states that bacteria do form a thermostable non-protein toxin (pelamotoxin) in scombroid fishes but this has not been confirmed.

The conclusion is that standards must be different in different countries, and must depend on the taste of the consumer. Further, spoilage, especially under controlled conditions, may improve the digestibility of fish products, and the consumption of "spoiled" fish in the east may well be due to a tacit recognition of this fact.

Spoilage may be considered under three heads: (1) toxic spoilage, (2) microbial spoilage, and (3) autolysis. The last, not being microbial, concerns us only incidentally.

Toxic spoilage

In this type of spoilage, the food product is poisonous to human beings at least. The toxin is usually produced by microorganisms, but can, of course, be due to trade wastes, etc. We are only concerned with the former, especially with the toxic substances produced by bacteria, by certain *Goniaulax* species and by some blue-green algae. Toxins due to spoilage are not to be confused with those produced by the fish themselves, e.g., certain tropical fish which have poisonous flesh, and the puffer fish which have a toxin in the gall bladder, etc., which toxin can pervade the tissues and kill human beings if the gall is ruptured during cleaning.

Paralytic shellfish poisoning

In 1927, an outbreak of mussel poisoning occurred in San Francisco and along the northern coast of California, but similar outbreaks had been known previously, and others have occurred in the same region. Sommer and his co-workers (SOMMER and MEYER, 1937; SOMMER et al., 1937) showed that this poisoning was caused by blooms of *Goniaulax catenella*, a dinoflagellate which was ingested by the mussels. The toxin was isolated and shown to be a neurotoxin (COVELL and WHEDON, 1937), acting as a depressor of respiration, inhibitor of cardiac action, and vasomotor activity. Sommer and his co-workers showed a strong correlation between mussel poisoning and the occurrence of *G. catenella*, and also that the toxicity of the mussels varied with the numbers of *G. catenella* in the diet. There was no correlation between mussel toxicity and the other species of *Goniaulax* or diatoms. Further, seawater containing large quantities of *G. catenella* was toxic in proportion to the amount of *G. catenella* present. The identity of *G. catenella* toxin with that of the California mussel and the Alaskan butter clam has been confirmed by BURKE et al. (1960).

NEEDLER (1949) and MEDCOF et al. (1947) relate mussel toxicity on the Atlantic coast of Canada to the presence of *Goniaulax tamarensis*, though the correlation is not always convincing. Toxicity in European waters is ascribed by WOLOSZYNSKA and CONRAD (1939) to *Pyrodinium phoneus*, and by DESOUSA E SILVA (1963) to *Goniaulax tamarensis* and possibly *Glenodinium foliaceum*. *Pyrodinium bahamense* though causing luminosity in the Bahamas and Puerto Rico is not recorded as toxic.

Toxicity of sand crabs may be due to other dinoflagellates, possibly *Ceratium* or *Prorocentrum* species, though there is no definite evidence of this. KOCH (1939) records shellfish toxicity on the northwest coast of Europe and at Leith in Scotland. During ten years of study of dinoflagellates in Australia, no *Goniaulax catenella* was found, and there is no history of shellfish poisoning. Mussels are not generally eaten in that country, but there is a big oyster industry in the east coast estuaries.

Bacterial toxins

There are two important types of bacterial toxins—botulinus and staphylococcal toxins. The former is only important in canned products, or, by introduction of staphylococci in potatoes, etc., in fish cakes and similar products (APPLEMAN et al., 1964). Although Dr. W. Scott of C.S.I.R.O. at Ryde, Australia, has found *Clostridium botulinum* in marine muds, the organisms isolated were type B and not type E, the latter being the type usually associated with toxic fishery products. Type E, however, has been recorded from fish by DOLMAN (1960) and SHEWAN (1962). Scott's isolates were pathogenic to laboratory animals, but were unusually heat-labile, a fact which may account for their not appearing in canned fish products, though it does not account for their failure to appear under anaerobic conditions in fresh fish. Possibly, even in cooked fish, the redox potentials are not low enough for clostridia to develop. SHEWAN (1938) found *C. tetani* in the gut of haddock and yet there is no evidence that this organism derived from fish has ever caused harm to humans. Dr. Kimura of Tokyo told me that *C. botulinum* did not occur in Japan, and it is perhaps significant that the cooking temperature for canned crab in that country is lower than would be permissable elsewhere in the world, which also probably accounts for the superior quality and color of Japanese canned crab.

Strains of *C. botulinum* have been recorded as causing a mortality of ducks in swamps in the United States, and apparently occur in the muds there.

Most cases of fish poisoning, apart from those due to the eating of poisonous fish, are due to staphylococci. Investigations of local epidemics derived from prawns gave evidence of staphylococcal infection subsequent to cooking.

It would appear that, apart from rather rare clostridia and the *Pseudomonas* described by BEIN (1954) from Florida red tides, marine bacteria are not toxic in themselves, nor do they produce toxic substances in food products.

Algal toxins (see also p.169)

There have been a number of records of the poisoning of domestic animals by blooms of blue-green algae in fresh water lakes, ponds, and irrigation ditches. These organisms could also be toxic in the upper parts of estuaries under certain circumstances. However, other blue-green algae, e.g., *Nostoc* are edible, and are actually eaten by natives in Fiji.

The green microscopic alga *Chlorella* is stated to contain a poison, "chlorellin" (SPOEHR et al., 1949), which is possibly specific for a small group of microorganisms. SPOEHR's later work (1951) suggests that these algae are suitable for food, and LOOSANOFF and ENGLE (1947) found that the effect of overdoses of *Chlorella* on the oyster *Ostrea virginica* was to kill them by mechanically impeding the feeding and respiration. I was not able to kill the Sydney Rock oyster *(Crassostrea commercialis)* by overfeeding with 100,000 cells of *Navicula* or 5,000,000 of *Chlorella*/ml even after 7 days, though the oysters did show some distress by increasing their rate of pumping (WOOD, 1964). The larvae of the tube worm *Galeolaria* can utilize *Chlorella* as food, but those of *Balanus amphitrite* die, presumably of starvation, if supplied with this alga, which passes undigested into the faeces.

Apart from the dinoflagellate toxins dealt with above, and those related to certain "red tides" and discussed under that heading, I do not know of any toxicity attributed to marine algae in truly marine environments.

Microbial spoilage

Microbial spoilage may be divided into two classes: (*1*) spoilage by infection with human pathogens, and (*2*) spoilage due to off-flavours of microbial origin.

Spoilage with human pathogens

Fish as carriers of disease. Fresh water is known to carry organisms

producing diseases in human beings, including staphylococci, actinomycetes, and streptococci, which produce furunculoses, dermatitis,
and throat infections, and also may contain viruses and intestinal
pathogens, e.g., the bacteria of typhoid, cholera, etc., or the hepatitis
virus. Fresh water is bactericidal to some of these microorganisms,
but water-borne infections of cholera, typhoid, etc., are a well known
feature of many far-east countries. Where pollution is heavy, many
pathogenic bacteria are consumed by Protozoa (PURDY and BUTTER-
FIELD, 1918) and other organisms, or destroyed by bacteriophage
(HAUDUROY, 1923). In certain Asiatic rivers which were excessively
polluted, hygienic methods produced disastrous results because they
resulted in the elimination of the phage without preventing re-
pollution by human contamination.

In the sea, however, the bactericidal effect is very marked. As
early as 1889, DE GIAXA showed that enteric bacteria perish rapidly
in seawater, and other workers in the main agree with his findings.
ZOBELL (1936) showed that sewage bacteria are killed by natural
seawater more rapidly than by autoclaved, filtered or synthetic sea
water. This is shown in Table X which is taken from ZoBell.

Other authors quoted by ZOBELL (1946b) confirm these findings.
As we should expect from this, coliform organisms are rare in marine
environments, except in the vicinity of sewer outfalls and other
sources of faecal pollution. VENKATARAMAN and SREENIVASAN (1953)
found slow-lactose-fermenters in and on mackerel, and these bacteria
did not grow at all readily on fresh water media, and were therefore
regarded as being of marine origin.

TABLE X

SURVIVAL OF SEWAGE BACTERIA IN SEA WATER
(After ZOBELL, 1936)

Solution in which bacteria were suspended	Percentage survival after time in minutes				
	1	30	60	90	120
Formula C control	100	100	91	82	97
Natural sea water	82	47	31	15	3
Autoclaved sea water	85	56	38	28	36
Filtered sea water	88	39	20	23	19

AMYOT (1901) concluded that the colon bacillus is not a normal inhabitant of the intestinal tract of fish in fresh water and yet JOHN-STON (1904) found *E. coli* in 47 out of 67 fish from the Mississippi and Illinois rivers. HOUSTON (1904) found *E. coli* in 13% and typical lactose-fermenters in 52% of sea fish taken from an unpolluted area; EYRE (1904) found *E. coli* in all trawl fish examined in catches two miles off the Lincolnshire coast; BROWNE (1917) found lactose-fermenters in 73 out of 93 fish examined; GREENE (1920) regarded them as one of the principal groups in frozen herring; HUNTER (1920) found that 21 out of 43 cultures from Pacific salmon belonged to the colon-cloacae group of bacteria and FELLERS (1926) found the coli-aerogenes group in decomposing salmon, while GIBBONS (1934a,b) found them in 18.4% of the fish examined, but only in the fish from polluted waters; REED and SPENCE (1929) found only 4.6% of coli-aerogenes; THJØTTA and SØMME (1938, 1943) did not find coliform organisms except in the contaminated waters of Oslo Fjord, and consider that they are evidence of pollution. M. M. STEWART (1932), SHEWAN (1944), ASCHEHOUG and VESTERHUS (1940), and WOOD (1940, 1950b) either failed to find coliform organisms or *Proteus* or found them rarely and then only in proximity to faecal pollution. THJØTTA and SØMME (1938) found that their coli strains did not conform to the usual faecal type, but as their optimum temperature was 37 °C these authors considered them to be pollutants and not part of the normal flora of the cod. Latterly GLANTZ and KRANTZ (1965) found that *E. coli* serotypes in fish and water samples were related to terrestrial sources and not to the marine biotope.

Summarizing, the earlier students of the bacterial flora of fish found that infection by coliform organisms was frequent, while later workers considered that infection of fish by such bacteria was due to pollution. The difference may well be due to improvements in technique plus the possibility that the earlier samples were contaminated after capture, while greater precautions were taken by more recent workers.

Coliform organisms are far more prevalent in the gut of fresh water fish, and no doubt are derived from the water. I found during my work on Victorian waters (unpublished) that these streams, many of which are used for town water supplies, although screened from human pollution, contained many coliform organisms of non-faecal types, resembling those described by MINKEWITCH and TROFIMUK

(1928, 1929). These authors found *B. aquatilis communis, B. cloacae* and varieties of *B. coli* may well be considered the chief intestinal flora of fresh water fish, but that the typical *B. coli* of warm-blooded animals were present in only five cases out of 252 specimens representing 15 species of fish. These cases were from sewage-polluted waters. STUTZER (1926) found a similar flora in fish and frogs. He concludes that a great part of the fresh water flora owes its origin to the intestines of fish and frogs, but my evidence suggests the opposite, i.e., that, as in the sea, the fish derive their intestinal flora from the environment. HAVENS and DEHLER (1923) found that the minnow, *Gambusia affinis*, caused the disappearance of *E. coli* from polluted waters, and regard this as due to the antibiotic effect of *Pseudomonas pyocyaneus*. It may well be due to the digestion of the bacteria by the minnows. TAMAKI (1928) states that the colon bacilli from fish have an optimum temperature of 22–23 °C and show slight indol formation, marked gelatin liquefaction and ferment arabinose but not glycerol, all in contradistinction to those from birds and mammals. TANIKAWA (1939) found that the intestinal floras of fish with different feeding habits differ, and that coliform bacteria, streptococci and *Clostridium welchi* were more abundant in carnivores than in herbivores. This may be due to the digestion of bacteria by the herbivores.

I think we must conclude that in fresh water fish the presence of faecal coli is indicative of local pollution, and that in sea fish, the occurrence of any coliform bacteria or *Proteus* types is indicative that the fish have recently been feeding in a polluted area. This important conclusion means that, in practice, should fish show coliform organisms and these organisms be not traceable to handling or to contaminating ice, the area in which the fish were caught is suspect and that fishing there should cease until pollution has stopped.

Coliform organisms have been shown to inhabit the intestines of live seals (OPPENHEIMER and KELLY, 1952) but this seems to be an independent association, in which the organisms are transmitted by contact from one mammal to another.

Despite the frequent pollution of fresh water streams and lakes, the transmission to humans of intestinal diseases by fish are rare. In sea water, the bactericidal effect of sea water is usually sufficient protection. Lake Macquarie in New South Wales has an area of 35 square miles and is surrounded by a human population of at least 100,000. Examination for coliform organisms over several months in the summer failed to show *E. coli* and gave very few coliform organisms, even in densely populated and unsewered areas. The examination was made in connection with a local typhoid epidemic, and I failed to find any evidence that there was a danger of human intestinal infection from such a lagoon.

In Copenhagen (Denmark) and Hobart (Tasmania), fish are marketed alive, and are kept for sale in tanks. This method was also tried at Oslo, but Dr. Thjøtta told me that contamination by coliform organisms rendered it unsafe. I could get no information of the extent of pollution at the Copenhagen fish market, and do not know of any tests having been made at Hobart, but the marketing of fish in this way, while ensuring perfect freshness, does increase the possibility of transmitting intestinal diseases by fish. However, the fact that no epidemics appear to have been traced to this practice suggests that the theoretical danger is not realized.

Shellfish and hygiene. The pollution of shellfish by bacteria pathogenic to man is much more serious than that of free-swimming animals. The reason is that bacteria form part of the diet of shellfish, so that a goodly number of live bacteria can usually be isolated from the fish. Moreover, shellfish are usually eaten whole, and often raw, so the danger of infection, especially by intestinal bacteria, is great. Studies on shellfish contamination have been made by DODGSON (1928), HUNTER and HARRISON (1928), SHERWOOD and THOMSON (1953), etc. Recently an epidemic of hepatitis has been traced to the eating of shellfish from the Raritan River, New Jersey.

The physiology of the shellfish has been used for getting rid of unwanted bacteria. If molluscs are removed from the source of contamination, and placed in clean sea water, they rapidly pump away the undigested bacteria and clean themselves. Oysters and mussels pump up to 20 l of water/h, so the cleaning process is very rapid. There are two methods for utilizing this process. Firstly, the shellfish can be taken from a heavily polluted area, cultivated in an unpolluted region, and marketed with perfect safety. In this way, not only do the shellfish get rid of the infecting bacteria, but dilution and the bactericidal nature of sea water towards such organisms remove the bacteria from the vicinity. This is a fact not usually recognized by health authorities, who often prevent even the removal of spat from polluted areas.

The second application is that worked out by DODGSON (1928) at Conway in Wales for the purification of mussels and oysters where they are growing in close proximity to sewer outfalls. The process is simple and very effective.

The shellfish are spread thinly on wooden grids in concrete tanks, hosed thoroughly and flooded with sea water or artificial sea water (ALLEN et al., 1950), sterilized by 3 p.p.m. of chlorine which is neutralized by sodium thiosulphate. The sterile water is left in contact with the shellfish for 24 h, and the bacteria encased in the faecal pellets or mucous slime fall to the bottom of the tank, from which they are removed by draining and a second hosing. The process is completed by a second 24 h treatment with sterile water, a third hosing and a final treatment with chlorinated water containing 3 p.p.m. residual chlorine to sterilize the outer surface of the shell. The shellfish remain closed throughout the final treatment, and are not affected by the chlorine. As mussels remain active at a lower temperature than oysters, which require 13 °C, the water used for oyster purification has to be heated in the winter in cooler climates. In warm climates, where the water is always above 13 °C this difficulty does not arise. Dodgson's method of purification results in coliform counts of less than five organisms/ml of flesh. If the shellfish, after purification, are transported in dirty bags, or watered at any stage of their journey to market by polluted water (a not-infrequent occurrence) they may easily become polluted again and require further treatment. The Dodgson technique has been improved for use by individual shellfish producers, and re-laying in unpolluted areas may also be used for purification.

It is interesting to note that BEASON and EHRINGER (1922) found a typhoid-like organism in oysters, but it was salt-tolerant and non-pathogenic to animals.

In assessing the possibility of human infection by eating either fish or shellfish, it is to be remembered that the count of faecal coli is merely an index of the degree of faecal pollution, hence of the chance of infection by an intestinal pathogen such as typhoid, paratyphoid, cholera or dysentery bacilli. This means that, in areas where intestinal diseases are rife, the ratio of typhoid, etc., to coli is likely to be high, and therefore the criteria of pollution should be strict. In countries such as Australia, where cholera is unknown, and typhoid cases total less than 0.01% of the population, the possibility of infection by eating fish or shellfish is exceedingly remote, and in fact there is no authentic record of such an infection. This makes it exceedingly difficult to set standards, even in any one country. In the case of an export trade, the problem is much greater, for example, fresh shellfish imported into Australia from Japan or Singapore would need much more rigid standards than shellfish sent from Australia to those places.

Methods of estimation of pollution in shellfish has been studied by a number of workers, and the literature reviewed by CLEGG and SHERWOOD (1947). These authors consider that the control of bivalve pollution by market tests is not generally desirable, except in tests for pollution in transit by bags or by standing in insanitary places, in which case individual shell tests should be made. Clegg and Sherwood conclude that control should lie in tests made on the beds, and that pooled samples are then admissible. In selecting samples, tidal conditions, currents, etc., should be taken into consideration as we are looking for a maximum pollution, not for a representative sample.

Univalves such as periwinkles, whelks, etc., which graze and do not filter must be sampled in consideration of the area on which they have been grazing.

Clegg and Sherwood examine shellfish by draining off the shell water after opening, chopping up the body, and scraping the gills to free the bacterial clumps. The flesh and exuded liquor are added to 5–10 ml of sterile water in a sterile 100 ml cylinder, the flesh volume being found by displacement. Sterile water is added to bring the total volume up to three times that of the body tissue. Univalves are ground in a sterile mortar.

The prepared material is inoculated into MacConkey agar using 1 ml of liquor (or 0.1 ml if pollution is expected to be heavy). These authors use roll-tubes with a modified medium containing 2% gelatine and 5% agar. Incubation is at 44 °C ($\pm$ 0.2) and the colonies of coliform organisms are counted after 24 h.

The London Fishmongers' Company have a somewhat similar method, but sample each shell individually, retaining the shell water and using 0.2 ml inoculum into bile salt broth, glucose and litmus milk. They look for coliform bacteria, streptococci and *C. welchi* (KNOTT, 1951).

Clegg and Sherwood require the absence of faecal coli from 1 ml

of body tissue in four out of five cases; Knott requires the same
standard freshness, fish that are 70% clean are viewed with suspicion,
and anything below this requires investigation of the beds, of handling and transport.

Spoilage due to off-flavors of microbial origin

Because of the limitations of my subject, I shall not discuss spoilage
due to contamination during the handling of marine products, e.g.,
bad cannery practice, unhygienic packaging, unclean fish markets,
etc., although some of these concern us to the extent that the organisms concerned may, in the first instance, be of marine origin. Autolytic spoilage by enzyme action is also outside the scope of this work.
It is not always easy to determine which effects are autolytic and
which microbial, e.g., the rancidity of fats, which is usually regarded
as autolytic, may be due in part to fat-splitting bacteria. On the other
hand, the splitting of urea in elasmobranch fish muscle is mainly
bacterial, but the urease of shark blood can also split the urea in the
flesh (WOOD, 1950b). However, as far as we know, the production
of trimethylamine from trimethylamine oxide is considered due to
bacteria, and largely to one group, the gram-negative, non-pigmented
rods with peritrichous flagella (WATSON, 1939), though J. M. Shewan
(personal communication) has failed to show the connection between
spoilage and any individual bacterium.

Fish spoilage is essentially bacterial. No fungi have been recorded,
and very few yeasts. Where the latter have been isolated, it has not
been possible to show that they were playing any part (WOOD, 1953).
Spoilage is essentially an aerobic phenomenon. FELLERS (1926),
REED and SPENCE (1929), PROCTOR and NICKERSON (1935), M. M.
STEWART (1932), THJØTTA and SØMME (1938), SNOW and BEARD
(1939), ASCHEHOUG and VESTERHUS (1940), SHEWAN (1944) and
WOOD (1940, 1950b) all failed to find anaerobes in the slime or in
spoiling fish muscle. SHEWAN (1938) found *Clostridium tetani* in the
gut of line-caught halibut and BROWNE (1917) isolated *Cl. welchii*.
Clostridium botulinum Type E has been recorded by DOLMAN (1960)
and SHEWAN (1962) as the cause of food poisoning in fisheries products. The organism has also been found in sediments from northwestern Canada, the Baltic Sea, the American Great Lakes and the
Caspian Sea. Further, the authors who have studied spoilage agree
that it is a surface phenomenon, and that the bacterial count decreases

rapidly with depth in the flesh, e.g., Wood (1953) who showed that
the bacterial population of shark flesh fell from 10^9 bacteria / g at the
surface to 10^7 at 0.5 cm, and 10^4 at 2.5 cm depth (see Fig.29).

Watson (1939) gives the Eh of the surface of cod muscle as
$+300$ mV with the interior at -50 to -100 mV. He correlates
trimethylamine oxide reduction with facultative anaerobes *(Achromobacter)*, but this does not march with the surface nature of spoilage.
The question is obviously the possession of a hydrogenase by the
bacteria concerned, and the organisms are probably acting as gradient

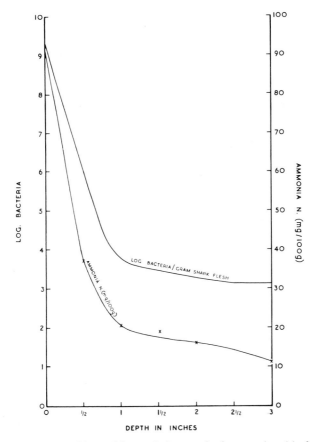

Fig.29. Decrease of bacterial populations and of ammonia with depth in
shark flesh.

organisms, i.e., require an oxidizing environment above, a reducing below the bacterial film.

Wood also showed that, for shark spoilage bacteria, the rate of reproduction fell off, and ammonia production decreased with decreased oxygen tension and increasing carbon dioxide.

Although fish spoilage results in the general degradation of the flesh, the unpleasant odors associated with spoilage are due to volatile amines or ammonia. In teleost or bony fishes, trimethylamine predominates though di- and mono-amines and ammonia are also found in varying quantities. In elasmobranch fish (sharks and rays) ammonia predominates, being derived mainly from the urea which occurs in quantities in excess of 2% of the total organic matter in the flesh, and in other parts of the fish. Other volatile amines are also present, and are broken down in spoilage. Because the odors are accepted commercially as a measure of the freshness of fish, studies of microbial spoilage have centred on the production of volatile amines and ammonia rather than on proteolysis. Moreover, the most active proteolysis occurs after the volatile amines have reached a peak.

Although spoilage occurs mainly at the surface of the flesh, the volatile substances do penetrate the flesh to some extent. However, shark tails giving off strong odors of ammonia and methylamines could be rendered odorless by cutting off 2 or 3 cm of flesh, showing that penetration is limited.

The authors cited above have all assumed that the primary infection of fish is derived from the bacterial flora of living fish, and have consequently studied the flora of the gills, slime, and intestines of different species of fish. Such investigations have been made by ASCHEHOUG and VESTERHUS (1940), THJØTTA and SØMME (1938, 1943) in Norway; M. M. STEWART (1932) and SHEWAN (1938, 1944, 1953, 1960) in Britain; GIBBONS (1934a,b), REED and SPENCE (1929) in Canada; HUNTER (1920), FELLERS (1926), etc., in the United States; WOOD (1940, 1950b) in Australia; and VENKATARAMAN and SREENIVASAN (1954) in India.

Unfortunately, many of these authors have endeavored to use the classification of bacteria as set out in *Bergey's Manual of Determinative Bacteriology*, although they found that many of their strains would not fit any description contained therein. Further, gram-positive and gram-negative forms were lumped together as *Achromobacter* and *Flavobacterium*, and non-motile forms or those in which motility was not determined were disposed of rather arbitrarily, usually in these two genera also. This makes it exceedingly difficult to compare the results of any two workers. In later work (WOOD, 1953) the gram-negative, pleomorphic organisms which are so abundant in marine environments, have been ascribed to the genus *Mycoplana*, and not to *Pseudomonas*, *Vibrio* and *Spirillum;* the gram-positive rods showing snapping cell division were put in *Corynebacterium*. While *Mycoplana* has had limited acceptance, fish spoiling corynebacteria are now generally conceded as *Arthrobacter*. If these two genera are accepted as containing a large number of fish spoiling bacteria, one can find a place for the aberrant forms described by Stewart, Aschehoug and Vesterhus, and Thjøtta and Sømme. Many previously described *Achromobacter*, *Flavobacterium*, *Pseudomonas* strains belong to *Mycoplana* and *Corynebacterium*. I have not been able to sort out the strains I described from fish (WOOD, 1940), but I feel sure that, if the classification of the water and soil bacteria (should we coin a new term, Edaphohydric?) could have been rationalized and simplified, the similarity of the findings of all workers on fish spoilage would be most striking. The recent work of Shewan and his group (SHEWAN et al., 1960a,b; LISTON, 1960; COLWELL and LISTON, 1961; and COLWELL et al., 1965), shows considerable similarity in marine pseudomonads and it is a pity that previous studies cannot be reinterpreted in the light of this work. Unfortunately sufficient data are rarely available for such an evaluation.

As would be expected, the gills, slime, and skin harbor large numbers of bacteria. The flora of the gills has been studied by Hunter, Aschehoug and Vesterhus, Wood, and Thjøtta and Sømme. Hunter regarded the gills as the source of contamination of the visceral cavity of salmon if the fish had not been feeding. Wood found that the flora of the gills contained fewer species than the slime, but that these species were also represented in the slime. He reports yellow-orange pigmented and non-pigmented cocci, "*Achromobacter*", "*Flavobacterium*", "*Corynebacterium*", *Pseudomonas*, *Bacillus* and one strain of a coliform from a polluted area. Aschehoug and Vesterhus listed *Pseudomonas*, *Achromobacter*, *Flavobacterium*, *Micrococcus* and *Proteus*. From their descriptions some of the cultures belonged to *Corynebacterium*, and others possibly to *Mycoplana*. The general picture given by Thjøtta and Sømme is very similar, so we find a marked similarity between the gill flora of fish in various parts of the world.

Flora of the slime. The slime of teleost fish has been studied by a large number of workers including Fellers (1926), Harrison et al. (1926), Sanborn (1930), Gibbons (1934a), M. M. Stewart (1932), Asche-houg and Vesterhus (1940), Wood (1940), Thjøtta and Sømme (1943). Wood compared his findings in some detail with those of other workers but was hampered by the difficulties of classification. Shewan (1944) remarked: "At the outset it may be said that it is often very difficult to place these non-pathogenic bacteria isolated from fish with any degree of certainty into their respective specific groupings. Many of the species isolated fail to fit into any of the descriptions given, e.g., in Bergey". Shewan even used agglutination tests without success, and commented on the need for a study of variability. Similar difficulties had been recorded by Stewart and by Thjøtta and Sømme. The last-mentioned authors recorded marked pleomorphism in the gram-negative organisms which they isolated. This placed them in *Mycoplana* which agrees with the findings of Wood (1953). Thus, the need for a revision of the gram-negative spoilage forms was realized by the earlier workers, but adequate computers had not been developed.

Some authors have claimed that slime is bactericidal, and others (e.g., Fellers, 1926) that it is a good bacterial medium and the main source of contamination. Apparently, during life, the slime is continually extruded and removed, thus keeping down the bacteria. Inhibitors may be present also. On the death of the fish, however, the inhibition is removed and slime becomes a good medium for bacterial growth until it dries, when it again appears to become inhibitory—hence the unsettled argument as to the benefit or otherwise of removing slime from fish after capture. My own experiments on this aspect gave equivocal results. In this work, fish were kept on ice, half with the slime removed and half with it intact. Bacterial counts made on fish agar from the flesh just under the skin (taken with aseptic precautions) showed no appreciable difference over 7 days, and the agreement between observers on organoleptic tests was poor.

The bacterial flora of elasmobranch showed a greater occurrence of corynebacteria on the skin. Sharks and rays do not possess the slime excreted by the teleosts, and the shark skin contains a considerable amount of urea. These two factors, especially the latter, possibly account for the difference, since the shark corynebacteria were nearly all urea-splitters (WOOD, 1950a,b). Wood found that the elasmobranch flora of the skin belonged to *Corynebacterium*, *Micrococcus*, *Sarcina*, *Pseudomonas*, (*Ps. putida*) and *Mycoplana* (*M. dimorpha*) in that order, with one strain of a pink *Torula*. VENKATARAMAN and SREENIVASAN (1955b) found nine corynebacteria, ten staphylococci (micrococci), nine *Bacillus* (some pigmented), three *Achromobacter*, one *Flavobacterium*, one *Vibrio*, one *Nocardia*, and a yeast. TSUCHIYA et al. (1951) found a very similar shark flora. GEORGALA (1958) produced evidence to show that there is a seasonal variation in the flora of the skin of North Sea cod and that this can be correlated with plankton outbursts.

Flora of the intestinal tract. OBST (1919) first made the observation that the gut of fish which have not been feeding is sterile. HUNTER (1920), FELLERS (1926) and WOOD (1940) amply confirmed this. Wood also found that the gut of mullet (*Mugil cephalus*) and Australian salmon (*Arripis truttae*) was frequently sterile during the spawning migrations, when the gut is usually empty.

As mullet are so-called "detrital feeders", i.e., ingest epontic diatoms and blue-green algae with the accompanying bacterial flora, and also surface mud with its large bacterial flora, the sterilization of the gut can only be explained by the digestion of the bacteria by the gastric juices. It also means that the bacterial flora of mullet and other fish does not play an essential part in the digestion of food as it does in warm-blooded animals. There is thus no specific intestinal flora of fish.

Table XI (modified from SHEWAN, 1944) gives the percentage of bacteria general found in slime and intestines by different authors.

The important point to be noticed is that SHEWAN (1939), BROWNE (1917), DOLMAN (1960) and REED and SPENCE (1929) are the only authors who found obligate anaerobes in the fish, and in each case the fish was a bottom feeder. The other authors for whom negative findings are indicated in the table, specifically mention that they failed to find strict anaerobes though these were sought. Facultative anaerobes however were present, in fact WOOD (1953) found that, with the exception of the corynebacteria and some other species isolated from elasmobranchs, almost all marine bacteria will grow anaerobically.

It will be noticed that, in addition to the presence or absence of

TABLE XI

BACTERIA IN THE SLIME AND GUT OF FISH

Author	Fish species		Achromobacter	Micrococcus	Flavobacter	Pseudomonas	Bacillus	Misc. aerobes	Clostridia
Reed and Spence (1929)	Canadian haddock	slime	23	4	8	22	24	18	0
		gut	4.4	1	5.6	8.7	5.7	10	×
Stewart (1932)	North sea haddock	slime	57	22	11	5	0	0	0
		gut	80	0	4.5	0	4.5	4.5	0
Shewan (1938)	Shetland herring haddock	slime	43	24	13	11	0	11	0
		gut						9	×
		gut							×
Aschehoug and Vesterhus	Winter herring	slime	24.5	16.7	17.7	40	0	1.1	0
		gills	33.4	3.9	13.7	47.0	0	3.0	0
		gut	72.5	3.4	0	24.1	0	0	0
Thjotta and Somme	Norway cod	slime	48	14	25	5	0	8	0
		gut	55	11	0	0	0	33	0
Wood (1940)	Australia Misc.	slime	19	48	17	7	9	0	0
		gills	30	45	13	7	5	0	0
		gut	30	21	1	10	35	0	0

clostridia, the percentages of the different genera vary considerably with both the species of fish and the locality. SHEWAN (1953) and LISTON (1960) also record a seasonal difference. These differences are not surprising, seeing that different species of fish behave in different ways, and would therefore expose themselves to different bacterial floras. It will be also seen that, when we consider the studies of marine environments of ZoBELL (1946b) and WOOD (1953), allowing for the changes in outlook on taxonomy in recent years, there are some striking differences, e.g., the greater importance of micrococci recorded by the latter author. This increase in micrococci appeared in fish, sea water and mud (WOOD, 1940, 1950b, 1953), and it is also recorded by VENKATARAMAN and SREENIVASAN (1954), so it does seem probable that the fish flora is influenced by that of the environment of the fish, though modified by the substrate. Liston suggests that the occurrence of maximal bacterial populations can be correlated with plankton outbursts. The large occurrence of the genus *Bacillus* in the gut of Australian fish shown in the table is comparable with the high *Bacillus* content of the muds recorded by WOOD (1953), most of the fish being bottom feeders.

One cannot however push this analogy too far, for the elasmobranchs (WOOD, 1950) show a flora which has little in common with the rest of the marine environment, and, in fact, resembles the soil flora to a much greater extent. In this case, however, we are dealing with an unusual and rather selective environment, and this selection is obviously very active. It also persists throughout the spoilage of shark so that we do not get a succession of genera as Wood and others have recorded for the teleosts and crustaceans.

The flora of blood. PROCTOR and NICKERSON (1935) made a bacteriological study of fish blood, and concluded that it is normally sterile, unless it has become infected with a blood parasite.

Flora of fish muscle. It is generally considered that, in the living state, fish muscle is sterile. As slime is considered to have bactericidal or protective powers, and as the gut becomes sterile after the food has been digested, it is only to be expected that the muscle would be sterile. It is not easy to maintain sterility in sampling fish muscle, and careful perusal of papers alleging a bacterial flora of living fish muscle shows that the technique is suspect. BRUNS (1909), OBST

(1919), FELLERS (1926), HUNTER (1920), LUMLEY et al. (1929), M. M. STEWART (1932), PROCTOR and NICKERSON (1935), SCHONBERG (1938), BEDFORD (1937), ASCHEHOUG and VESTERHUS (1940) and WOOD (1940) agree on the sterility of fish muscle. Gee found *Bacillus mesentericus* but his methods are suspect, especially as the organism is a sporer.

BISSET (1948), studying fresh water fish, claims the finding of living bacteria in the peritoneal cavity, but his technique seems to have been somewhat inadequate. In his summary, he mentions bacteria in muscle, but gives no experimental evidence. He claims that the organisms isolated were the usual gram-negative fresh water bacteria. VENKATARAMAN and SREENIVASAN (1954) mention a number of bacterial species isolated from the flesh of fresh water fish, but again give no description of the technique by which they were isolated. Only if the outer surface of the fish has been adequately seared with a hot spatula before cutting into the flesh or belly cavity could the presence of a bacterial flora in these places be effectively demonstrated.

The rate at which bacteria invade fish muscle depends on a number of factors. Fish such as whiting which have been penned until the gut is empty and packed in the round after the onset of *rigor mortis* will keep for 7 days or more packed in ice, and the bacterial content of the muscle at the end of this period will be around 10–100 organisms/g. This means that, under such conditions, bacteria have a difficulty in penetrating the tissues, but penetration does occur slowly from the gills and through the skin; possibly because many of the commercial fish have an open vascular system, invasion through the blood is slow. Bacterial counts from various parts of the fish confirm the findings of those who have studied the qualitative aspects of spoilage that the skin, slime, and gills are the source of spoilage bacteria.

The flora of fish spoilage. The bibliography of fish spoilage is very extensive and only the most important papers can be quoted here. This aspect of microbial hydrobiology is the most extensively studied of all, no doubt because of its great economic importance. Unfortunately, most of the workers have confined themselves to the one aspect, and the services of a number of really good microbiologists have been lost to marine and aquatic microbiology in general.

Fish muscle, like other muscular tissue, is buffered on the acid side of neutrality and shows buffer plateaux around pH 6.0 and 3.4 (COLLINS et al., 1940). One would expect therefore that a considerable degree of selection of the flora would occur, as the aqueous environment is usually more alkaline. There is, however, a marked resemblance between the floras of teleost fish and of other marine environments (WOOD, 1953, fig.7, table I). This suggests that the flora is very adaptable, especially as regards pH and salt tolerance. WOOD (1940) did not find any great difference in numbers of types when using tap-water or sea-water media, but SHEWAN (1953) and LISTON (1956) do find a difference. This may be due to the fact that Wood was dealing largely with an estuarine fishery.

The elasmobranch fish are a special case due to their high urea content (see above).

Teleost fish. The earlier work on the spoilage of teleost fish was directed to bacterial counts and to descriptive bacteriology. Because the Canadian workers considered that the estimation of trimethylamine would serve as a criterion of freshness, they directed their energies in this direction and the general proteolytic and other changes of microbial origin have not received the attention they deserve. GIBBONS and REED (1930) showed that spoilage bacteria are proteolytic, breaking down the proteins to simpler, non-coagulable substances, ammonia and volatile amines. However, the details of this proteolysis, the fate of glycogen, lactic acid, etc., have only recently been studied (MACLEOD et al., 1954; VENKATARAMAN and SREENIVASAN, 1955b). BAIRD and WOOD (1944) found that the micrococci did not reduce trimethylamine oxide, so it has become generally accepted that these organisms are unimportant in spoilage, although WOOD (1940) showed that some of his cocci did attack trimethylamine oxide. Wood also found a succession of organisms in teleost spoilage beginning with gram-positive rods and cocci, through non-pigmented rods *(Achromobacter)* to fluorescent pseudomonads, and a similar succession has been recorded in crustacea by TOBIN et al. (1941), ALFORD et al. (1942). This is almost certainly a metabiotic relationship in which each organism prepares the way for the next, since it occurs even in fish which have been placed alive in sterile tubes.

Spoilage flora of fish have been listed by a number of authors including SANBORN (1930, 1932), FELLERS (1926), HARRISON (1929),

REED et al. (1929), GIBBONS (1934a) and WOOD (1940). Sanborn was the first to use fish muscle as the criterion of proteolysis and found that the various micrococci, flavobacteria and pseudomonads were proteolytic. Other authors, including the Canadians, tend to discount the activity of the first two groups. WOOD (1940) also used a preparation of fish muscle juice (this time filtered through a Seitz filter) to determine proteolysis, and found that all the genera present, i.e., *Staphylococcus (Micrococcus)*, "*Achromobacter*", "*Flavobacterium*" (including *Corynebacterium, Pseudomonas* and *Bacillus*) showed a number of proteolytic strains; moreover, the usual criterion of proteolysis, gelatine liquefaction, did not correlate at all well with the lysis of fish muscle juice—not a very surprising fact after all, as gelatine is not very easily lysed.

FELLERS (1926) found that salmon remains sterile for 20–50 h after death. Of 41 purified cultures from salmon, 31% were cocci, 4.5% sporulating aerobes, 17.5% non-sporing chromogenic rods, 6.8% yeasts, 2% obligate anaerobes, and 1.7% spirilla.

HARRISON et al. (1926) consider that "the marked preponderance of these two groups *(Achromobacter* and *Pseudomonas)* in stale and decaying fish indicates that they are mainly responsible for its decomposition". Fellers considers *Achromobacter* to be inert, while WATSON (1939) believes this group to be of the greatest importance because of its action on trimethylamine oxide. Reed, Rice and Sinclair stress the importance of *Pseudomonas*, and Gibbons found a flora very similar to that of Wood.

The latter author gives a table, which shows the change in the flora with progressive spoilage (Table XII).

The changes in the bacterial flora of the skin of stored fish from the North Sea show an overall similarity (SHEWAN et al., 1960b; Table XIII, XIV).

The decline in *Flavobacterium*, slower diminution of *Micrococcus* and increase of *Achromobacter* and *Pseudomonas* are obvious. SHEWAN (1944) pictures spoilage of teleosts thus:

(*1*) 0–6 days. Little visible alteration; dimethylamine is produced mainly by cocci from a purine; carbohydrate is broken down by cocci to lactic acid. Flora is *Achromobacter* 57%, micrococci 22%, Flavobacteria 10%.

(*2*) 6–14 days. Spoilage begins; acetic and lower fatty acids formed;

TABLE XII

BACTERIAL GENERA IN SPOILING FISH, SHOWING PROGRESSIVE CHANGES IN
THE FLORA
(expressed as percentages)

Genus	Ports	Trawlers	Market	Retail
Achromobacter	8	30	18	45
Micrococcus	42	30	52	14
Flavobacterium	50	10	11	3
Pseudomonas	0	21	8	27
Bacillus	0	9	10	10

with reduction of trimethylamine oxide by *Achromobacter* (64%), with flavobacteria 20%, cocci 10%, *Pseudomonas* 6%.

(3) 14–21 days. Acceleration of these changes with rapid proteolysis and a large increase in ammonia, probably due to deamination. The third stage, although Shewan does not state it, is accompanied by an increase in *Pseudomonas*, which, in my experience is the only genus to give free ammonia in teleost spoilage.

Wood found that all the pigmented organisms decreased with spoilage.

SHEWAN (1953) lists a larger number of genera from fish than do previous workers, but stresses the difficulties of classification of marine bacteria. He also suggests the use of sea water in media and as a diluent, and the use of low nutrient concentrations in media for fish spoilage.

SHEWAN et al. (1960a) again record a change in the composition of teleost fish with time, corynebacteria and micrococci diminishing in numbers from up to 49% of the flora to about 2%, being replaced by *Achromobacter* and *Pseudomonas* which measured from up to 50% to 90%. These authors confirm the conclusion of Castell and his co-workers (CASTELL and ANDERSON, 1948; CASTELL and GREEN-OUGH, 1957; CASTELL et al., 1959) that the spoilage of fish is "probably a direct result of the action of non-pigmented *Pseudomonas* strains in the fish muscle". LISTON (1960) also stressed the importance of *Pseudomonas* in fish from the northeast Pacific.

Further studies on fish spoilage include a review by TARR (1954)

TABLE XIII

CHANGES IN THE PROPORTIONS AND NUMBERS OF DIFFERENT BACTERIA ON THE SKIN OF FISH STOWED AT 0–1.5° FOR VARIOUS PERIODS DURING EXPEDITION 1, JUNE 1959

Fishing ground	Genus and/or kind of bacteria	Proportions (P)* and calculated nos. (N)† of various bacteria on fish stowed at 0–1.5° for (days)							
		0		5		10		15	
		P*	N†	P	N	P	N	P	N
North Cape	*Pseudomonas* nonfluorescent	12	15.79	6	9.63	45	299.25	62	12,809
	fluorescent	2	2.64	11	17.65	5	33.25	20	4,132
	Achromobacter	33	43.40	49	78.65	38	252.50	14	2,893
	Flavobacterium	4	5.27	0	0.00	0	0.00	2	413
	Coryneforms	41	53.90	33	52.97	12	80.00	2	413
	Micrococcus	8	10.50	1	1.60	0	0.00	0	0
	Unidentified	0	0.00	0	0.00	0	0.00	0	0
	Total colony count‡		131.50		160.50		665.00		20,660
Faroes	*Pseudomonas* nonfluorescent	11	2.26	66	315.48	45	1,269.0	79	47,005
	fluorescent	0	0.00	18	86.04	5	141.0	11	6,545
	Achromobacter	59	12.10	13	62.14	31	874.2	0	0
	Flavobacterium	1	0.20	0	0.00	3	84.6	1	595
	Coryneforms	20	4.10	2	9.56	9	253.8	5	2,975
	Micrococcus	9	1.84	1	4.78	7	197.4	2	1,190
	Unidentified	0	0.00	0	0.00	0	0.0	2	1,190
	Total colony count‡		20.50		478.00		2,820.0		59,500
North Sea	*Pseudomonas* nonfluorescent	26	24.49	18	88.74	71	9,372.0	71	39,660
	fluorescent	0	0.00	15	73.95	13	1,716.0	11	6,145
	Achromobacter	33	31.09	26	128.18	7	924.0	13	7,262
	Flavobacterium	0	0.00	8	39.44	0	0.0	0	0
	Coryneforms	25	23.55	12	59.16	8	1,056.0	3	1,676
	Micrococcus	14	13.19	21	103.53	0	0.0	0	0
	Unidentified	2	1.88	0	0.00	1	132.0	2	1,117
	Total colony count‡		94.20		493.00		13,200.0		55,860

* Percentages, based on 100 isolates at each examination. † Numbers (10³/cm² of skin), calculated from the percen-

CHANGES IN THE PROPORTIONS AND NUMBERS OF DIFFERENT BACTERIA ON THE SKIN OF FISH STOWED AT 0–1.5° FOR VARIOUS PERIODS DURING EXPEDITION 2, SEPTEMBER 1959

Fishing ground	Genus and/or kind of bacteria	Proportions (P)* and calculated nos. (N)† of various bacteria on fish stowed at 0–1.5° for (days)									
		0		5		10		15		20	
		P*	N†	P	N	P	N	P	N	P	N
North Cape	Pseudomonas nonfluorescent	35	4.48	50	67.50	31	1,237	32	517	45	73,350
	fluorescent	0	0.00	1	1.35	0	0	1	16	6	9,780
	Achromobacter	24	3.07	41	55.35	46	1,835	38	614	9	14,670
	Flavobacterium	1	0.13	2	2.70	0	0	14	226	20	32,600
	Coryneforms	22	2.82	5	6.75	18	718	8	129	14	22,820
	Micrococcus	18	2.30	1	1.35	5	200	7	113	5	8,150
	Unidentified	0	0.00	0	0.00	0	0	0	0	1	1,630
	Total colony count‡		12.80		135.00		3,990		1,615		163,000
Faroes	Pseudomonas nonfluorescent	26	12.70	23	9.24	20	391	42	6,058	38	9,521
	fluorescent	0	0.00	24	9.65	4	78	3	433	10	2,506
	Achromobacter	19	9.27	26	10.45	26	508	13	1,875	10	2,506
	Flavobacterium	4	1.95	1	0.40	0	0	26	3,750	5	1,253
	Coryneforms	48	23.42	17	6.82	25	489	7	1,009	23	5,763
	Micrococcus	3	1.46	8	3.22	25	489	8	1,154	10	2,506
	Unidentified	0	0.00	1	0.40	0	0	1	144	4	1,000
	Total colony count‡		48.80		40.18		1,955		14,423		25,055
North Sea	Pseudomonas nonfluorescent	30	8.94	39	20.98	48	4,986	59	33,850	68	238,816
	fluorescent	0	0.00	11	5.92	16	1,664	21	12,030	9	31,608
	Achromobacter	32	9.54	24	12.91	6	630	5	2,867	15	52,680
	Flavobacterium	10	2.98	2	1.07	1	104	5	2,867	4	14,048
	Coryneforms	25	7.45	23	11.84	16	1,664	9	5,162	3	10,536
	Micrococcus	0	0.00	1	0.54	11	1,144	0	0	0	0
	Unidentified	3	0.89	1	0.54	2	208	1	574	1	3,512
	Total colony count‡		29.80		53.80		10,400		57,350		351,200

* Percentages, based on 100 isolates at each examination. † Numbers ($10^3/cm^2$ of skin), calculated from the percentages and the total colony counts/cm^2 of skin. ‡ Total colony counts, observed values, in $10^3/cm^2$ of skin.

which is concerned with post mortem changes and therefore only touches on our subject, and by SHEWAN (1956O).

Elasmobranch fish. The sharks and rays have not been studied extensively, either in regard to their chemical constitution or to their spoilage. Biochemical studies have been made by SUYAMA et al. (1950), and by SIMIDU and OISI (1952), and TSUCHIYA et al. (1951) who agree with WOOD (1950) that spoilage is chiefly microbial. The last author found himself handicapped by the absence of information regarding the composition of elasmobranch flesh and the enzyme reactions concerned with autolysis. It is known that sharks possess an arginase (HUNTER, 1929), and Wood was able to show that blood and flesh possess a urease which can produce ammonia by autolysis, the blood urease lysing the flesh urea and vice versa. At the same time, a large majority of the bacteria isolated from the surface, gills and muscle of sharks and rays contained urease.

A very interesting point is the predominance in and on elasmobranchs studied by Wood of the genus *Corynebacterium*, (recently placed in *Arthrobacter*) which totalled 162 out of 266 cultures examined, followed by cocci (46), and *Pseudomonas* (29). Strains of these four genera attacked urea, but the corynebacteria were most consistent, which probably accounts for their predominance. VENKATARAMAN and SREENIVASAN (1955c) and Tsuchiya et al. also found corynebacteria and cocci to predominate in shark flesh, but VELANKAR and KAMASASTRI (1955) found gram-negative rods and no corynebacteria. TSUCHIYA et al. (1951) only found four out of fourteen of their cultures would split urea.

There appears to be no succession of genera as in teleosts and crustacea, but this may in part be due to the fact that the ammonia taint is produced early in spoilage, and the fish is discarded before it becomes heavily spoiled.

In commercial practice, the production of ammonia is unpredictable, and this suggests that both microbes and autolysis are active, and their relative activity depends on conditions. The bacterial content of shark flesh does not indicate the degree of spoilage.

SHEWAN (1962) compared the flora isolated from fish in several parts of the world by several investigators (Table XV).

The origin of the spoilage flora is obviously the skin and gills, as these have essentially the same flora as the spoiling muscle, with the addition in muscle of occasional strains of *Bacillus*, *Pseudomonas*, *Proteus* and *Aerogenes*. The muscle of living elasmobranchs was shown by Wood to be sterile. The flora of elasmobranchs resembles the soil flora as described by TOPPING (1937) and TAYLOR and LOCHHEAD (1938).

The exogenic flora of spoiling fish. It is now generally accepted that proteus and coliform organisms found in spoiling fish are a sign of pollution, either in the water in which the fish was living prior to capture, or during the marketing and handling of the fish. The genus *Bacillus* (except for the pigmented strains, which appear to be characteristically hydric) is probably also largely exogenic, although sporers do occur in muds. The presence of bacteria with terminal spores (e.g., *B. sphaericus*) suggests the influence of the mud flora. Bilges, fish holds, transports, canneries and markets soon become contaminated with bacterial flora from the fish as Table XVI will show.

SHEWAN (1962) compared the bacterial flora of sea water and the fish which was caught therein (Table XVII).

The tap water in which fish is washed has quite a different flora from any marine environment, with a much higher proportion of *Pseudomonas*. In point of fact, the washing facilities in markets are usually so arranged that there is heavy contamination with spoiling organisms, and I have seen cases where unpurified river water with a high degree of pollution was used for fish washing.

Ice is regarded as a great potential source of contamination, but its action is probably very largely to carry the intrinsic flora of the fish over the surfaces and into cavities as it melts, hence the need for the disinfection of ice. Perusal of the papers on the subject does not suggest any change in the ratio of species due to fresh water flora introduced by ice.

One form of spoilage affecting living fish is so-called earthy fish. This is due to an Actinomycete which occurs in brackish water at certain times. The organism produces a soluble excretion which is apparently absorbed through the gills of fish swimming in the water, and reaches the flesh, which it taints, so that the fish, though perfectly healthy, has an earthy flavour when eaten. When katadromous fish such as mullet *(Mugil cephalus)* pass through brackish water at certain times on their journey from the upper reaches of a river to the mouth,

TABLE XV

AEROBIC BACTERIAL FLORA OF FRESH FISH EXPRESSED AS PERCENTAGE OF
TOTAL NUMBER OF ORGANISMS ISOLATED

Source	Species	Medium	Source of sample
Dyer	Canadian-Atlantic cod	Tap water at 20°C	Slime Intestines
Anderson	Canadian-Atlantic cod *(Gadus morrhua)*	Sea-water	Slime
Pivnick	Canadian-Atlantic cod *(Gadus morrhua)*	Sea-water	(a) Slime (b) Slime
Fischer	Baltic cod	Fish agar at 22°C	Intestines
Georgala	N. Sea cod	Sea-water agar at 20°C Sea-water agar at 0°C	Slime Slime
Aschehoug and Vesterhus	Norwegian winter herring	Fish agar and nutrient agar at 22°C	Slime Gills Intestines
Liston	N. Sea skate	Sea-water	Slime
		Sea-water Sea-water	Gills Intestines
	N. Sea lemon sole	Salt water	Slime
		Salt water	Gills
		Salt water	Intestines
Gianelli	Middle Adriatic hake *(Merluccius merluccius)*	Iced before sampling. 119 cultures isolated at 18–20°C	Slime
Georgala	W. Coast South African hake	Sea-water at 20°C	Slime
	E. Coast South African hake	Sea-water at 20°C	Slime
Wood	Australian spp. Teleosts Elasmobranchs		Slime Slime
Venkataraman and Sreenivasan	Indian shark *(Carcharius sp.)*	Sea-water	Slime
Venkataraman and Sreenivasan	Indian mackerel	Sea-water	Slime Gills Intestines Whole fish

Pseudomonas	Achromobacter	Coryneforms	Flavobacter	Micrococci incl. Sarcina	Bacillus	Vibrio	Miscellaneous
4.5	3.6	—	1.8	78.5	—	—	11.5 (Yeasts)
5.6	3.7	—	5.6	65.0	—	—	1.8 *(Proteus)* 14.6 (Others)
41.5	31.3	—	33.4	10.0	0	—	7.1 *(Proteus)* 0.7 *(Serratia)*
21.7	56.5	—	8.7	8.7	0	—	4.4
6.9	45.8	—	43.1	1.4	0	—	2.8
9.3	65.0	—	4.7	17.0	—	—	3.0 *(Serratia)* 1.0 *(Kurthia)*
44.0	32.4	8.7	6.0	1.1	—	5.9	1.9
51.5	41.3	1.0	1.5	0.7	—	3.3	0.7
40.0	24.5	—	17.7	16.7	—	—	1.4
47.0	33.4	—	13.7	3.9	—	—	3.0
24.1	72.5	—	—	3.4	—	—	—
63.0	8.6	3.4	10.2	—	—	—	6.4 *(Alkalig.)* 6.4 (Others)
59.5	13.7	4.0	11.3	—	—	—	6.9
26.7	12.2	1.6	4.9	—	—	48.0	2.4 *(Alkalig.)*
57.0	16.7	—	9.5	—	—	—	9.5 *(Alkalig.)* 7.3 (Others)
62.0	14.5	—	11.1	—	—	1.1	10.0 *(Alkalig.)* 1.1 (Others)
34.6	7.7	5.8	9.6	—	—	34.6	1.9 *(Alkalig.)*
6.7	21.0	—	16.0	29.4	4.2	—	5.9 *(Proteus)* 4.2 *(Gaffkya)* 2.5 *(Escherichia)* 10.9 (Others)
27.8	52.5	8.2	6.6	3.3	0	0	1.6
4.2	4.2	33.3	—	37.5	0	0	20.8
16.0	0	12.0	0	60.0	8.0	—	4.0
11.0	0	61.0	0	17.0	2.0	—	9.0
0.0	8.6	28.5	2.9	28.5	25.7	2.9	2.9
5.6	33.3	—	—	5.6	55.6	—	—
—	—	—	—	14.3	85.8	—	—
—	33.3	—	—	—	33.3	—	—
—	11.5	—	8.0	54.0	19.0	—	7.5

TABLE XVI

BACTERIAL FLORA OF CONTAMINATING ENVIRONMENTS AS PERCENTAGES OF
CULTURES EXAMINED
(After WOOD, 1940)

Genus	Slime	Gut	Gills	Sea-water	Market air	Market surfaces	Tapwater
Flavobacterium	17	1	12	18	12	15	8
Micrococcus	48	21	41	34	50	27	4
Pseudomonas	7	10	7	10	12	18	50
Bacillus	9	35	9	12	12	37	8
Achromobacter	19	30	31	26	14	13	30

TABLE XVII

COMPARISON OF THE AEROBIC FLORA OF NEWLY CAUGHT FISH WITH THAT OF
THE SEA-WATER IN WHICH IT WAS CAUGHT
(Expressed as a percentage of the total number of organisms isolated)

Author	Area	Sample	No. of colonies investigated
Wood	Australia	Sea-water	50
		Fish slime	?
Wood	Australia	Sea-water	706
		Elasmobranchs	266
		Telcosts	679
Venkataraman and Sreenivasan	Calicut—India	Sea-water	72
		Mackerel	65
Shewan and Hodgkiss	N. Sea	Sea-water	100
		Cod	200
Shewan and Hodgkiss	N. Cape—Norway	Sea-water	100
		Cod	100

catches from this region will taste earthy, but when the school reaches the sea the taint disappears.

Protozoan spoilage

"Milky" fish, caused by myxosporidia, chiefly *Chloromyxum*, is a form of spoilage that has economic significance, especially in barracouta or snoek *(Thyrsites atun)*.

Spoilage of whale meat

ROBINSON et al. (1953) discuss in considerable detail the bacteriology of whale meat and the hygienic implications thereof. Whales being mammals, the bacterial flora of whale meat resembles that of land animals more than that of fish. These authors assume that the muscle of living whales contain bacteria, or that bacteria readily invade the tissues immediately after death, so they divide the flora into two groups: (1) Intrinsic flora consisting of clostridia. (2) An extrinsic flora consisting of psychrophilic achromobacter, pseudo-

Pseudo- monas	Achro- mobacter	Coryne- form	Flavo- bacter	Micro- cocci and Sarcina	Bacillus	Vibrio	Miscellaneous
10.0	26.0	—	18.0	34.0	12.0	—	—
7.0	19.0	—	17.0	48.0	9.0	—	—
0.9	0	71.0	—	19.0	7.5	—	1.7
11.0	0	61.0	0	17.0	2.0	—	9.0
16.0	0	12.0	0	60.0	8.0	—	4.0
18.0	11.6	—	9.7	18.1	40.3	1.4	1.4
1.5	13.8	—	3.0	27.0	50.8	—	3.0
94.0	6.0	—	—	—	—	—	—
71.0	13.5	5.5	7.0	—	—	—	3.0
0.0	14.0	25.0	1.0	55.0	—	—	—
9.0	51.0	20.0	9.0	8.0	—	—	3.0

monads and cocci, with at times, *Proteus*, streptococci and mesophilic staphylococci as contaminants.

A difficulty in accepting this theory of an intrinsic flora is the paucity of true anaerobes in sea water. Since whales feed on plankton organisms, it is difficult to imagine where the clostridia come from unless they are contaminants from the flensing operations or are normal inhabitants of the gut. The clostridia include *Cl. perfringens*, *Cl. tertium*, *Cl. novyi*, *Cl. sporogenes* and *Cl. histolyticum*. The authors believe that, as whale meat contains a negligible amount of trimethylamine oxide, the ability of the clostridia to reduce this substance does not actually cause off-flavors in whale meat. No *Cl. botulinum* has been isolated from whale meat, and the *Cl. perfringens* type A, which occurs therein has not been shown to give rise to food poisoning. The possibility of gas-gangrene infection from whale meat is no different from that of beef or mutton. On the whole, we must conclude with the authors that the clostridia are not dangerous.

Streptococci were found in nearly every whale examined by Robinson et al. and were similar to those associated with warm-blooded terrestrial animals. The streptococci from the muscle resembled those from whale faeces and from krill, and it was suggested that they represent contaminants from the gut. Gram-negative rods were only 9% of the flora, and two strains of a coliform were isolated, although this organism does not appear to be a normal inhabitant of the whale. The other organisms isolated were gram-positive sporing aerobes and a few corynebacteria with 34% micrococci, all but one being coagulase-negative.

All but the streptococci and the clostridia appear to fit in with the normal marine flora, and the streptococci seem to take the place of the coliform organisms usual in the gut of mainly land mammals. The transmission of the intestinal flora to the offspring would parallel the transmission in land animals.

The blood of whales appears to be normally sterile, and was not found to contain bacteria until 8 hours (aerobes) to 13 hours (anaerobes) after death. Robinson et al. consider, however, that bacteria from the intestinal tract are disseminated through the blood during the long death struggle, enmeshed by the capillaries, and multiply in the liver and muscles as external factors allow.

External contamination is largely comprised by the same flora as the internal. This is only to be expected, since the docks, etc., will be exposed to an overall infection from the whales themselves.

The conclusion is that, unless toxin-producing bacteria such as salmonellas or staphylococci are introduced into the meat by bad practices, whale meat does not represent a source of infection to humans.

Further, it has been shown that more than 99% of the clostridia and most of the aerobes are rendered non-viable by the freezing and storage processes used on board whalers. However, the subsequent increase of bacteria after thawing was shown to depend on the degree of spoilage prior to freezing. After thawing, the meat spoils in about 2 days at 15 °C (Robinson et al.).

Quantitative aspects of spoilage

The qualitative aspects have been discussed first because they represent ecological and biochemical processes that control the course of spoilage. The total number of bacteria present tells only part of the story, and on its own cannot even indicate whether the fish are palatable or likely to be injurious. FELLERS (1926) found that the bacterial count of raw salmon rose from 0 to 2.5×10^6 bacteria/g in 5–6 days at 64 °F. REAY (1935) states that, with fish in ice, the bacterial count increases from about $10^4–10^5$ bacteria/g between the 7th and 10th days and that stale fish generally contains from 1×10^5 to 4×10^6 bacteria/g. Watson considers that the actual spoilage is due to what he calls "reducing Achromobacter" i.e., organisms which are facultative anaerobes and reduce trimethylamine oxide. HAINES showed (1933) that carbon dioxide reduced the rate of spoilage by increasing the lag phase of bacterial multiplication. These two findings appear to be contradictory, and the truth appears to be that one cannot estimate spoilage by any one criterion, e.g., trimethylamine, and that the main processes are aerobic.

REAY (1935) considers that organoleptic tests are more sensitive and more reliable than the numerous chemical tests which have been devised for measuring freshness in fish. This is no doubt due to the fact that the skilled operative in his organoleptic tests sums up the changes in fish muscle by feel and sight as well as by smell, and thus assesses a large number of factors, both autolytic and microbial. I heartily agree with Reay's statements, having tried out a number of tests, including bacterial counts, di- and trimethylamine estimations, buffer capacity and fluorescence to ultra-violet light. In all cases, an experienced fishmonger could determine freshness more rapidly and far less expensively than I could. The criterion of accuracy was the prediction of the subsequent spoilage of the fish.

Salt

In the preparation of solar salt from sea water, microbial reactions are extensively employed, especially in the more primitive methods of manufacture. Sulfate-reducing bacteria remove the iron and colloidal calcium sulfate by precipitation as iron sulfides and calcium carbonate (by removal of carbon dioxide).

The blue-green algae, e.g., *Microcoleus* form a mat in the salterns between the black sulfides and the salt, making harvesting easier, while the mat also assists in the diffusion of the hygroscopic magnesium salts away from the sodium chloride (BAAS BECKING, 1938).

Solar salt also contains a large number of halophilic bacteria which form a serious source of spoilage of salt fish. It is an open question whether these halophils are derived from the marine bacterial flora by selection.

CHAPTER X

SOME GEOBIOLOGICAL ASPECTS

The importance attributed to biological agents in geological processes has varied considerably from time to time. It should be emphasized that photosynthesis is the only biological process which, from the geologist's point of view, is unique in that it results in a net gain of energy to the earth, this being obtained from the sun. All other biological processes are exothermic overall, i.e., the organisms gain energy (growth) at the expense of the environment. In this case, an exothermic reaction must supply the source of energy, e.g., the exothermic anaerobic reduction of sulfate to sulfide supplies the energy whereby *Desulfovibrio* reduces carbon dioxide to provide nutriment. Studies by BAAS BECKING and KAPLAN (1956a,b) have shown that it is possible to draw up a thermodynamic balance sheet for the organisms occurring in the sulfur cycle, and a similar method may prove applicable to other geomicrobiological reactions. From paleontological evidence it is shown that microbes have been important geological agents in sedimentary rocks from the Algonkian era.

MICROORGANISMS IN PALEONTOLOGY

Table XVIII shows the major groups of microorganisms which are important in fossil records, and relates them to geological eras. The geological classification of fossil microorganisms differs at times from the biological one, because the remains of organisms found as fossils are frequently confined to the hard parts, and cannot always be homologised with present-day organisms.

Table XIX gives a classification of microbes, which are of interest in paleontology, though it might not be entirely accepted by taxonomic purists studying living forms. To us, as microbiologists the important organisms in geobiology are the smaller algae, the Protozoa and the bacteria and fungi. The processes include the formation of certain sediments, the production of certain ore bodies, the produc-

TABLE XVIII

MICRO-ORGANISMS OCCURRING IN GEOLOGICAL ERAS

Era	Period	Micro-organisms
Caenozoic	Quaternary Recent Pleistocene Tertiary Neogene Pliocene Miocene Palaeogene Oligocene Eocene Palaeocene	All present-day groups represented, Silicoflagellates declining Many present-day forms, e.g., diatoms
Mesozoic	Cretaceous Jurassic Triassic	Silicoflagellates appear, Calpionellidae disappear. Coccolithophores common, Dinoflagellates appear, Calpionellidae and diatoms
Palaeozoic	Permian Carboniferous Devonian Silurian Ordovician Cambrian	Foraminifera from Cambrian, Radiolaria from late Palaeozoic, bacteria and fungi present as fossils, Algae present
Proterozoic (Algonkian) Archaeozoic		Algae, bacteria and marine worms No life

tion, migration and accumulation of petroleum, the removal of nitrogen from coal, and the formation of sulfur, calcium carbonate, dolomite and gypsum.

THE CHEMICAL AND ECOLOGICAL IMPORTANCE OF MICRO-ORGANISMS

Effects of algae

The algae, in which we include the diatoms, have been recorded in the sediments since pre-Cambrian times (BARGHORN and SCHOPF, 1965) and have several geological effects.

(*1*) They form surface films and carpets, especially in the intertidal zone, and thus protect from erosion the rock, sand, or mud on which they are growing. Such film-forming algae include *Microcoleus*, *Nostoc*, and other blue-greens, a number of unicellular and filamentous green algae, e.g., *Vaucheria*, *Microdictyon*, and diatoms, such as the Schizonema group of Naviculoids. In Lake Macquarie, New South Wales, for instance, *Navicula grevillei* hardens the muds of *Zostera* beds so that they erode only round the edges of the felt, which is thus raised above the flat to form a sort of false shore line. A similar effect is produced at Coila Lake by *Chaetomorpha* and *Cladophora*, and at Lake Conjola by *Microcoleus*. The *Salicornia* flats are usually protected from wind and water by algal felts, some of which fix nitrogen from

TABLE XIX

GROUPS OF MICRO-ORGANISMS OF VALUE IN PALEONTOLOGY

A. Protozoa
    (*1*) Flagellata
        Phytomastigina
            Chrysomonadina
            Coccolithophoroidea
            Silicoflagellata
            Dinoflagellata
    (*2*) Sarcodina
        Rhizopoda
            Foraminifera
        Actinopoda
            Radiolaria
    (*3*) Ciliata
        Calpionellidae?

B. Algae
    Bacillariales
      Centrales
      Pennales
    Myxophyceae (blue-green algae)?

C. Bacteria and fungi

D. Miscellaneous micro-organisms of uncertain identity

the atmosphere, and all of which, as they decompose, add nutriment to the substrate, thus accelerating the growth of the shore-line vegetation including *Spartina*, *Atriplex*, the Goodenias and others. In the Laguna Madre of South Texas, the algal felts form alternating layers with the sand, silt and sea grasses. These beds, in some places, have a total thickness of six to twelve inches and suggest the early stages in the formation of ligneous shales.

(2) Minute algae can also cause erosion and sedimentation by alternately raising and lowering the pH of the environment on rock surfaces so as to precipitate and redissolve calcium carbonate and by producing acid substances which can attack alkaline rocks. This can be of great importance in limestone regions, especially in the tropics. The blue-green algae are very important in this, especially in coral reefs and in shell beds. Many of these precipitate calcium carbonate around the trichomes and thus assist in the formation of marls as in the Everglades of Florida. Although they have no hard parts, and not much is known of them from the fossil record, their primitive character, and wide diversity of environments are biological evidence that they have been very important throughout geological time.

(3) The more resistant parts of algae become incorporated with the bottom sediments, e.g., lignins, porphyrins, to form marine humus. A similar process in fresh water swamps and bogs has led to the formation of coal. The siliceous tests of diatoms have precipitated to form diatomaceous ooze which has consolidated into diatomaceous earth (Kieselguhr), e.g., the Tertiary diatomaceous earths of New South Wales, which were formed mainly of *Melosira* (Sussmilch, 1922). In the oceans, there is an almost continuous band of siliceous diatom ooze in the Antarctic, and a similar belt in the northern Pacific (see Sverdrup et al., 1949). The presence of *Ethmodiscus* ooze in the Pacific (Hanazawa, 1933; Wiseman and Hendey, 1953) and a *Coscinodiscus* ooze in Walvis Bay, South Africa (Brongersma-San-ders, 1948) is evidence that some of these oozes are formed by an autochthonous, heterotrophic diatom flora (see Wood, 1956). The diatoms of these oozes form a community very distinct from present day planktonic communities, and the amount of material involved makes it certain that these oozes must have been deposited over vast periods of time or that conditions for growth must have been very different when the major part of deposition occurred.

(4) The algae cause rapid oxidation at the surface of sediments in shallow waters and thus influence the rate and character of the chemical changes in the environment.

(5) Metals may be concentrated by algae, and this could be important in red tide blooms of such species as *Gymnodinium brevis*, which is reported by COLLIER (1953) to concentrate titanium and zirconium.

Effects of Protozoa

The Protozoa have a marked effect in some regions on the formation of sedimentary rocks. Among the flagellates, the calcareous coccoliths of the coccolithophores (BRAARUD et al., 1955) and the siliceous skeletons of the silicoflagellates are found in extensive deposits; of the Rhizopoda, the Foraminifera, with mainly calcareous tests, form very large deposits of foraminiferal limestone in many parts of the world, and are important as stratigraphic indicators because there has been a marked variation in form throughout geological ages, and many of these variants were short-lived. The Actinopoda are represented by the Radiolaria, which have formed vast deposits of ooze on the sea bottom in various geological ages. For example, in the Silurian strata of New South Wales, there are, at Jenolan, radiolarian cherts of more than 1,000 ft. in thickness, where Radiolaria in enormous numbers are preserved in chalcedonic casts (SUSSMILCH, 1922). Because the Radiolaria did not vary much in form during geological ages, they are not of much use as indicators of the age of the strata. Thus, whole strata can be, and in the past, have been formed by the Protozoa. Many present-day Radiolaria and Foraminifera contain zooxanthellae, which fact brings them into the primary producing microorganisms of the oceans, analogous with the flowering plants of the land.

Bacteria and fungi

While bacteria and fungi do not form geological strata, their geobiological effects are greater and more lasting than those of any other group, not excluding the photosynthetic plants. From the earliest dawn of life on this planet, bacteria have been active in transforming materials, and in assisting chemical transformations, and fossil bacteria have been recorded from the Proterozoic (Algonkian) era

(WALCOTT, 1955; BEERSTECHER, 1954), and fungi by BERRY (1916) from all geological horizons. Soil and marine microbiology are relatively new disciplines, and the influence of bacteria in these environments is ill recognized and little understood. At the outset, it should be stated that bacteria do not initiate or carry out chemical reactions that are not possible by purely chemical means, but they do catalyse at ordinary temperatures, reactions that would require a considerable amount of heat or pressure or even ultraviolet light if they were due to chemical agency alone.

The finding of ZoBELL (1952) that bacteria will live and reproduce at pressures up to 1,000 atm on the sea floor greatly increases the possible scope of their activities as geobiological agents. ZoBell's work has largely been connected with petroleum, but the field he has opened has, as he fully realizes, a very much wider significance, so much so that it is safe to predict that the bacteriologist will, in the future, be called upon to assist the geologist in his interpretation of mineral deposition in sedimentary strata, and probably of the formation of rocks such as kaolinite and laterite. The work of my colleagues and myself on estuarine sediments, though it has revealed much information, only allows us a vague guess at the possibilities afforded us by this discipline. One of the difficulties is the fact mentioned above, that bacterial and non-bacterial transformations frequently run parallel and may occur together or may replace one another with only a slight change in the environmental conditions. An example of this is the oxidation of sulfide to sulfur which can occur anaerobically by bacterial photosynthesis or, in the presence of iron, by photochemical reaction, and aerobically by the Verhoop reaction or by the activity of sulfur bacteria (BAAS BECKING and WOOD, 1955).

Among the reactions which we know can be catalysed by bacteria are:

(1) Reduction of sulfates to sulfides, which in aqueous environments, are precipitated in the form of hydrotroilite (FeSH.OH) in lakes and estuaries, and this is converted in part into pyrites (FeS$_2$) in estuarine and oceanic sediments (EMERY and RITTENBERG, 1952). This reaction can also cause the dissolution of rock gypsum in the presence of water and organic matter (BAAS BECKING and KAPLAN, 1956a).

(2) Iron can be reduced from the ferric to the ferrous state. This

is a frequent concomitant of sulfate reduction, hydrogen sulfide reacting with ferric phosphate and other ferric salts to form ferrous sulfide.

(*3*) Phosphates are released from insoluble compounds such as ferric or calcium phosphates by microbial action.

(*4*) Ferrous iron can be oxidized to ferric iron and precipitated by iron bacteria or by heterotrophs.

(*5*) Sulfides may be oxidized to sulfur biologically.

(*6*) Sulfur may be oxidized to sulfate.

(*7*) Sodium chloride brines are purified by the precipitation of sulfate (derived from magnesium and calcium sulfate) as sulfide, and iron is removed in the same reaction, i.e., sulfate reduction.

(*8*) Hydrogen and methane are produced by anaerobic bacteria and carbon dioxide by aerobic bacteria and fungi. These reactions are the precursors of other biological or chemical reactions which may profoundly affect the milieu.

(*9*) Bacteria may synthesize hydrocarbons, and thus form oil (ZoBELL and RITTENBERG, 1948), and may aid in the translation and storage of oil by adsorption and desorption phenomena (ZoBELL, 1946a; BEERSTECHER, 1954).

(*10*) The release of nitrogen and the increase of the carbon-nitrogen ratio in the formation of peat and coal is due to bacteria and fungi. In fact, the loss of nitrogen in this way is a general phenomenon in sedimentation (see Emery and Rittenberg).

(*11*) Calcium carbonate may be precipitated from sea water by an increase in alkalinity or by the removal of carbon dioxide. The precipitation by denitrification has been demonstrated by DREW (1914), BAVENDAMM (1931, 1932) and GREENFIELD (1963). The production of ammonia from amines, amino-acids, etc., by heterotrophs or the assimilation of carbon dioxide by autotrophic bacteria would also precipitate calcium carbonate. Such reactions would be most active in shallow water, e.g., on sea-grass flats or in lagoons of coral cays.

(*12*) Gypsum may be formed by the oxidation of sulfides by thiobacilli and other sulfur-oxidizing organisms.

(*13*) Microorganisms can concentrate many elements and are regarded as responsible for the formation of ores of aluminum, manganese, vanadium and other metals.

(*14*) Bacterial activity, e.g., that of the sulfur cycle can assist in the translocation of metals and in mineralization (OPPENHEIMER, 1960).

(15) The weathering of rocks is in part due to bacteria and fungi, both autotrophs and heterotrophs playing a part in this process (WAKSMAN, 1932; POLYNOV and MUIR, 1937). Many of the reactions mentioned above are concerned.

PRODUCTS OF MICROBIAL ACTIVITY

Calcium, magnesium and strontium minerals

The precipitation of calcium carbonate and sulfate has been discussed (see also OPPENHEIMER, 1961). Magnesium minerals may also be of microbial origin, while strontium sulfate forms the skeleton of *Actipylea* (a radiolarian) and is precipitated in this form.

The precipitation of silica

The subject of silica precipitation in the tests of diatoms, Radiolaria, etc., has already been mentioned. As this silica is concentrated from the water by the microorganisms, it completes the cycle begun by the solution of silica on land by meteoric water.

Production of the ores

Ores are frequently associated with igneous activity, but there are certain circumstances where a microbial or partly microbial origin may be suggested. Such apply to the Precambrian ore deposits in central Australia, which are associated with coral limestones. These deposits consist of sulfides of copper, zinc and lead, associated with pyrites and uranium minerals. EMERY and RITTENBERG (1952) have shown that the marine sediments of the California Basin differ from those in shallow waters in that pyrite is formed rather than hydrotroilite. Lead sulfide can be formed directly (SHIPLEY, 1922; VON WOLZOGEN KUHR, 1939) and copper sulfide is probably produced by the replacement of iron by copper in accordance with the respective solubility products of their sulfides. The microbial origin of copper sulfide has already been suggested by SCHNEIDERHÖHN (1923),

TRASK (1925), THIEL (1926, 1927) and BASTIN (1933), while THIEL (1927) has explained the formation of bauxite and other oxides of aluminum with the aid of *Desulfovibrio*. The presence of *Desulfovibrio* in calcareous muds was demonstrated by BAVENDAMM (1932), so it seems safe to assume the microbial origin of sulfide ores associated with coral limestones (see also ZoBELL and RITTENBERG, 1948). The association of uranium with microbial sulfide ores is not easy to explain, especially as uranium is toxic to microorganisms. The concentration of uranium may be due to adsorption on organic matter in this environment.

Oil

That petroleum is derived from marine organic matter by the aid of microorganisms is generally conceded, but the precise processes and organisms involved in the changes are little known despite a great deal of research. The reason for this is that oil is not found in situ but has flowed away from its source. The origin of oil is discussed in some detail by BEERSTECHER (1954) and by DAVIS and UPDEGRAFF (1954). BRONGERSMA-SANDERS (1948) suggests that red tides supply the primary material for the production of oil. In her view, massive red tides such as those occurring at the present time in the Walvis Bay region of South Africa cause a heavy fish mortality and result in the formation of a copious diatom ooze. She ascribes the presence of these phenomena to regions of upwelling water and the concentration of nutrients. This explanation of the origin of red tides seems only partly satisfactory, but the concentration of organic matter is undoubted, and certainly the concentrations are a prerequisite of oil formation. That the primary source of oil is of marine origin is generally agreed.

ZoBELL (1946a, 1947, 1950a,b,c, 1952), ROSENFELD (1946), MÜLLER and SCHWARTZ (1953) suggest that sulfate-reducing bacteria can reduce carbonaceous material to hydrocarbons, and there is some evidence that Clostridia as well as *Desulfovibrio* can perform this feat. It would appear that bacteria possessing a hydrogenase are potentially capable of forming hydrocarbons. Whether the hydrogen utilized by the bacteria is derived from organic matter, or in part from magmatic hydrogen is uncertain. The hydrocarbons higher than methane appear to be products of microbial assimilation rather than excretory products. KNÖSEL and SCHWARTZ (1954) have shown the presence of autochthonous bacteria in oil, but it could not be determined whether these organisms were derived from the original oil-producing organisms or had invaded the oil at a later date. ZOBELL (1947) has shown that methane- and hydrogen sulfide-producing bacteria may aid in the release and transfer of oil from the source to the oil-bearing sands. One cannot say whether these organisms are derived from original marine strains, but such a derivation is not impossible. It is certain, too, that bacteria are responsible for the reduction of the nitrogen-carbon ratio in sediments, i.e., in the removal of the nitrogenous matter from the organic precursor of oil.

Sulfur and its compounds

The sulfur cycle has already been discussed, and the formation of pyrites and other sulfide ores has been mentioned. KAPLAN (1957) found that the bacteria of the sulfur cycle were abundant, and almost omnipresent, in the New Zealand sulfur springs that he examined. Moreover, BUTLIN and POSTGATE (1954) have shown beyond all doubt the microbial origin and course of formation of sulfur in the Cyrenaican lakes. Here sulfate reduction is the first step, and the sulfide thus produced is oxidized to sulfur by purple and green sulfur bacteria. Kaplan's observations suggest that even sulfur of volcanic origin may have bacterial processes concerned with its deposition, while lacustrine deposits may be present-day examples of the mode of deposition of stratified sulfur deposits such as those of Louisiana. Fig.27 gives a clear exposition of the main biological processes in the sulfur cycle. To the diagram, should be added for completeness, the Verhoop and Bunsen reactions for the aerobic, direct oxidation, and the anaerobic photochemical oxidation respectively, of sulfides to sulfur. This oxidation may well, in nature, supplement the biological processes suggested by these two authors. Recent studies by BAAS BECKING and KAPLAN (1956b) on sulfur nodules formed at Lake Eyre (a salt lake in South Australia), have shown that these are formed from gypsum and organic matter (flood detritus, *Dunaliella*, etc.) the limiting factor in this case being in all probability the supply of organic matter and possibly water. In this case, the purple and green sulfur bacteria were absent, and the sulfur must be due to the oxidation of sulfide by thiobacilli or by abiological means. These authors showed that, in the laboratory, *Desulfovibrio* will form reduction zones along the cleavage planes of gypsum crystals, thus decomposing the crystal and increasing the surface available for reaction.

Iron

While iron bacteria have been found as fossils from early geological ages, the actual effectiveness of these organisms in precipitating iron is probably limited, due to the fact that they are gradient organisms, and occur in films (BAAS BECKING et al., 1956). They may, however, be important in the formation of ferruginous cements in sandstones and other rocks. No trace of iron bacteria was observed in the limestone vaces at Jenolan, New South Wales, but, as has been stated elsewhere, the environment was completely oxidizing. A more widespread microbial effect in iron precipitation and solution is that of the heterotrophs, algae and other microbes in altering pH-Eh conditions, utilization or production of carbon dioxide and so on.

NUTRIENT CYCLES IN THE SEAS
(summaries)

Nitrogen cycle

$N_2 \rightarrow NH_3$ or $-NH_2$, electric storms; blue-green algae in estuaries, coral reefs and tropical oceans; anaerobic, autotrophic and heterotrophic bacteria, mainly in sediments.

$NH_3 \rightarrow NO_2 \rightarrow NO_3$, nitrifying bacteria (mainly in sediments).

$NO_3 \rightarrow NO_2 \rightarrow N_2$, denitrifying bacteria (pseudomonads).

$NO_3 \rightarrow -NH_2$, in algal cells.

$-NH_2 \rightarrow NH_3$, (deamination) bacteria and autolytic.

Nitrification is exothermic in aerobic environments, endothermic in anaerobic systems.

Nitrogen assimilation is endothermic, frequently associated with the photosynthetic process in blue-green algae, etc.

Denitrification is endothermic in aerobic, exothermic in anaerobic systems.

Sulfur cycle

—$SO_4 \rightarrow H_2S$,   (exothermic in anaerobic environments) abiological: *Desulfovibrio*.

—$SH^- \rightarrow H_2S$,   facultative and obligate heterotrophic anaerobes.

$H_2S \rightarrow S$ (anaerobic) green sulfur bacteria, purple sulfur bacteria, photocatalytic with Fe; *Thiobacillus denitrificans*; (aerobic) abiological; Thiobacilli and other sulfur-oxidizing organisms, e.g., *Thiovulum*, *Thiothrix*, *Beggiatoa*.

$S \rightarrow SO_4$,   (anaerobic) purple sulfur bacteria; (aerobic) Thiobacilli.

GLOSSARY OF TERMS

Adsorption: Attachment of small particles or molecules to a larger particle by electric charge.

Aerobe: An organism which lives in a milieu containing gaseous oxygen which it uses as a hydrogen acceptor.

Agamont: A sexual stage of Foraminifera.

Allochthonous: Derived from an environment other than that in which it is found.

Allogamous: Sexual stage with differentiated gametes.

Anaerobe: An organism which flourishes in the absence of oxygen, i.e., uses other hydrogen acceptors.

Antibiotic: Substance inhibiting growth or reproduction, generally of biological origin.

Aphotic Zone: The region below the photic zone, i.e., below the region of light penetration.

Aufwuchs: (Periphyton) attached algal community.

Autoantagonism: Production by organisms of substances which inhibit their own growth.

Autochthonous: Occurring in their natural environment, endemic.

Autotroph: Organism which can obtain its energy in an entirely inorganic medium, i.e., utilizes chemical or photochemical energy for assimilation of carbon.

Auxospore: Diatom spore resulting in an increase in vegetative cell size.

Auxotroph: An organism which requires organic growth factors.

Barophil: An organism which grows at high pressure rather than at atmospheric pressure.

Benthos: Organisms of the sediment community.

Bewuchs: Organisms attached to artificial material in the water.

Biomass: Mass of living matter present.

Chemoautotroph: An organism which obtains its energy from light-independent chemical reactions in an organic environment.

Chemotaxis: Response to chemical stimuli by movement.

Chlorinity: Quantity of chlorine ion contained in water (includes other halides as it is measured by silver nitrate titration).

Community: A grouping of plants (and animals) in a given environment.

Compensation depth: The depth at which photosynthesis is calculated to provide energy equal to that used up in respiration.

Compensation point: The light intensity at which photosynthetic assimilation equals respiratory loss.

Composite: A fungal-algal association in aqueous environments.

Conservative properties: Chemical and physical properties of a water mass which are characteristic of that water mass.

Convergence: An area or region where water masses meet and the overall movement of the water is downward.

Critical depth: Depth at which production is zero, i.e., total photosynthesis per unit of surface area equals total respiration. This applies to a body of water and not to the organisms occurring therein.

Deep scattering layer: A layer consisting of marine organisms so numerous as to reflect or partially reflect electronic beams such as Sonar or Asdic. It frequently moves vertically with a diurnal rhythm.

Density: Density of water depends on temperature and salinity and is expressed as $\sigma\ t$.

Detritus: Particulate (organic) material which is only partly disintegrated.

Direct counts: Microscopic counts of microorganisms collected on slides or filters.

Divergence: An area or region where the overall movement of water is upward, due to the meeting of two water masses, e.g., upwelling.

Ecosystem: An ecological unit consisting of the organisms and their environment.

Endemic: Occurring in a natural habitat.

Endothermic: A chemical reaction in which energy is consumed overall.

Epilimnion: That part of a lake or stream which is above the thermocline, when there is stratification.

Epilithic: Plants attached to rocks, stones or shells.

Epipelic: Organisms growing on the sediments.

Epiphytic: Attached to plants.

Epiphytotic: A disease of plants.

Epontic: Attached organisms (general term).

Epizootic: A disease of animals.

Euryhaline: Tolerant of wide salinity ranges.

Eurythermal: Tolerant of a wide temperature range.

Exothermic: A chemical reaction giving off energy.

Extinction coefficient: The amount of light absorbed in its passage through water.

Facultative: Being able to adapt to alternate environments, e.g., facultative anaerobe, facultative halophil.

Frustule: External skeleton of cell.

Gamete: A haploid sex cell which combines with another gamete to form a *Zygote*.

Gamont: Sexual stage of Foraminifera.

Gyral: A rotating water mass, usually low in nutrients.

Halophil: An organism which grows preferentially in high salinities.

Halophyte: A plant which grows preferentially in high salinities.

Heteroantagonism: Production by an organism of inhibitors for other organisms, e.g., antibiotics.

Heterotroph: An organism which uses soluble organic carbon compounds as a source of carbon, rather than carbon dioxide.

Holophytic: Plant-type nutrition, photoautotrophic.

Holozoic: Animal-type nutrition, using particulate or living organic matter as food.

Hypolimnion: The region below the thermocline in stratified waters.

Indicator Species: Species peculiar to a particular regime or water mass and which can be used to identify it, e.g., *Fragilaria antarctica* which is peculiar to sub-Antarctic and Antarctic waters.

Isogamous: Having equal gametes (i.e., no distinction between male and female).

Lorica: Sheath of Tintinnids, closed at one end and open at the other.

Marine: Including oceanic and estuarine environments.

Meiosis: Reducing cell division.

Mesohaline: Preferring moderate salinities.

Mesophil: Organism found in moderate salinities or temperatures.

Mesothermal: Organism requiring moderate temperatures, i.e., with optimum around 25 °C and maximum about 37 °C.

Metabiosis: Organisms in the same habitat which are metabolically interdependent.

Metaphyton: Plants growing amongst, but not restricted or attached to, the *Periphyton.*

Microbiology: The study of all unicellular or functionally unicellular organisms.

Microplankton: The smaller elements of the plankton including the small flagellates—variously set at less than 5–10μ. Also called *Nanoplankton, Ultraplankton* or *μ-plankton.*

Mitosis: Chromosome division in cell division.

μ-plankton: Synonym for microplankton.

Myxotrophy: Combining two or more means of carbon assimilation.

Nanoplankton: Often spelled *Nannoplankton,* synonym for *Microplankton.*

Neritic: Close to shore, usually demarcated by the continental shelf.

Oogonium: Cell containing ova.

Palmella stage: Flagellate cells forming clumps joined by gelatinous material; sometimes these clumps are of large size; flagella may be retained or lost.

Parasitic: Growing inside a host cell and causing detriment thereto.

Periphyton: Algae attached to larger plants *(Aufwuchs, Bewuchs).*

Phagotrophy: Gaining nutriment by ingesting (and digesting) organic particles or organisms.

Photic zone: Zone of light penetration; often considered to be the zone to which 1% of surface light can penetrate.

Photoautotroph: An organism which obtains its carbon by using light energy; usually considered as utilizing light by photosynthesis or photoreduction to assimilate carbon dioxide, though it may also use other, lower energy-yielding reactions.

Photoreduction: Reduction of carbon dioxide with hydrogen, hydrogen sulfide or an organic hydrogen donor; and no release of oxygen.

Photosynthesis: Reduction of carbon dioxide with water as the hydrogen donor, and release of oxygen.

Phototaxis: Movement in response to light.

Phytophagous: Plant-eating (in contrast to carnivorous).

Plankton: Organisms suspended in the water but unable to stem the currents.

Production: The amount of material produced in unit time.

Productivity: The ability or potential to produce per unit time.

Pseudoperiphyton (Metaphyton): Plants associated with *Periphyton* as part of the community but not attached.

Psychrophil: Organisms with low temperature optima (below 20 °C) and maxima.

Psychrotolerant: Organisms growing at 0 °C but tolerating temperatures above 20 °C.

Red Tides: Colored water masses produced by very large plankton blooms, the plants being so closely associated as to impart the color.

Respiration: The complete oxidation of an organic compound to carbon dioxide and water with molecular oxygen serving as the ultimate electron acceptor.

Salinity: Salt content of water, measured by conductivity and includes ions other than halides e.g., sulfate.

Saprobic: (Saprophytic) Obtaining nutrients from dead organic matter.

Saprotrophic: See Saprobic.

Schizont: A sexual stage of Foraminifera (see *Agamont*).

Seston: Suspended material in the oceans.

Spermatogonium: Receptacle for sperms.

Standing crop: Amount of living plant matter in a given place at a given time.

Standing stock: Amount of living animal material in a given place at a given time.

Stenohaline: Tolerating only a narrow salinity range.

Stenothermal: Tolerating only a narrow temperature range.

Sub-photic zone: Zone below the photic zone.

Symbiosis: Living together of two organisms with mutual advantage and without losing their identity.

Synergic reaction: One in which a chemical reaction is carried to completion by the combined activity of two or more organisms.

Tambak: A Javanese brackish water fish pond.

Tapetic: Carpet- or felt-forming.

Taxis: Response to stimuli by motion.

Test: The exoskeleton of microorganisms.

Thermocline: A sharp difference in temperature between two water masses.

Thermophil: An organism with a high temperature optimum (usually about 40 °C).

Ultraplankton: Minute plankton (see plankton, etc.).

Upwelling: Vertical movement of a water mass bringing it to or near the surface.

Viable counts: Microbial counts made by culturing the organisms.

Zoochlorellae: Symbioses between green algae and animals.

Zoocyanellae: Symbioses between blue-green algae and animals.

Zooxanthellae: Symbioses between dinoflagellates and animals.

REFERENCES

AARONSON, S. and BAKER, H., 1959. A comparative biochemical study of two species of *Ochromonas. J. Protozool.*, 6:282–284.

ADAIR, E. J. and VISHNIAC, H. S., 1958. Marine fungus requiring vitamin B$_{12}$. *Science*, 127:147–148.

ALEEM, A., 1950. The diatom community inhabiting the mud flats at Whitstable. *New Phytologist*, 49:176–188.

ALFORD, J. A., TOBIN, L. C. and McCLESKEY, C. S., 1942. Bacterial spoilage of iced fresh crab meat. *Food Res.*, 7:353–359.

ALLEN, L. A., THOMAS, G., THOMAS, C. C., WHEATLAND, A. B., THOMAS, A. N., JONES, E. E. and HUDSON, J., 1950. Repeated reuse of sea water as a medium for the functioning and self-cleaning of molluscan shellfish. *J. Hyg.*, 48:431.

ALLEN, M. B., 1963a. Nitrogen-fixing organisms in the sea. In: C. H. OPPENHEIMER (Editor), *Marine Microbiology*. Thomas, Springfield, Ill., pp.85–92.

ALLEN, M. B., 1963b. Comparative biochemistry of photosynthetic reactions. *Proc. Intern. Congr. Biochem., 5th, Moscow, 1961*, 6:138–150.

ALLEN, M. B. and DAWSON, E. Y., 1960. Production of antibacterial substances by benthic tropical marine algae. *J. Bacteriol.*, 79:459–460.

ALLEN, M. B., FRIES, L., GOODWIN, T. W. and THOMAS, D. M., 1964. The carotenoids of Algae; pigments from some cryptomonads, a heterokont and some Rhodophyceae. *J. Gen. Microbiol.*, 34:259–267.

AMYOT, J. A., 1901. Is the colon bacillus a normal inhabitant of the intestinal tract of fish? *Rept. Public Health Assoc.*, 27:400–401.

ANDERSON, C. G. and BANSE, K., 1963. Hydrography and phytoplankton production. *Wash. State Univ., Dept. Oceanog., Contr.*, 250: 21 pp.

ANDERSON, C. G. and BANSE, K., 1965. Chlorophills in marine phytoplankton; correlation with carbon uptake. *Deep-Sea Res.*, 12:531–533.

ANGST, E. C., 1923. The fouling of ships' bottoms by bacteria. *U.S. Navy Dept., Letter, Bur. Construct. Repair*, 7:49–63.

ANGST, E. C., 1929. Some new agar-digesting bacteria. *Publ. Puget Sound Biol. Sta., Univ. Wash.*, 7:49–63.

ANTIA, N. J., McALLISTER, C. D., PARSONS, T. R., STEPHENS, K. and STRICKLAND, J. D. H., 1963. Further measurements of primary production using a large-volume plastic sphare. *Limnol. Oceanog.*, 88:166–183.

APPLEMAN, M. D., BAIN, N. and SHEWAN, J. M., 1964. A study of some organisms of public health significance from fish and fishery products. *J. Appl. Bacteriol.*, 27:69–77.

ASCHEHOUG, V. and VESTERHUS, R., 1940. Investigation on the bacterial flora of fresh herring. *Zentr. Bakteriol. Parasitenk., Abt. II,* 106:5–27.

ATKINS, W. R. G., 1922. Respirable organic matter of sea water. *J. Marine Biol. Assoc. U. K.,* 12:772–780.

ATKINS, W. R. G., 1923. The phosphate content of sea water in relation to the growth of algal plankton. *J. Marine Biol. Assoc. U. K.,* 13:119–150.

ATKINS, W. R. G., 1924. The phosphate content of sea water in relation to the growth of algal plankton. *J. Marine Biol. Assoc. U. K.,* 14:447.

BAARS, J., 1930. *Over Sulfaatreduktie door Bakterien.* Thesis, Tech. Univ. Delft, 164 pp.

BAAS BECKING, L. G. M., 1938. On the cause of high acidity in natural waters especially in brines. *Koninkl. Ned. Akad. Wetenschap., Proc., Ser. B,* 41(1074):193.

BAAS BECKING, L. G. M. and KAPLAN, I. R., 1956a. Biological processes in the estuarine environment, III, IV. *Koninkl. Ned. Akad. Wetenschap., Proc., Ser. B,* 59:85–108.

BAAS BECKING, L. G. M. and KAPLAN, I. R., 1956b. The microbial origin of the sulfur nodules of Lake Eyre. *Trans. Roy. Soc. S. Australia,* 79:52–65.

BAAS BECKING, L. G. M. and MACKAY, M., 1956. Biological processes in the estuarine environment, V. *Koninkl. Ned. Akad. Wetenschap., Proc., Ser. B,* 59:190–213.

BAAS BECKING, L. G. M. and WOOD, E. J. F., 1955. Biological processes in the estuarine environment, I, II. *Koninkl. Ned. Akad. Wetenschap., Proc., Ser. B,* 58:168–181.

BAAS BECKING, L. G. M., WOOD, E. J. F. and KAPLAN, I. R., 1956. Biological processes in the estuarine environment, VIII. *Koninkl. Ned. Akad. Wetenschap., Proc., Ser. B,* 59:398–407.

BAAS BECKING, L. G. M., WOOD, E. J. F. and KAPLAN, I. R., 1957. Biological processes in the estuarine environment, X. *Koninkl. Ned. Akad. Wetenschap., Proc., Ser. B,* 60:88–102.

BAIRD, E. A. and WOOD, A. J., 1944. Reduction of trimethylamine oxide by bacteria. *J. Fisheries Res. Board Can.,* 6:143.

BAIRD-PARKER, A. C., 1965. The classification of staphylococci and micrococci from world-wide sources. *J. Gen. Microbiol.,* 38:363–387.

BARGHOORN, E. S. and LINDER, D. H., 1944. Marine Fungi, their taxonomy and biology. *Farlowia,* 1:395–467.

BARGHOORN, E. S. and SCHOPF, J. W., 1965. Microorganisms from the Late Precambrian of central Australia. *Science,* 150:337–339.

BASTIN, E., 1933. The chalcosite and native copper types of ore deposits. *Econ. Geol.,* 28:107–146.

BAVENDAMM, W., 1931. Die Frage der bakteriologischen Kalkfallung in der tropischen Seen. *Ber. Deut. Botan. Ges.,* 49:282–287.

BAVENDAMM, W., 1932. Die mikrobiologische Kalkfallung in der tropischen Seen. *Arch. Mikrobiol.,* 3:205–276.

BAYLOR, E. R. and SUTCLIFFE JR., W. H., 1963. Dissolved organic matter in sea water as a source of particulate food. *Limnol. Oceanog.,* 8:369–371.

Bé, A. W. H., 1959. Ecology of recent Foraminifera. *Micropaleontology*, 5:77–98.

Beason, A. and Ehringer, G., 1922. A new bacillus isolated from oysters. *Compt. Rend. Soc. Biol.*, 87:107.

Becker, G. und Kohlmeyer, J., 1958a. Holzzerstörung durch Meerespilze in Indien und besondere Bedeutung für Fischereifahrzeuge. *Arch. Fischereiwiss.*, 1:29–39.

Becker, G. and Kohlmeyer, J., 1958b. Deterioration of wood by marine Fungi in India and its special significance for fishing crafts. *J. Timber Dryers*, 4:1–10.

Becker, G., Kampf, W. D. und Kohlmeyer, J., 1957. Zur Ernährung der Holzbohrasseln der Gattung *Limnoria*. *Naturwissenschaften*, 44:473–474.

Bedford, R. H., 1937. Bacteria in the gut of line-caught halibut. *Pacific Biol. Sta. Can., Progr. Rept.*, 33:23–24.

Beerstecher Jr., E., 1954. *Petroleum Microbiology*. Elsevier, Houston, Texas, 375 pp.

Bein, S. J., 1954. A study of certain chromogenic bacteria isolated from "red tide" water, with a description of a new species. *Bull. Marine Sci. Gulf Caribbean*, 4:110–119.

Berkner, L. V. and Marshall, L. C., 1965. On the origin and rise of oxygen concentration in the earth's atmosphere. *J. Atmospheric Sci.*, 22:225–261.

Bernard, F., 1963. Vitesse de chute en mer des amas palmelloides de *Cyclococcolithus*; ses conséquences pour le cycle vitale des mers chaudes. *Pelagos*, 1:5–34.

Bernard, F., 1964. Le nannoplancton en zone aphotique des mers chaudes. *Bull. Inst. Oceanog.*, 2(2):5–32.

Bernard, F. et Lecal, J., 1960. Plancton unicellulaire récolté dans l'Océan Indien par le "Charcot" (1950) et le "Norsel" (1955–1956). *Bull. Inst. Oceanog.*, 1(166):1–59.

Bernatowicz, A. J., 1952. Marine monocotyledonous plants of Bermuda. *Bull. Marine Sci. Gulf Caribbean*, 2:338–345.

Berry, W., 1916. Remarkable fossil Fungi. *Mycologia*, 8:73–79.

Bisset, K. A., 1948. Seasonal changes in the normal flora of fresh water fish. *J. Hyg.*, 46:94–97.

Braarud, T., 1951. Taxonomic studies of marine dinoflagellates. *Nytt Mag. Naturv.*, B88:43–48.

Braarud, T., 1958. Observations on *Peridinium trochoideum* (Stein) Lemm. in culture. *Nytt Mag. Botan.*, 6:39–42.

Braarud, T., 1960. On the coccolithophorid genus *Cricosphaera* n. gen. *Nytt Mag. Botan.*, 8:211–212.

Braarud, T., 1961. Cultivation of marine organisms as a means of understanding environmental influences on populations. In: M. Sears (Editor), *Oceanography*. Am. Assoc. Advan. Sci., Washington, D.C., pp.271–298.

Braarud, T., 1962. Species distribution in marine phytoplankton. *J. Oceanog. Soc. Japan*, 20:628–649.

BRAARUD, T., 1963. Reproduction in the marine coccolithophorid *Coccolithus huxleyi* in culture. *Pubbl. Staz. Zool. Napoli*, 33:110–116.

BRAARUD, T., DEFLANDRE, G., HALLDAL, O. and KAMPTNER, E., 1955. Terminology, nomenclature and systematics of the Coccolithophoridae. *Micropaleontology*, 1:157–159.

BREED, R. S., MURRAY, E. G. D. and SMITH, N. D., 1961. *Bergey's Manual of Determinative Bacteriology*. Williams and Wilkins, Baltimore, Md., 1094 pp.

BRONGERSMA SANDERS, M., 1948. The importance of upwelling water to vertebrate paleontology and oil geology. *Verhandel. Koninkl. Ned. Akad. Wetenschap., Afdel. Natuurk., Sect. I*, 45(4):1–112.

BROWN, A. D., 1964. Aspects of bacterial response to the ionic environment. *Bacteriol. Rev.*, 28:296–329.

BROWNE, W. W., 1917. The presence of *B. coli* and *B. welchii* groups in the intestinal tract of fish *(Stenomus chrysops)*. *J. Bacteriol.*, 2:417–422.

BRUCE, J. R., KNIGHT, M. and PARKE, M., 1940. The rearing of oyster larvae on an algal diet. *J. Marine Biol. Assoc. U. K.*, 24:337–374.

BRUNS, H., 1909. Über das bakteriologische Verhalten des Fischfleisches nach der Zubereitung. *Arch. Hyg. Bakteriol.*, 67:209–236.

BUNT, J. S., 1964. Primary productivity under sea-ice in Antarctic waters, I, II. *Natl. Sci. Found., Antarctic Res. Ser.*, 1:13–31.

BUNT, J. S., 1965. Measurement of photosynthesis and respiration in a marine diatom with the mass spectrometer and with carbon 14. *Nature*, 207:373–375.

BUNT, J. S. and WOOD, E. J. F., 1963. Micro-algae of Antarctic sea-ice. *Nature*, 199:1254–1255.

BURKE, J. M., MARCHISOTTO, J., McLAUGHLIN, J. J. A. and PROVASOLI, L., 1960. Analysis of the toxin produced by *Goniaulax catenella* in axenic culture. *Ann. N. Y. Acad. Sci.*, 90:837–842.

BURKE, J. M., PRAGER, J. and McLAUGHLIN, J. J. A., 1962. Preliminary studies on nutritional and physiological factors which determine ecological dominance in phytoplankton blooms. *J. Protozool.*, 8:7.

BURKHOLDER, P. R., 1963. Some nutritional relationships among microbes of sea sediments and waters. In: C. H. OPPENHEIMER (Editor), *Marine Microbiology*. Thomas, Springfield, Ill., pp.133–150.

BURKHOLDER, P. R., BURKHOLDER, L. M. and ALMODOVAR, L. R., 1960. Antibiotic algae of some marine algae of Puerto Rico. *Botan. Marina*, 2:149–156.

BURSA, A. S., 1963. Phytoplankton successions in the Canadian Arctic. In: C. H. OPPENHEIMER (Editor), *Marine Microbiology*. Thomas, Springfield, Ill., pp.625–628.

BUTCHER, R. W., 1959. An introductory account of the smaller algae of British coastal waters, I. *Gt. Brit., Min. Agr., Fisheries Food, Fisheries Invest.*, 4:73 pp.

BUTCHER, R. W., 1961. An introductory account of the smaller algae of British coastal waters, II. *Gt. Brit., Min. Agr., Fisheries Food, Fisheries Invest.*, 8:17 pp.

BUTLIN, K. R. and POSTGATE, J. R., 1954. The microbiology of sulphur of Cyrenaican lakes. In: *Biology of Deserts*. Inst. Biol., London, p.112.

BUTLIN, K. R. and VERNON, W. H. J., 1949. Underground corrosion of metals; causes and prevention. *J. Inst. Water Engrs.*, 3:627–637.

CALLAME, B. et DEBYSER, J., 1954. Observations sur les mouvements des diatomées à la surface des sédiments marins de la zone intercotidiale. *Vie Milieu*, 5:243.

CAMPBELL, A. S., 1942. The oceanic Tintinnoidea of the plankton gathered during the last cruise of the "Carnegie". *Sci. Results "Carnegie" Expedition. 2. Biology*, 7: 1–163.

CASTELL, C. H. and ANDERSON, G. W., 1948. Bacteria associated with the spoilage of cod fillets. *J. Fisheries Res. Board Can.*, 7:370–377.

CASTELL, C. H. and GREENOUGH, M. F., 1957. The action of *Pseudomonas* on fish muscle, I. *J. Fisheries Res. Board Can.*, 14:617–625.

CASTELL, C. H., GREENOUGH, M. F. and JENKINS, N. L., 1957. The action of *Pseudomonas* on fish muscle, II. *J. Fisheries Res. Board Can.*, 14:775–782.

CASTELL, C. H., GREENOUGH, M. F. and DALE, J., 1959. The action of *Pseudomonas* on fish muscle, III. *J. Fisheries Res. Board Can.*, 16:13–19.

CASTRACANE, F., 1886. Report on the Diatomaceae collected by H.M.S. "Challenger" during the years 1873–1876. In: C. W. THOMSON (Editor), *Report on the Scientific Results of the Voyage of H.M.S. "Challenger". 2. Botany*. Eyre and Spottiswoode, London, 170 pp.

CHALLENGER, F., BYWOOD, R., THOMAS, P. and HAYWARD, B. J., 1957. Studies on biological methylation, XVII. *Arch. Biochem. Biophys.*, 69:514–523.

CHESTERS, G. G. C. and STOTT, J. A., 1956. Production of antibiotic substances by seaweeds. *Intern. Seaweed Symp.*, *2nd, Trondheim, 1955*, pp.49–53.

CHRISTENSEN, T., 1964. The gross classification of the algae. In: D. F. JACKSON (Editor), *Algae and Man*. Plenum Press, New York, N.Y., pp.59–64.

CHU, S. P. and KUO, K. C., 1959. A decade of marine phytoplankton research in China. *Oceanol. Limnol. Sinica*, 2:229–232.

CIERESZKO, L. S., 1962. Chemistry of coelenterates, III. Occurrence of antimicrobial terpenoid compounds in the zooxanthellae of Alcyonarians. *Trans. N. Y. Acad. Sci.*, 2(24):502–503.

CLARKE, G. L. and BACKUS, R. H., 1964. Interrelations between the vertical migration of deep scattering layers, bioluminescence and changes of daylight in the sea. *Bull. Inst. Oceanog.*, 64(1318):36 pp.

CLARKE, G. L. and DENTON, E. J., 1962. Light and animal life. In: M. N. HILL (Editor), *The Sea*. Interscience, New York, N.Y., 1:456–468.

CLARKE, G. L. and GELLIS, S. S., 1935. The nutrition of copepods in relation to the food cycle of the sea. *Biol. Bull.*, 68:231–246.

CLARKE, G. L. and KELLY, M. G., 1964. Variation in transparency and in bioluminescence on longitudinal transects in the western Indian Ocean. *Bull. Inst. Oceanog.*, 64(1319):20 pp.

CLEGG, L. F. and SHERWOOD, H. F., 1947. The bacteriological examination of molluscan shellfish. *J. Hyg.*, 45:504.

CLEVE, P. T., 1900. Plankton from the red sea. *Övers. Kgl. Vetenskapsakad. Forsökssta.*, 127(9):1025–1038.

CLEVE, P. T., 1903. Plankton researches in 1901–1902. *Kgl. Svenska Vetenskapsakad. Handl.*, 36:53–81.

COE, W. R. and ALLEN, W. E., 1937. Growth of sedentary marine organisms on experimental plates and blocks for nine successive years at the Scripps Institution of Oceanography. *Bull. Scripps Inst. Oceanog. Univ. Calif., Tech. Ser.*, 4:101.

COLE, H. A., 1936. Experiments on the breeding of oysters *(Ostrea edulis)* in tanks, with special reference to the food of larvae and spat. *Gt. Brit., Min. Agr., Fisheries Food, Fisheries Invest., Ser. II*, 15(4):1–27.

COLLIER, A., 1953. Titanium and zirconium in blooms of *Gymnodinium brevis. Science*, 118:329.

COLLINGWOOD, C., 1868. Observations on the microscopic alga which causes the discoloration of the sea. *Trans. Microscopol. Soc. London*, 16.

COLLINS, V. K., KUCHEL, C. C. and BEATTY, S. A., 1940. Studies on fish spoilage, IX. *J. Fisheries Res. Board Can.*, 5:203.

COLWELL, R. R. and LISTON, J., 1961. Taxonomic relationships among the pseudomonads. *J. Bacteriol.*, 82:1–14.

COLWELL, R. R., CITARELLA, R. V. and RYMAN, I., 1965. Deoxyribonucleic acid base composition and Adnasonian analysis of heterotrophic, aerobic pseudomonads. *J. Bacteriol.*, 90:1148–1149.

CONOVER, J. T. and SIEBURTH, J. McN., 1964. Effects of *Sargassum* distribution on its epibiota. *Botan. Marina*, 6:147–157.

COPENHAGEN, W. J., 1934. Sulfur as a factor in the corrosion of iron and steel structures in the sea. *Trans. Roy. Soc. S. Africa*, 22:103–127.

COVELL, W. P. and WHEDON, W. F., 1937. Effects of paralytic shell fish poison on nerve cells. *Arch. Pathol.*, 23:411–418.

CRIBB, A. B. and CRIBB, J. W., 1955. Marine Fungi from Queensland. *Univ. Queensland Botan. Papers*, 3(10):77–81.

CVIIC, V., 1953. Attachment of bacteria to slides submerged in sea water. *Biljeske Inst. Oceanog. Ribar*, 6.

DAISLEY, K. W., 1957. Vitamin B_{12} in ecology. *Nature*, 180:1042.

DANFORTH, W. M., 1962. Substrate assimilation and heterotrophy. In: R. A. LEWIN (Editor), *Biochemistry and Physiology of Algae*. Academic Press, New York, N.Y., pp.99–103.

DAVIS, J. B. and UPDEGRAFF, D. M., 1954. Microbiology in the petroleum industry. *Bacteriol. Rev.*, 18:215–238.

DEFLANDRE, G., 1950. Contribution à l'étude des silicoflagellides actuels et fossiles. *Microscopie (Paris)*, 272:1–82 (extr.).

DEFLANDRE, G., 1952a. Classe des silicoflagellides. Dans: P. P. GRASSÉ (Rédacteur), *Traité de Zoologie*. Masson, Paris, 1:425.

DEFLANDRE, G., 1952b. Classe des xanthomonadines. Dans: P. P. GRASSÉ (Rédacteur), *Traité de Zoologie*. Masson, Paris, 1:212–226.

DE GIAXA, J., 1889. Über die Verhalten einiger pathogener Mikroorganismen in Meereswasser. *Z. Hyg.*, 6:162–225.

DEMNY, T. C., MILLER, I. M. and WOODRUFF, H. B., 1961. Occurrence of a variety of actinomycetes isolated from marine materials. *Bacteriol. Proc.*, D10:47.

DESIKACHARY, T. V., 1960. *Cyanophyta*. Academic Press, New York, N.Y., 660 pp.

DESOUSA E SILVA, E., 1963. Les "red waters" à la lagune d'Orbidos, ses causes probables et ses rapports avec la toxicité des bivalves. *Notas Estudios Inst. Biol. Maritimo*, 27:265–275.

DI SALVO, L. H., 1965. *Eniwetok Atoll Reef Studies*. Thesis, Univ. Arizona, Tucson, Ariz., 50 pp.

DODGE, J. D., 1964. Nuclear division in the dinoflagellate *Goniaulax tamarensis. J. Gen. Microbiol.*, 36:269–276.

DODGSON, R. W., 1928. Report on mussel purification. *Fisheries Invest. Serv.*, 2(10):535 pp.

DOLMAN, C. E., 1960. Type E botulism; a hazard of the North. *Arctic*, 13:230–256.

DREW, G. H., 1914. On the precipitation of calcium carbonate in the sea by marine bacteria and on the action of denitrifying bacteria in tropical and temperate seas. *Carnegie Inst. Wash., Papers Tortugas Lab.*, 5:7–45.

DROOP, M. R., 1957a. Vitamin B_{12} in ecology. *Nature*, 180:1041.

DROOP, M. R., 1957b. Auxotrophy and organic compounds in the nutrition of marine plankton. *J. Gen. Microbiol.*, 16:286–293.

DROOP, M. R., 1962. Organic micronutrients. In: R. A. LEWIN (Editor), *Biochemistry and Physiology of Algae*. Academic Press, New York, N.Y., pp.141–159.

DROOP, M. R., 1963a. Algae and invertebrates in symbiosis. *Symbiotic Associations—Symp. Soc. Gen. Microbiol.*, 13.

DROOP, M. R., 1963b. A feeding experiment. *Brit. Phycol. Bull.*, 2:278.

DROST-HANSEN, W., 1956. Discontinuities in the slope of the temperature dependence of the thermal expansion of water. *Naturwissenschaften*, 22:511–512.

DUGDALE, R. G., GOERING, D. J. and RYTHER, J. H., 1964. High nitrogen fixation rates in the Sargasso Sea, and the Arabian Sea. *Limnol. Oceanog.*, 9:507–510.

DUURSMA, E. K., 1960. *Dissolved Organic Carbon, Nitrogen and Phosphorus in the Sea*. Thesis, Univ. Amsterdam, 147 pp.

ECKLUND, M. W. and POYSKY, F., 1965. *Closterium botulinum* type F from marine sediments. *Science*, 150:306.

EMERY, K. O. and RITTENBERG, K. C., 1952. Early diagenesis of California Basin sediments in relation to the origin of oil. *Bull. Am. Assoc. Petrol. Geologists*, 36:735–806.

EMERY, K. O., ORR, W. D. and RITTENBERG, S. C., 1955. Nutrient budgets in the ocean. *Essays in Honor Capt. Hancock*, pp.299–309.

EYRE, J. H., 1904. On the distribution of *B. coli* in nature. *Lancet*, 1:648–649.

EYSTER, C., 1964. Micronutrient requirements for green plants especially Algae. In: D. F. JACKSON (Editor), *Algae and Man*. Plenum Press, New York, N.Y., pp.86–119.

FELL, J., 1965. *Bionomics and Physiological Taxonomy of Marine Occurring Yeasts.* Thesis, Univ. Miami, Miami, Fla., 181 pp.

FELLERS, C. R., 1926. Bacteriological investigations on raw salmon spoilage. *Wash. State Coll., Publ. Fisheries*, 1(8):157–188.

FLEMING, R. H., 1939. The control of diatom populations by grazing. *J. Conseil, Conseil Perm. Intern. Exploration Mer*, 14:1–18.

FOGG, G. E., 1962a. Nitrogen fixation. In: R. A. Lewin (Editor), *Biochemistry and Physiology of Algae.* Academic Press, New York, N.Y., pp.161–170.

FOGG, G. E., 1962b. Extracellular products. In: R. A. LEWIN (Editor), *Biochemistry and Physiology of Algae.* Academic Press, New York, N.Y., pp.475–489.

FOGG, G. E., 1963. The role of algae in organic production in aquatic environments. *Brit. Phycol. Bull.*, 2:195–206.

FOGG, G. E., 1964. Environmental conditions and the pattern of metabolism in algae. In: D. F. JACKSON (Editor), *Algae and Man.* Plenum Press, New York, N.Y., pp.77–85.

FOGG, G. E. and WOLFE, M., 1954. The nitrogen metabolism of the blue-green Algae (Myxophyceae). *Symp. Soc. Gen. Microbiol.*, 4:99–125.

FOGG, G. E., NALEWAJKO, C. and WATT, W. D., 1964. *Extracellular Products of Phytoplankton Photosynthesis.* (Manuscript).

FRENKEL, A., GAFFRON, H. and BATTLEY, E. H., 1949. Photosynthesis and photoreduction by a species of blue-green algae. *Biol. Bull.*, 97:269.

FRIEND, J. N., 1922. Corrosion of iron. *Iron Steel Inst. (London), Spec. Rept.*, 11:1.

GAARDER, K. R., 1962. Electron microscope studies on holococcolithophorids. *Nytt Mag. Botan.*, 10:35–50.

GAARDER, K. R. and HASLE, G. R., 1962. On the assumed symbiosis between diatoms and coccolithophorids in *Brenneckella. Nytt Mag. Botan.*, 9:145–149.

GAINES, R. H., 1910. Bacterial activity as a corrosive influence in soil. *Ind. Eng. Chem.*, 2:128.

GALTSOFF, P. S., 1940. Wasting disease causing mortality of sponges in the West Indies and Gulf of Mexico. *Proc. Pan Am. Sci. Congr., 8th*, p.111.

GARVEL, L. J. and GILMOUR, C. M., 1965. Nitrate respiration of inshore marine sediments. *Bacteriol. Proc.*, 15.

GEORGALA, D. A., 1958. The bacterial flora of the skin of the North Sea cod. *J. Gen. Microbiol.*, 18:84–91.

GIBBONS, N. E., 1934a. The slime and intestinal flora of the haddock. *Contrib. Can. Biol. Fisheries*, 8:275–290.

GIBBONS, N. E., 1934b. Lactose-fermenting bacteria from the intestinal contents of marine fishes. *Contrib. Can. Biol. Fisheries*, 8:291–300.

GIBBONS, N. E. and REED, G. B., 1930. The effect of autolysis in sterile tissues on subsequent bacterial decomposition. *J. Bacteriol.*, 19:73–88.

GLAESSNER, M. F., 1948. *Principles of Micropaleontology.* Wiley, New York, N.Y., 295 pp.

GLANZ, P. J. and KRANZ, G. E., 1965. *Escherichia coli* serotypes isolated from fish and their environment. *Bacteriol. Proc.*, 15.

GOLD, K., 1965. A note on the distribution of luminescent dinoflagellates in Phosphorescent Bay, Puerto Rico. *Ocean Sci. Ocean Eng.*, 1:77–80.

GOLDBERG, E. D., WALKER, T. J. and WHISENAND, A., 1951. Phosphate utilization by diatoms. *Biol. Bull.*, 101:274–284.

GRAY, P. H. H. and THORNTON, E. G., 1928. Soil bacteria that decompose certain organic compounds. *Zentr. Bakteriol. Parasitenk.*, *Abt. II*, 73:74–96.

GRAY, S., 1821. *A Natural Arrangement of British Plants.*

GREENE, H. I., 1920. Report on experiments on cold storage of herring carried out at North Shields. *J. Hyg.*, 19:75.

GREENFIELD, L. H., 1963. Metabolism and concentration of calcium and magnesium and precipitation of calcium carbonate by a marine bacterium. *Ann. N. Y. Acad. Sci.*, 109:23–45.

GREIN, A. and MEYERS, S. P., 1958. Growth characteristics and antibiotic production of actinomycetes isolated from littoral sediments and materials suspended in sea water. *J. Bacteriol.*, 76:457–463.

GRINDLEY, J. R. and TAYLOR, F. J. R., 1964. Red water and marine fauna mortality near Cape Town. *Trans. Roy. Soc. S. Africa*, 37:111–130.

GRØNTVED, J., 1960. On the productivity of microbenthos and phytoplankton in some Danish fjords. *Medd. Komm. Danmarks Fiskeri Havundersøgelse*, 3(3):55–92.

GRØNTVED, J., 1962. Preliminary report on the productivity of microbenthos and phytoplankton in the Danish Waddensee. *Medd. Komm. Danmarks Fiskeri Havundersøgelse*, 3(12):55–92.

HAINES, R. B., 1933. The influence of carbon dioxide on the rate of multiplication of certain bacteria as judged by viable counts. *J. Soc. Chem. Ind. (London)*, 1:52, 13T.

HALL, W. T. and CLAUS, G., 1962. Electron microscope studies on ultrathin sections of *Oscillatoria chalybea* MARTENS. *Protoplasma*, 54:355–368.

HALL, W. T. and CLAUS, G., 1963. Ultrastructural studies on the blue-green algal symbiont in *Cyanophora paradoxa* KORSCHIKOFF. *J. Cellular Biol.*, 19:551–563.

HALLDAL, P., 1957. Importance of calcium and magnesium ions in phototaxis of marine algae. *Nature*, 179:215–216.

HAMBURGER, G. L. und VON BRUDDENBROCK-HEIDELBERG, C., 1907. Nordische Ciliata mit Ausschluss der Tintinnoidea. *Nordisches Plankton*, 3(1):152.

HAMILTON, R. D., 1964. Photochemical processes in the inorganic nitrogen cycle of the sea. *Limnol. Oceanog.*, 9:107–111.

HANAZAWA, S., 1933. Diatom *(Ethmodiscus)* ooze obtained from the tropical south-western Northern Pacific. *Oceanog. Records Oceanog. Works (Japan)*, 7:37–44.

HANNAN, P. J., 1964. Effect of pressure on oxygen production by Algae. *Developments in Industrial Microbiology*, 6(24):229–237.

HARDER, R. und OPPERMAN, A., 1953. Über antibiotische Stoffe bei Grünalgen *Stichococcus bacillaris* und *Protosiphon botryoides*. *Arch. Mikrobiol.*, 19:398–401.

HARDY, A., 1935. The plankton of the South Georgia whaling ground and adjacent waters, 1926–1927. The plankton community and the whale fishery and the hypothesis of animal exclusion. *Discovery Rept.*, 11:273–370.

HARRISON, F. C., 1929. The discoloration of halibut. *Can. J. Res.*, 1:214–239.

HARRISON, F. C., PERRY, H. M. and SMITH, P. W. P., 1926. The bacteriology of certain sea fish. *Natl. Res. Council Can.*, *Rept.*, 19:1048.

HART, T., 1942. Phytoplankton periodicity in Antarctic surface waters. *Discovery Rept.*, 21:261–356.

HARVEY, H. W., 1934. Measurement of phytoplankton populations. *J. Marine Biol. Assoc. U. K.*, 19:761.

HARVEY, H. W., 1955. *Biology and Fertility of Sea Water*. Cambridge Univ. Press, London, 224 pp.

HASLE, G. R., 1956. Phytoplankton and hydrography of the Pacific part of the Antarctic Ocean. *Nature*, 117:617.

HASLE, G. R., 1960a. Plankton coccolithophorids from the sub-antarctic and equatorial Pacific. *Nytt Mag. Botan.*, 8:77–88.

HASLE, G. R., 1960b. Phytoplankton and ciliate species from the tropical Pacific. *Skrifter Norske Videnskaps-Akad. Oslo, I: Mat.-Naturv. Kl.*, 1960(2):1–50.

HASLE, G. R., 1964. *Nitzschia* and *Fragilariopsis* species studied in the light and electron microscopes, I, II. *Skrifter Norske Videnskaps-Akad. Oslo, I: Mat.-Naturv. Kl.*, 1964(16):48 pp.; 1964(18):45 pp.

HAUDUROY, P., 1923. Recherches sur le bactériophage de d'Hérelle; présence du principe dans l'eau de mer. *Bull. Inst. Oceanog.*, 1923: 433–434.

HAVENS, L. C. and DEHLER, S. A., 1923. The effect of *Gambusia affinis* on the *B.coli* index of pollution of water. *Am. J. Hyg.*, 3:296–299.

HENDEY, N. I., 1937. The plankton diatoms of the southern seas. *Discovery Rept., II*, 16(2):153–364.

HENDEY, N. I., 1951. Littoral diatoms of Chichester Harbour with special reference to fouling. *J. Roy. Microscop. Soc.*, 71:1–86.

HENRICI, A. T., 1933. Studies of fresh-water bacteria. I. A direct microscopic technique. *J. Bacteriol.*, 25:277–278.

HENRICI, A. T. and JOHNSON, D. E., 1935. Studies on fresh-water bacteria, II. Stalked bacteria, a new order of the Schizomycetes. *J.Bacteriol.*,30:61–93.

HILEN, E. J., 1923. Report on a bacterial study of ocean slime. *U.S. Navy Dept., Rept. Bur. Construct. Repair.*

HOBBS, G., CANN, D. C., GOWLAND, G. and BYERS, H. D., 1964. A serological approach to the genus *Pseudomonas*. *J. Appl. Bacteriol.*, 27:83–92.

HÖHNK, W., 1955. Studien zur Brack- und Seewassermikrobiologie, V. *Veröffentl. Inst. Meeresforsch. Bremerhaven*, 3:199–227.

HÖHNK, W., 1959. Ein Beitrag zur ozeanischen Mykologie. *Deut. Hydrograph. Z.*, B3:81–87.

HOLLANDE, A., 1952a. Classe des eugléniens. Dans: P. P. GRASSÉ (Rédacteur), *Traité de Zoologie*. Masson, Paris, pp.238–284.

HOLLANDE, A., 1952b. Classe des cryptomonadines. Dans: P. P. GRASSÉ (Rédacteur), *Traité de Zoologie*. Masson, Paris, pp.285–308.

HOLM-HANSEN, O., 1962. Assimilation of carbon dioxide. In: R. A. LEWIN (Editor), *Biochemistry and Physiology of Algae*. Academic Press, New York, N.Y., pp.25–35.

HOUSTON, A. C., 1904. Results of a number of separate bacteriological observations bearing on the general question of the pollution of estuarine waters and shellfish. *Roy. Comm. Sewage Disposal Dept.*, 4:191.

HULBURT, E. M., 1963. The diversity of phytoplanktonic populations in coastal and estuarine regions. *J. Marine Res. (Sears Found. Marine Res.)*, 21:81–93.

HULBURT, E. M., 1964. Succession and diversity in the plankton flora of the western North Atlantic. *Bull. Marine Sci. Gulf Caribbean*, 14:33–44.

HUMM, H. J., 1956. Annotated check-list of the marine fauna and flora of the St. George Sound–Apalachee Bay region. *Florida State Univ., Contrib. Oceanog. Inst.*, 66:1–78.

HUNTER, A., 1929. Further observations on the distribution of arginase in fishes. *J. Biol. Chem.*, 81:505–511.

HUNTER, A. C., 1920. Bacteriological decomposition of salmon. *J. Bacteriol.*, 5:543–552.

HUNTER, A. C. and HARRISON, C. W., 1928. Bacteriology and chemistry of oysters with special reference to regulatory control of production, handling and shipment. *U.S. Dept. Agr., Tech. Bull.*, 64:1–75.

HUTNER, S. H. and PROVASOLI, L., 1951. The phytoflagellates. In: S. H. HUTNER and A. LWOFF (Editors), *Biochemistry and Physiology of the Protozoa*. Academic Press, New York, N.Y., 1:27–121.

HUTNER, S. H. and PROVASOLI, L., 1954. Comparative biochemistry of the flagellates. In: S. H. HUTNER and A. LWOFF (Editors), *Biochemistry and Physiology of the Protozoa*. Academic Press, New York, N.Y., 2:17–56.

HUTNER, S. H. and PROVASOLI, L., 1964. Nutrition of algae. *Ann. Rev. Plant Physiol.*, 15:37–56.

INGRAM, M. and SHEWAN, J. M., 1960. Introductory reflections on the *Pseudomonas–Achromobacter* group. *J. Appl. Bacteriol.*, 23:373–378.

IRVINE, R., 1891. On the corrosion of iron. *J. Soc. Chem. Ind. (London)*, 10:237.

JOHANNES, R. E., 1964a. Uptake and release of dissolved organic phosphorus by representatives of a coastal marine ecosystem. *Limnol. Oceanog.*, 9:224–234.

JOHANNES, R. E., 1964b. Uptake and release of phosphorus by a benthic marine amphipod. *Limnol. Oceanog.*, 9:235–242.

JOHNSON, G. A., 1904. Isolation of *B. coli* from the alimentary tract of fish and the significance thereof. *J. Infect. Diseases*, 1:348.

JOHNSON, T. W. and SPARROW JR., F. K., 1961. *Fungi in Oceans and Estuaries*. Cramer, Weinheim, 665 pp.

JONES, G. E. and JANNASCH, H. W., 1956. Aggregates of bacteria in sea water as determined by treatment with surface active agents. *Limnol. Oceanog.*, 4:269–276.

JØRGENSEN, E. G., 1962. Antibiotic substances from cells and culture solutions of unicellular algae with special references to some chlorophyll derivatives. *Physiol. Plantarum*, 15:530–545.

KADOTA, H., 1951. Microbiological studies on the weakening of netting cords. *Bull. Japan. Soc. Sci. Fisheries*, 16:63–70.

KADOTA, H., 1955. Microbiological studies on the weakening of netting cords. *Bull. Japan. Soc. Sci. Fisheries*, 20:120–132.

KAMIMOTO, K., 1955. Studies on the antibacterial substances extracted from seaweeds on the growth of some pathogenic bacteria. *Japan. J. Bacteriol.*, 10:897–902.

KAPLAN, I. R., 1957. Evidence of microbiological activity in some geothermal regions of New Zealand. *New Zealand J. Sci. Technol.*, B, 37:639–662.

KAPLAN, I. R., EMERY, K. O. and RITTENBERG, S. C., 1963. The distribution and isotopic abundance of sulfur in recent marine sediments off Southern California. *Geochim. Cosmochim. Acta*, 27:297–331.

KARSTEN, G., 1905. Das Phytoplankton des Antarktischen Meeres nach dem Material der deutschen Tiefsee-Expedition. *Wiss. Ergeb. Deut. Tiefsee-Expedition Valdivia*, 2.

KARSTEN, G., 1906. Das Phytoplankton des Atlantischen Ozeans. *Wiss. Ergeb. Deut. Tiefsee-Expedition Valdivia*, 2:2.

KARSTEN, G., 1907. Das indische Phytoplankton. *Wiss. Ergeb. Deut. Tiefsee-Expedition Valdivia*, 2(2):3.

KATAYAMA, T., 1962. Volatile constituents. In: R. A. LEWIN (Editor), *Physiology and Biochemistry of Algae*. Academic Press, New York, N.Y., pp.467–473.

KEOSIAN, J., 1960. On the origin of life. *Science*, 131:479–482.

KIKKAWA, Y. and KOSUGI, K., 1937. The Fungi grown on dried bonito. *Bull. Japan. Soc. Sci. Fisheries*, 6:79.

KIMBALL, J. F. and WOOD, E. J. F., 1965a. A simple centrifuge for phytoplankton studies. *Bull. Marine Sci. Gulf Caribbean*, 14:539–544.

KIMBALL, J. F. and WOOD, E. J. F., 1965b. A dinoflagellate with characters of *Gymnodinium* and *Gyrodinium*. *J. Protozool.*, 12:577.

KIYOHARA, T., FUJITA, Y., HATTORI, A. and WATANABE, A., 1960. *J. Gen. Appl. Microbiol.*, 6:176–182.

KIYOHARA, T., FUKITA, Y., HATTORI, A. and WATANABE, A., 1962. *J. Gen. Appl. Microbiol.*, 8:165–168.

KNÖSEL, D. und SCHWARTZ, W., 1954. Untersuchungen zur Erdölbakteriologie, III. *Arch. Mikrobiol.*, 20:362–390.

KNOTT, F. A., 1951. Memorandum of the principles and standards for the bacteriological control of shellfish in the London markets. *Fishmongers Company*, pp.1–16.

KNUDSEN, M., 1901. *Hydrographische Tabellen*. Gad, Copenhagen, 63 pp.

KOCH, H. J., 1939. La cause des empoisonnements paralytiques provoqué par les moules. *Sci. Sean. Sess.*, 63:654–657.

KOFOID, C. A. and CAMPBELL, A. S., 1939. The Ciliata; the Tintinnoidea. *Bull. Museum Comp. Zool. Harvard Coll.*, 84.

KOFOID, C. A. and SKOGSBERG, T., 1928. Dinoflagellatae, the Dinophysoidea. *Bull. Museum Comp. Zool. Harvard Coll.*, 51.

KOHLMEYER, J., 1958a. Beobachtungen über mediterrane Meerespilze sowie das Vorkommen von marinen Moderfaule-Erregern in Aquariumseuchten holzzerstörender Meerestiere. *Ber. Deut. Botan. Ges.*, 71:98–106.

KOHLMEYER, J., 1958b. Holzzerstörende Pilze im Meereswasser. *Holz Roh Werkstoff*, 16:215–220.

KOHLMEYER, J., 1959. Neufunde holzbesiedelnder Meerespilze. *Nova Hedwigia*, 1:77–98.

KOHLMEYER, J., 1960. Wood-inhabiting marine fungi from the Pacific, northwest and California. *Nova Hedwigia*, 2:193–343.

KOHLMEYER, J., 1961. Pilze von nördlichen Pazifik-Küste der U.S.A. *Nova Hedwigia*, 3:85–91.

KOHLMEYER, J., 1964. Pilzfunde am Meer. *Z. Pilzkunde*, 30:43–51.

KOLBE, R. W., 1956. Diatoms from the equatorial Indian Ocean cores. *Rept. Swed. Deep-Sea Expedition, 1948–1949*, 9(1):1–51.

KROGH, A., 1931. Dissolved substances as food for aquatic organisms. *Rappt. Proces-Verbaux Réunions, Conseil Perm. Intern. Exploration Mer*, 75:1–36.

KUCERA, S. and WOLFE, R. S., 1957. A selective enrichment method for *Gallionella ferruginea*. *J. Bacteriol.*, 74:344–349.

KUENTZLER, E. J., GUILLARD, R. R. L. and CORWIN, N., 1963. Phosphate-free sea water for reagent blanks in chemical analyses. *Deep-Sea Res.*, 10: 749–755.

LASKER, R., 1964. Moulting frequency of a deep-sea crustacean, *Euphausia pacifica*. *Nature*, 203:96.

LEE, J. J. and FREUDENTHAL, H. D., 1963. Neglected amoebas in culture. *Nat. Hist. Mag.*, 1963: 54–61.

LEE, J. J., FREUDENTHAL, H. D., MULLER, W. A., KOSSOY, V., PIERCE, S. and GROSSMAN, R., 1963. Growth and physiology of Foraminifera in the laboratory. *Micropaleontology*, 4:449–466.

LEFÈVRE, M., 1964. Extracellular products of algae. In: D. F. JACKSON (Editor), *Algae and Man*. Plenum Press, New York, N.Y., pp.337–367.

LEVINA, R. I., 1961. Antagonism between planktonic algae and microflora in biological ponds. In: *The Purification of Waste-Waters in Biological Ponds*. Minsk. Akad. Nauk B.S.S.R., Minsk, pp.136–147.

LEWIN, J. C. and GUILLARD, R. R. L., 1963. Diatoms. *Ann. Rev. Microbiol.*, 17:373–414.

LIPMAN, C., 1924. A critical and experimental study of Drew's bacterial hypothesis on $CaCO_3$ precipitation in the sea. *Carnegie Inst. Wash., Dept. Marine Biol.*, 19:179–191.

LISTON, J., 1956. Quantitative variations in the bacterial flora of flatfish. *J. Gen. Microbiol.*, 15:304–314.

LISTON, J., 1960. The bacterial flora of fish caught in the Pacific. *J. Appl. Bacteriol.*, 23:469–470.

LOOSANOFF, L. and ENGLE, I. B., 1947. Feeding of oysters in relation to the density of microorganisms. *Science*, 105:260, 748.

LUMLEY, A., PIQUÉ, J. and REAY, G. A., 1929. Handling and storage of fresh fish at sea. *Gt. Brit. Food Min., Spec. Rept.*, 37.

LUND, J. W. G., 1949. Studies on *Asterionella formosa*, I. *J. Ecol.*, 37:389–419, 38:1–35.

LUND, J. W. G., 1955. The ecology of algae and waterworks practice. *Proc. Soc. Water Treat. Exam.*, 4:43–99.

MACKERETH, F. H., 1953. Phosphorus utilization by *Asterionella formosa* HAAS. *J. Exptl. Botany*, 4:296–313.

MACKIN, J., OWEN, H. M. and COLLIER, A., 1950. Preliminary note on the occurrence of a new protozoan parasite *Dermocystidium marinum* n.sp. in *Crassostrea virginica* GMELIN. *Science*, 111:328–329.

MACLEOD, R. A., 1965. The question of the existence of specific marine bacteria. *Bacteriol. Rev.*, 29:9–23.

MACLEOD, R. A. and HORI, A., 1960. Nutrition and metabolism of marine bacteria. *J. Bacteriol.*, 80:464–471.

MACLEOD, R. A. and ONOFREY, E., 1956. Nutrition and metabolism of marine bacteria, II. *J. Bacteriol.*, 73:661–667.

MACLEOD, R. A. and ONOFREY, E., 1957a. Nutrition and metabolism of marine bacteria. *J. Cellular Comp. Physiol.*, 50:389–401.

MACLEOD, R. A. and ONOFREY, E., 1957b. Nutrition and metabolism of marine bacteria. *Can. J. Microbiol.*, 3:573–579.

MACLEOD, R. A., ONOFREY, E. and NORRIS, M. E., 1954. Nutrition and metabolism of marine bacteria, I. *J. Bacteriol.*, 68:680–686.

MACLEOD, R. A., CLARIDGE, C. A., HORI, A. and MURRAY, J. F., 1957. Nutrition and metabolism of marine bacteria. *J. Biol. Chem.*, 232:829–834.

MACLEOD, R. A., HOGENKAMP, H. and ONOFREY, E., 1958. Nutrition and metabolism of marine bacteria. *J. Bacteriol.*, 75:460–464.

MACLEOD, R. A., HORI, A. and FOX, S. M., 1960a. Nutrition and metabolism of marine bacteria. *Can. J. Microbiol.*, 6:639–644.

MACLEOD, R. A., HORI, A. and FOX, S. M., 1960b. Nutrition and metabolism of marine bacteria. *Can. J. Biochem. Physiol.*, 38:693–701.

MANTON, I. and LEEDALE, G. F., 1963. Observations on the microanatomy of *Crystallolithus hyalinus* GAARDER and MARKALI. *Arch. Mikrobiol.*, 47:115–136.

MARKOV, V. R., 1939. Putrefaction of sea fish. *Zentr. Bakteriol. Parasitenk., Abt. II*, 101:151.

MARSHALL, S. M. and ORR, A. P., 1955a. Experimental feeding of the copepod *Calanus finmarchicus* (GUNNER) on phytoplankton cultures labelled with radioactive carbon (^{14}C). *Deep-Sea Res.*, 3:110–114.

MARSHALL, S. M. and ORR, A. P. 1955b. On the biology of *Calanus finmarchicus*, VIII. *J. Marine Biol. Assoc. U.K.*, 34:495–529.

MAUTNER, H. C., GARDNER, G. M. and PRATT, R., 1953. Antibiotic activity of seaweed extracts, II. *J. Pharm. Sci.*, 42:294–296.

McHUGH, J. L., 1954. Distribution and abundance of the diatom *Ethmodiscus rex* off the west coast of North America. *Deep-Sea Res.*, 1:216–223.

MEDCOF, J. C., LEIM, A. H., NEEDLER, A. B., GIBBARD, J. and NAUBERT, J.,

1947. Paralytic shellfish poisoning on the Canadian Atlantic coast. *Bull. Fisheries Res. Board Can.*, 75:1–32.

MERESCHOWSKY, C., 1902. Notes sur quelques diatomées de la mer noir. *J. Botany*, 16:319, 358, 416.

MERKEL, J. R., 1965. Proteolytic bacteria from the Bermuda area. *Bacteriol. Proc.*, 16.

MEYERS, S. P., 1953. Marine Fungi in Biscayne Bay, Florida. *Bull. Marine Sci. Gulf Caribbean*, 2:590–601.

MEYERS, S. P., 1954. Marine Fungi in Biscayne Bay, Florida, II. *Bull. Marine Sci. Gulf Caribbean*, 3:307–327.

MEYERS, S. P., 1957. Taxonomy of marine Pyrenomycetes. *Mycologia*, 49:475–528.

MEYERS, S. P. and MOORE, R. T., 1960. Thalassiomycetes, II. *Am. J. Botany*, 47:345–349.

MEYERS, S. P. and REYNOLDS, E. S., 1957. Incidence of marine fungi in relation to wood borer attack. *Science*, 126:969.

MEYERS, S. P. and REYNOLDS, E. S., 1958. A wood incubation method for the study of lignicolous marine fungi. *Bull. Marine Sci. Gulf Caribbean*, 8:242–247.

MEYERS, S. P. and REYNOLDS, E. S., 1959a. Marine fungi and wood borer attack. *Science*, 130:46.

MEYERS, S. P. and REYNOLDS, E. S., 1959b. Cellulolytic activity in lignicolous marine Ascomycetes. *Bull. Marine Sci. Gulf Caribbean*, 9:441–455.

MEYERS, S. P. and REYNOLDS, E. S., 1959c. Growth and cellulolytic activity of lignicolous Deuteromycetes from marine localities. *Can. J. Microbiol.*, 5:493–503.

MEYERS, S. P. and REYNOLDS, E. S., 1959d. Effect of wood and wood products on perithecial development by lignicolous marine Ascomycetes. *Mycologia*, 51:138–145.

MEYERS, S. P. and REYNOLDS, E. S., 1960a. Cellulolytic activity of lignicolous marine Ascomycetes and Deuteromycetes. *Developments in Industrial Microbiology*. Plenum Press, New York, N.Y., pp.157–168.

MEYERS, S. P. and REYNOLDS, E. S., 1960b. Occurrence of lignicolous fungi in northern Atlantic and Pacific marine localities. *Am. J. Botany*, 38:217–226.

MEYERS, S. P. and REYNOLDS, E. S., 1962. Studies on cellulolytic activity in lignicolous marine fungi. In: C. H. OPPENHEIMER (Editor), *Marine Microbiology*. Thomas, Springfield, Ill., pp.315–328.

MEYERS, S. P., PRINDLE, B. and REYNOLDS, E. S., 1960. Cellulolytic activity of marine fungi; degradation of lignocellulose material. *Tappi*, 43:534–538.

MINKEWITCH, I. und TROFIMUK, N. A., 1928–1929. Über Darmbakterien der Fische vom Standpunkt der hygienischen Beurteilung von Trinkwasser. *Z. Hyg. Infektionskrankh.*, 109:139–146.

MOORE, E. C., 1954. *Radiolarians and Tintinnids*. In: R. C. MOORE (Editor), *Treatise on Invertebrate Paleontology, D. Protista, 3*. Geol. Soc. Am., New York, N.Y., pp.2–93.

MOORE, R. T. and MEYERS, S. P., 1959. Thalassiomycetes, I. *Mycologia*, 51: 871–876.

MORITA, R. Y., 1957. Phosphatase activity by marine bacteria under hydrostatic pressure. *Deep-Sea Res.*, 4:254–258.

MORITA, R. Y. and HAIGHT, R. D., 1964. Temperature effects on the growth of an obligate psychrophilic marine bacterium. *Limnol. Oceanog.*, 9:103–106.

MÜLLER, A. und SCHWARTZ, W., 1953. Geomikrobiologische Untersuchungen. *Eiszeitalter Gegenwart*, 3:216–220.

NAKAMURA, H., 1937. Adaptation of algae to hydrogen sulfide. *Acta Phytochim.*, 9:189.

NEEDLER, A. B., 1949. Paralytic shellfish poisoning and *Goniaulax tamarensis. J. Fisheries Res. Board Can.*, 7:490–504.

NITZSCH, C. L., 1817. *Beitrag zur Infusorienkunde*. Halle, 3:1.

OBST, M. M., 1919. A bacteriological study of sardines. *J. Infect. Diseases*, 24:158–169.

OHEOCHA, C. and RAFTERY, M., 1959. Phycoerythrins and phycocyanins of cryptomonads. *Nature*, 184:1047–1052.

OMELIANSKY, W., 1922. *Principles of Microbiology*. (In Russian.)

O'NEIL, T. B., DRISKO, R. W. and HOCKMAN, H., 1961. *Pseudomonas creosotensis* sp. n., a creosote-tolerant marine bacterium. *Appl. Microbiol.*, 9:472–474.

OPPENHEIMER, C. H., 1960. Bacterial activity in sediments of shallow marine bays. *Geochim. Cosmochim. Acta*, 19:244–260.

OPPENHEIMER, C. H., 1961. Note on the formation of spherical aragonite bodies in the presence of bacteria from the Bahama Bank. *Geochim. Cosmochim. Acta*, 23:295–296.

OPPENHEIMER, C. H. and KELLY, A. L., 1952. *Escherichia coli* in the intestine of a wild sea lion. *Science*, 115:527–528.

OPPENHEIMER, C. H. and WOOD, E. J. F., 1962. Note on the effect of contamination on a marine slough and the vertical distribution of unicellular plants in the sediment. *Z. Allgem. Mikrobiol.*, 2:45–47.

OPPENHEIMER, C. H. and WOOD, E. J. F., 1965. Quantitative aspects of the benthic unicellular algal population of the Texas Bay systems. *Bull. Marine Sci. Gulf Caribbean*, 15:571–588.

OVERBECK, J., 1962a. Untersuchungen zum Phosphäthaushalt von Grünalgen. *Arch. Hydrobiol.*, 58:162–209.

OVERBECK, J., 1962b. Das Nannoplankton (µ-Algen) der Rügenschen Brackwasser als Hauptprodukt in Abhängigkeit vom Salzgehalt *Kiel. Meeresforsch.*, 18:157–171.

OVERBECK, J., 1964a. Der Fe/P Quotient des Sediments als Merkmal des Stoffumsatzes in Brackwasser. *Helgoländer Wiss. Meeresuntersuch.*, 10:430–447.

OVERBECK, J., 1964b. Über den Nachweis von freien Enzymen in Gewässer. *Arch. Hydrobiol.*, 60:107–114.

PAASCHE, E., 1964. A tracer study of the inorganic carbon uptake during coccolith formation and photosynthesis in the coccolithophorid *Coccolithus huxleyi. Physiol. Plantarum*, 3:82 pp.

PARKE, M., 1961. Some remarks concerning the class Chrysophyceae. *Brit. Phycol. Bull.*, 2:47–55.

PARKE, M. and DIXON, P. S., 1964. A revised check-list of British marine algae. *J. Marine Biol. Assoc. U.K.*, 44:499–542.

PARKE, M. and RAYNS, D. G., 1964. Studies on marine flagellates. *J. Marine Biol. Assoc. U.K.*, 44:209–217.

PARKE, M., MANTON, I. and CLARKE, B., 1955. Studies on marine flagellates. *J. Marine Biol. Assoc. U.K.*, 34:579–609.

PARKE, M., MANTON, I. and CLARKE, B., 1956. Studies on marine flagellates. *J. Marine Biol. Assoc. U.K.*, 35:387–414.

PARKE, M., MANTON, I. and CLARKE, B., 1959. Studies on marine flagellates. *J. Marine Biol. Assoc. U.K.*, 38:169–188.

PARKE, M., MANTON, I. and CLARKE, B., 1962. Studies on marine flagellates. *J. Marine Biol. Assoc. U.K.*, 42:391–404.

PARKER, C. D. and PRISK, J., 1953. The oxidation of inorganic compounds of sulfur by various sulfur bacteria. *J. Gen. Microbiol.*, 8:344–364.

PAVILLARD, J., 1926. Bacillariales. *Rept. Danish Oceanog. Expedition, 1908–1910, Biology*, 11(9).

PHILLIPS, R. C., 1963. Ecology of floating algal communities in Florida. *Quart. J. Florida Acad. Sci.*, 26:329–334.

PINTNER, I. J. and PROVASOLI, L., 1963. Nutrition characteristics of some chrysomonads. In: C. H. OPPENHEIMER (Editor), *Marine Microbiology*. Thomas, Springfield, Ill., pp.114–121.

POLYNOV, B. B. and MUIR, A., 1937. *The Cycle of Weathering*. Murby, London, 220 pp.

POMEROY, L. R., 1959. Algal productivity in the salt marshes of Georgia. *Limnol. Oceanog.*, 4:386–398.

POMEROY, L. R., 1960. Primary productivity of Boca Ciega Bay, Florida. *Bull. Marine Sci. Gulf Caribbean*, 10:1–10.

PRAGER, J. C., 1963. Fusion of the family Glenodiniaceae into the Peridineaceae, with notes on *Glenodinium foliaceum*. *J. Protozool.*, 10:195–204.

PRATT, R., DANIELLS, T. C., EILER, J. J., GUNNISON, J. B., KUMLER, W. D., ONETO, J. F., STRAIT, L. A., SPOEHR, H. A., HARDIN, G. J., MILNER, H. W., SMITH, J. H. C. and STRAIN, H. H., 1944. Chlorellin an antibacterial substance from *Chlorella*. *Science*, 98:351–352.

PRATT, R., MAUTNER, G., GARDNER, G. M., SHA, Y. and DUFRENOY, J., 1951. Report on antibiotic activity of seaweed extracts. *J. Pharm. Sci.*, 40:575–579.

PRESCOTT, G. W., 1964. Contributions of current research to algal systematics. In: D. F. JACKSON (Editor), *Algae and Man*. Plenum Press, New York, N.Y., pp.1–30.

PRÉVOT, A. R., 1958. Utilité de la bactériologie marine dans le présent et l'avenir. *Bull. Inst. Oceanog.*, 1114:22 pp.

PRINGSHEIM, E. G., 1948. Taxonomic problems in the Euglenaceae. *Biol. Rev. Cambridge Phil. Soc.*, 23:46–61.

PRINGSHEIM, E. G., 1949. The relationship between bacteria and myxophyceae. *Bacteriol. Rev.*, 13:47–98.

PRINGSHEIM, E. G., 1964. Heterotrophism and species concepts in Beggiatoa. *Am. J. Botany*, 51:898–913.

PRINGSHEIM, E. G. und WIESSNER, W., 1961. Ernährung und Stoffwechsel von *Chlamydobotrys* (Volvocales). *Arch. Mikrobiol.*, 40:231–246.

PROCTOR, B. E. and NICKERSON, J. T. R., 1935. An investigation on the sterility of fish tissues. *J. Bacteriol.*, 30:377–382.

PROVASOLI, L. and McLAUGHIN, J. J. A., 1963. Limited heterotrophy of some photosynthetic dinoflagellates. In: C. H. OPPENHEIMER (Editor), *Marine Microbiology*. Thomas, Springfield, Ill., pp.105–113.

PROVASOLI, L. and PINTNER, I. J., 1954. Cultural characteristics of *Phormidium persicinum*, an auxotrophic marine red-pigmented blue-green alga. *Congr. Intern. Botan., 8th, Paris, 1954*, 17:39–40.

PSHENIN, L. H., 1963. Distribution and ecology of *Azotobacter* in the Black Sea. In: C. H. OPPENHEIMER (Editor), *Marine Microbiology*. Thomas, Springfield, Ill., pp.383–391.

PURDY, W. C. and BUTTERFIELD, T. C., 1918. The effect of plankton on bacterial death rates. *Am. J. Public Health*, 8:499–505.

PÜTTER, A., 1907a. Die Ernährung der Wassertiere. *Z. Allgem. Physiol.*, 7:283–320.

PÜTTER, A., 1907b. Der Stoffhaushalt des Meeres. *Z. Allgem. Physiol.*, 7:321–368.

RAY, D. L. and STUNTZ, D. E., 1959a. Possible relation between marine fungi and *Limnoria* attack on submerged wood. *Science,* 129:93–94.

RAY, D. L. and STUNTZ, D. E., 1959b. Marine Fungi and *Limnoria*. *Science*, 130:46–47.

REAY, G. A., 1935. Some observations on the methods of estimating the degree of preservation of white fish. *J. Soc. Chem. Ind. (London)*, 1:54, 14T:96–98.

REED, G. B. and SPENCE, C. M., 1929. The intestinal and slime flora of the haddock. *Contrib. Can. Biol. Fisheries*, 4:257–264.

REED, G. B., RICE, C. E. and SINCLAIR, A. J., 1929. A comparative study of autolysis and bacterial decomposition in haddock, lobster, and clam muscle. *Contrib. Can. Biol. Fisheries*, 4:229–255.

RENN, C. E., 1940. Effects of marine mud on the aerobic decomposition of plankton materials. *Biol. Bull.*, 78:454–462.

REYES VASQUEZ, G., 1965. *Studies on the Diatom Flora Living on Thalassia testudinum* KONIG *in Biscayne Bay*. Thesis, Univ. Miami, Miami, Fla., 81 pp.

REYNOLDS, E. S. and MEYERS, S. P., 1957. *Office Naval Res., Res. Rev.*, 1957:6–11.

REYNOLDS, E. S. and MEYERS, S. P., 1959. Marine Fungi and *Limnoria* attack. *Science*, 130:46.

RILEY, G. A., 1963. Organic aggregates in sea water and the dynamics of their formation and utilization. *Limnol. Oceanog.*, 8:372–381.

RILEY, G. A., STOMMEL, H. and BUMPUS, D. F., 1949. Quantitative ecology of the plankton of the western North Atlantic. *Bull. Bingham Oceanog. Coll.*, 12:1–169.

RILEY, G. A., WANGERSKY, P. J. and VAN HEMERT, D., 1964. Organic aggregates in tropical and sub-tropical surface waters of the North Atlantic Ocean. *Limnol. Oceanog.*, 9:546–550.

RITTENBERG, S. C., EMERY, K. O. and ORR, W. L., 1955. Regeneration of nutrients in sediments of marine basins. *Deep-Sea Res.*, 3:23–45.

ROBERTSON, A. C. and WRIGHT, W. H., 1930. Investigation on the deterioration of nets in Lake Erie. *U.S. Bur. Fisheries Doc., Rept. U.S. Comm. Fisheries*, 1083:149–176.

ROBINSON, R. H. M., INGRAM, M., CASE, R. A. M. and BENSTEAD, J. G., 1953. Whalemeat; bacteriology and hygiene. *Gt. Brit., Dept. Sci. Ind. Res., Food Invest., Spec. Rept.*, 59.

RODHE, W., 1963. In: G. A. RILEY (Editor), *Proceedings of the First Conference on Marine Biology*. Am. Inst. Biol. Sci., Washington, D.C., 286 pp.

ROGERS, T. H., 1945. The inhibition of sulfate-reducing bacteria by dyestuffs. *J. Soc. Chem. Ind. (London)*, 64:292–295.

ROOS, H., 1957. Untersuchungen über das Vorkommen antimikrobieller Substanzen in Meeresalgen. *Kiel. Meeresforsch.*, 13:41–48.

ROSENFELD, W. D., 1946. Lipolytic activities of anaerobic bacteria. *Arch. Biochem. Biophys.*, 10:145–154.

ROUND, E. F., 1964. The ecology of benthic Algae. In: D. F. JACKSON (Editor), *Algae and Man*. Academic Press, New York, N.Y., pp.138–184.

SAITO, K. and SAMESHIMA, J., 1955. Studies on antibiotic action of algal extracts. *J. Agr. Chem. Soc. Japan*, 29:427–430.

SANBORN, J. R., 1930. Certain relationships of marine bacteria to the decomposition of fish. *J. Bacteriol.*, 19:375–382.

SANBORN, J. R., 1932. Marine bacteria commonly found on fresh fish. *J. Bacteriol.*, 23:349–351.

SCAGEL, R. F. and STEIN, J. R., 1961. Marine nannoplankton from a British Colombia fjord. *Can. J. Botany*, 39:1205–1214.

SCHAFER, R. D. and LANE, C. E., 1957. Some preliminary observations bearing on the nutrition of *Limnoria*. *Bull. Marine Sci. Gulf Caribbean*, 7:289.

SCHNEIDERHOHN, H., 1923. Calkographische Untersuchung der Mansfelder Kupferschiefers. *Neues Jahrb. Geol. Palaeontol. Abhandl.*, 47:1038.

SCHOLES, R. B. and SHEWAN, J. M., 1964. The present status of some aspects of marine microbiology. *Advan. Marine Biol.*, 2:133–169.

SCHONBERG, F., 1938. Über die wissenschaftlichen Grundlagen zu der Fischerhaltung der Seefisch. *Vorratspflege Lebensm.*, 1:133–142.

SCHRÖDER, B., 1911. Adriatisches Phytoplankton. *Sitzber. Kaiserl. Akad. Wiss. Wien, Math.-Naturw. Kl.*, 120:601–657.

SCHWIMMER, D. and SCHWIMMER, M., 1964. Algae and medicine. In: D. F. JACKSON (Editor), *Algae and Man*. Plenum Press, New York, N.Y., pp.368–412.

SEKI, H. and TAGA, N., 1963. Microbiological studies on the decomposition of chitin in the marine environment, I–V. *J. Oceanog. Soc. Japan*, 19:101–111, 143–161.

SENEZ, J. C., 1953. Investigations in biological corrosion in anaerobic soils by sulfate-reducing bacteria. *Corrosion Anti-Corrosion*, 1:131–132.

SGUROS, P. L. and SIMMS, J., 1963. Role of marine fungi in the oceans. *Can. J. Microbiol.*, 9:585–591.

Sguros, P. L. and Simms, J., 1964. Role of marine fungi in the oceans. *J. Bacteriol.*, 88:346–355.

Sherwood, H. P. and Thomson, S., 1953. Bacteriological examination of shellfish as a basis for sanitary control. *Monthly Bull. Min. Health Public Health, Lab. Ser.*, 103.

Shewan, J. M., 1938. The strict anaerobes in the slime and intestines of the haddock *(Gadus aeglefinus)*. *J. Bacteriol.*, 35:397–405.

Shewan, J. M., 1944. The bacterial flora of some species of marine fish and its relation to spoilage. *Proc. Soc. Exptl. Bacteriol.*, 1:1–5.

Shewan, J. M., 1953. Some recent progress in the bacteriology of marine fish. *Intern. Congr. Microbiol., 6th, Rome, 1953*, 7:361–365.

Shewan, J. M., 1960. The microbiology of sea-water fish. In: G. Borgstrom (Editor), *Fish as Food. 1. Production, Biochemistry, Microbiology.* Academic Press, New York, N.Y., pp.487–560.

Shewan, J. M., 1962. Food poisoning caused by fish and fishery products. In: G. Borgstrom (Editor), *Fish as Food. 2. Nutrition, Sanitation, Utilization.* Academic Press, New York, N.Y., pp.443–466.

Shewan, J. M., Hobbs, G. and Hodgkiss, W., 1960a. A determinative scheme for the identification of certain genera of gram-negative Bacteria with special reference to the Pseudomonadaceae. *J. Appl. Bacteriol.*, 23:379–390.

Shewan, J. M., Hobbs, G. and Hodgkiss, W., 1960b. The *Pseudomonas* and *Achromobacter* groups of Bacteria in the spoilage of marine white fish. *J. Appl. Bacteriol.*, 23:463–468.

Shipley, J. W., 1922. The corrosion of cast iron and lead pipes in alkaline soils. *J. Soc. Chem. Ind. (London)*, 41:311.

Sieburth, J. McN., 1960. Acrylic acid as an "antibiotic" principle in *Phaeocystis* blooms in Antarctic waters. *Science*, 132:676–677.

Sieburth, J. McN., 1962. Biochemical warfare among the microbes of the sea. *Rhode Island, Univ., Honors. Lectures*, 1962: 13 pp.

Sieburth, J. McN., 1964a. Antibacterial substances produced by marine algae. *Develop. Ind. Microbiol.*, 5:124–134.

Sieburth, J. McN., 1964b. Polymorphism of a marine bacterium *(Arthrobacter)* as a function of multiple temperature optima and nutrition. *Proc. Symp. Exptl. Marine Ecol., Occasional Publ.*, 2:11–16.

Sieburth, J. McN., 1965. Hiemal development of a psychrophilic bacterial flora in a temperate estuary. *Bacteriol. Proc.*, 16.

Sieburth, J. McN. and Pratt, D. M., 1962. Anticoliform activity of sea water associated with the termination of *Skeletonema costatum* blooms. *Trans. N.Y. Acad. Sci.*, 24:498–501.

Silva, P. C., 1962. Classification of algae. In: R. A. Lewin (Editor), *Biochemistry and Physiology of Algae*. Academic Press, New York, N.Y., pp.827–837.

Silvestri, L. G. and Hill, L. R., 1965. Agreement between deoxyribonucleic acid base composition and taxometric classification of gram-positive cocci. *J. Bacteriol.*, 90:136–140.

Simidu, W. and Oisi, K., 1952. Studies on the putrefaction of aquatic products. V. On urea in the elasmobrancheate fish. *Bull. Japan. Soc. Sci. Fisheries*, 16:547–549.

SKERMAN, T. M., 1956. The nature and development of primary films on surfaces submerged in the sea. *New Zealand J. Sci. Technol., B*, 38:44–57.

SMITH, F. G. W., 1941. Sponge disease in British Honduras and its transmission by water currents. *Ecology*, 22:415–420.

SNOW, J. E. and BEARD, P. J., 1939. Studies on the bacterial flora of north Pacific salmon. *Food Res.*, 4:563–585.

SOMMER, H. and MEYER, K. F., 1937. Paralytic shellfish poisoning. *Arch. Pathol.*, 24:560–598.

SOMMER, H., WHEDON, W. F., KOFOID, C. A. and STOHLER, R., 1937. Relation of paralytic shellfish poison to certain plankton organisms of the genus *Goniaulax*. *Arch. Pathol.*, 24:537–559.

SPENCER, C. P., 1956. The bacterial oxidation of ammonia in the sea. *J. Marine Biol. Assoc. U.K.*, 35:621, 630.

SPENCER, R., 1963. Bacterial viruses in the sea. In: C. H. OPPENHEIMER (Editor), *Marine Microbiology*. Thomas, Springfield, Ill., pp.350–365.

SPENCER, R. S., 1959. Some aspects of the ecology of Lake Macquarie, N.S.W., II. *Australian J. Marine Freshwater Res.*, 10:279–296.

SPOEHR, H. A., 1951. *Chlorella* as a source of food. *Proc. Am. Phil. Soc.*, 96: 62–67.

SPOEHR, H. A., SMITH, J. H. C., STRAIN, H. H., MILNER, H. W. and HARDIN, G. J., 1949. Fatty acid antibacterials from plants. *Carnegie Inst. Wash. Publ.*, 586:1–67.

SPRUYT, C. J. P., 1962. Photoreduction and anaerobiosis. In: R. A. LEWIN (Editor), *Biochemistry and Physiology of Algae*. Academic Press, New York, N.Y., pp.47–60.

SREENIVASAN, A., 1956. New species of marine bacteria tolerating high concentration of copper. *Current Sci. (India)*, 25:92–93.

STANBURY, F. A., 1944. Experiments on the growth of marine plants with special reference to effects of copper and mercury salts. *Marine Corrosion Comm. Rept. Iron, Steel Corrosion Comm.*, manuscript.

STANIER, R. Y., 1961. Photosynthetic mechanisms in bacteria; development of a unitary concept. *Bacteriol. Rev.*, 25:1–17.

STARKEY, R. L., 1953. The relationship of sulfate-reducing bacteria to iron corrosion in the marine environment. *Intern. Congr. Microbiol., 6th, Rome, 1953*, 7:347–349.

STARKEY, R. L., 1956. Transformations of sulfur by microorganisms. *Ind. Eng. Chem.*, 48:1429–1437.

STARKEY, R. L., 1957. Susceptibility of matrix-constituents of anti-fouling paints to microbial attack in sea water. *Can. J. Microbiol.*, 3:231–238.

STARKEY, R. L. and SCHENONE, J. D., 1946. Decomposition of marine paints and paint constituents in sea water. *J. Bacteriol.*, 52:401 (abstr.).

STARKEY, R. L. and SCHENONE, J. D., 1947. Relations of sulfate-reducing bacteria to corrosion of steel in sea water. *J. Bacteriol.*, 54:46 (abstr.).

STARKEY, R. L. and WIGHT, K. M., 1945. Anaerobic corrosion of iron in soil. *Am. Gas Assoc. Rept.*, 1.

STARR, T. J. and JONES, M. E., 1957. The effect of copper on the growth of bacteria isolated from marine environments. *Limnol. Oceanog.*, 2:33–36.

STARR, T. J., JONES, M. E. and MARTINEZ, D., 1957. The production of vitamin B_{12}-active substances by marine bacteria. *Limnol. Oceanog.*, 2:114–119.

STARR, T. J., DEIG, E. F., CHURCH, K. K. and ALLEN, M. B., 1962. Antibacterial and antiviral activities of algal extracts studied by acridine orange staining. *Texas Rept. Biol. Med.*, 20:271–278.

STAUDT, E., 1925. Korrosion von Kupferröhr durch Petroleum. *Chem. Z.*, 49:952.

STEELE, J. H., 1956. Plant production on the Fladen Ground. *J. Marine Biol. Assoc. U.K.*, 35:1–33.

STEELE, J. H., 1964. A study of production in the Gulf of Mexico. *Bull. Marine Res.*, 22:211–222.

STEEMANN-NIELSEN, E., 1955. The production of antibiotics by plankton algae and its effect upon bacterial activities in the sea. *Deep-Sea Res.*, 3:281–286.

STEWART, M. M., 1932. The bacterial flora of the slime and intestinal contents of the haddock *(Gadus aeglefinus)*. *J. Marine Biol. Assoc. U.K.*, 18:35–50.

STEWART, W. D. P., 1964a. Nitrogen fixation by Myxophyceae from marine environments. *J. Gen. Microbiol.*, 36:415–422.

STEWART, W. D. P., 1964b. Assimilation of ^{15}N by marine blue-green algae. *Soc. Gen. Microbiol., Abstr.*, 1964:6–8.

STUTZER, M. J., 1926. Darmbakterien der Kaltbluder. *Zentr. Bakteriol. Parasitenk., Abt. II*, 66:344–354.

SUSSMILCH, C. A., 1922. *Introduction to the Geology of New South Wales.* Angus and Robertson, Sydney, 269 pp.

SUYAMA, I. M., TOKUHIRO, T. and SUYAMA, Y., 1950. On the urea content and the ammonia formation of the muscle of shark flesh. *Bull. Japan. Soc. Sci. Fisheries*, 16:211.

SVERDRUP, H. U., JOHNSON, M. W. and FLEMING, R. N., 1949. *The Oceans.* Prentice Hall, New York, N.Y., 1077 pp.

SWEENEY, B. M., 1958. A persistent diurnal rhythm of luminescence in *Goniaulax polyedra*. *Biol. Bull.*, 115:440–458.

SYRETT, P. J., 1962. Nitrogen assimilation. In: R. A. LEWIN (Editor), *Biochemistry and Physiology of Algae.* Academic Press, New York, N.Y., pp.177–188.

TAMAKI, S., 1928. Mikrobiochemische Studien über die Coli-Gruppe der verschiedenen Tierarten. *Fukuoka Acta Med.*, 21:257–286.

TANIKAWA, E., 1939. Über der Einfluss der Ernährung auf die Darmflora der Fische. *Arch. Mikrobiol.*, 10:26–71.

TARR, H. L. A., 1954. Microbial deterioration of fish post mortem, its detection and control. *Bacteriol. Rev.*, 18:1–15.

TAYLOR, C. B. and LOCHHEAD, A. G., 1938. Quantitative studies of soil microorganisms, II. *Can. J. Res., C*, 16:162–173.

TELITCHENKO, M. M., DAVYDOVA, N. V. and FEDOROV, V. D., 1962. The interrelation of algae and microorganisms, II. *Nauchn. Dokl. Vysshei Shkoly, Biol. Nauki*, 4:157–163.

THIEL, G. A., 1926. The Mansfeld Kupferschiefer. *Econ. Geol.*, 21:299–300.

THIEL, G. A., 1927. The enrichment of bauxite deposits through the activity of microorganisms. *Econ. Geol.*, 22:480–493.

THJØTTA, TH. and SØMME, O. M., 1938. The bacterial flora of normal fish. (A preliminary report.) *Acta Pathol. Microbiol. Scand.*, 37:514–525.

THJØTTA, TH. and SØMME, O. M., 1943. The bacterial flora of normal fish. *Skrifter Norske Videnskaps-Akad. Oslo, I: Mat.-Naturv. Kl.*, 1943(4):1–86.

THODE, H. G., McNAMARA, J. and FLEMING, W. H., 1953. Sulfur isotope fractionation in nature and biological and geological time scales. *Geochim. Geophys. Acta*, 3:235–243.

TOBIN, L. C., ALFORD, J. A. and McCLESKEY, C. S., 1941. The bacterial flora of iced fresh crabmeat. *J. Bacteriol.*, 41:96 (abstr.).

TOPPING, L. E., 1937. The predominant microorganisms in soil. *Zentr. Bakteriol. Parasitenk., Abt. II*, 97:289–304.

TRASK, P. D., 1925. The origin of the ore of the Mansfeld Kupferschiefer, Germany. A review. *Econ. Geol.*, 20:746–761.

TSUCHIYA, Y., TAKAHASHI, I. and YOSHIDA, S., 1951. Studies on the formation of ammonia and trimethylamine in shark. *Tohoku J. Agr. Res.*, 2:119–126.

VACCA, D. D. and WALSH, R. A., 1954. The antibacterial extract obtained from an extract of *Ascophillum nodosum. J. Pharm. Sci.*, 43:24–26.

VAN BAALEN, V., 1962. Studies on marine blue-green algae. *Botan. Marina*, 4:129–139.

VAN LANDINGHAM, S., 1964. Some physical and genetic aspects of fluctuations in non-marine plankton diatom populations. *Botan. Rev.*, 30:437–478.

VEILLON, R., 1935. Du rôle des bactéries et notamment des anaerobies dans la corrosion d'acier. *Compt. Rend. Soc. Biol.*, 120:1045–1047.

VELANKAR, N. K. and KAMASASTRI, P. V., 1955. Shark spoilage bacteria. *Current Sci. (India)*, 24:272–273.

VENKATARAMAN, R. and SREENIVASAN, A., 1953. A marine species of slow-lactose-fermenting bacterium. *Current Sci. (India)*, 22:120.

VENKATARAMAN, R. and SREENIVASAN, A., 1954. Bacterial flora of sea water and mackerels off Tellicherry (Malabar). *Proc. Natl. Acad. Sci., India, Sect. A*, 20:651–655.

VENKATARAMAN, R. and SREENIVASAN, A., 1955a. Mussel pollution at Korpuzha estuary (Malabar) with an account of certain coliform types. *India. J. Fisheries*, 2:314–324.

VENKATARAMAN, R. and SREENIVASAN, A., 1955b. Utilization of various nitrogenous compounds by certain *Pseudomonas* cultures from marine environments. *Proc. Indian Acad. Sci.*, 42:31–38.

VENKATARAMAN, R. and SREENIVASAN, A., 1955c. Bacterial content of fresh shark. *Current Sci. (India)*, 24:380–381.

VISHNIAC, H. S., 1960. Salt requirements of marine phycomycetes. *Limnol. Oceanog.*, 5: 362–365.

VON MÜLLER, O. F., 1783. Om et besondelight Vaesen i Strandvandet. *Kgl. Danske Videnskab. Skrifter.*

VON WOLZOGEN KUHR, C. A. H., 1923. Sulphate reduction as the cause of corrosion of cast iron pipe lines. *Water Gas*, 7:277–284.

VON WOLZOGEN KUHR, C. A. H., 1939. The corrosion of lead and copper pipes in soil. *Water*, 23:215; *J. Am. Water Works Assoc.*, 37:355–358.

WAKSMAN, S. A., 1932. *Principles of Soil Microbiology*. Williams and Wilkins, Baltimore, Md., 894 pp.

WAKSMAN, S. A., JOHNSTONE, D. B. and CAREY, C. L., 1943. The effect of copper on the development of bacteria in sea water and the isolation of specific bacteria. *J. Marine Res. (Sears Found. Marine Res.)*, 5:136–152.

WALCOTT, C. D., 1955. Discovery of Algonkian bacteria. *Proc. Natl. Acad. Sci. U.S.*, 1:256–257.

WANGERSKY, P. J. and GUILLARD, R. R. L., 1960. Low molecular weight organic base from the dinoflagellate *Amphidinium carteri*. *Nature*, 185: 689–690.

WATSON, D. W., 1939. Studies on fish spoilage, IV. *J. Fisheries Res. Board Can.*, 4:252–266.

WHEDON, W. F., 1942. Report to Buships. (Mimeo rept.)

WHITTON, B. A., 1965. Extracellular products of blue-green algae. *J. Gen. Microbiol.*, 40:1–11.

WIEBE, W. J. and LISTON, J., 1965. Observations on the physiology of selected marine bacteria. *Bacteriol. Proc.*, 16.

WIESSNER, W., 1962. Inorganic micronutrients. In: R. A. LEWIN (Editor), *Biochemistry and Physiology of Algae*. Academic Press, New York, N.Y., pp.267–286.

WILLINGHAM, C. A., 1965. *Studies on the Mechanisms of Mild Steel Corrosion in the Marine Environment with Special Reference to the Sulfate Reducing Bacteria*. Thesis, Univ. Miami, Miami, Fla.

WILLINGHAM, C. A. and BUCK, J. D., 1965. A preliminary comparative study of fungal contamination in non-sterile water samples. *Deep-Sea Res.*, 12:693–695.

WILSON, D. P., 1955. The role of microorganisms in the settlement of *Ophelia bicornis* Savigny. *J. Marine Biol. Assoc. U.K.*, 34:531–543.

WILSON, I. M., 1960. Marine Fungi; a review of the present position. *Proc. Limnol. Soc., London*, 171:53–70.

WINOGRADSKY, S., 1890. Recherches sur les organismes de la nitrification. *Ann. Inst. Pasteur*, 4:213–231.

WINOGRADSKY, S., 1949. *Microbiologie du Sol. Problèmes et Méthodes*. Masson, Paris, 862 pp.

WISEMAN, J. D. H. and HENDEY, N. I., 1953. The significance and diatom content of a deep-sea floor sample from the neighbourhood of the greatest oceanic depth. *Deep-Sea Res.*, 1:47–59.

WOLOSZYNSKA, J. et CONRAD, W., 1939. *Pyrodinium phoneus* sp.n. agent de la toxicité des moules du canal maritime de Bruges à Zeebrugge. *Bull. Musée Roy. Hist. Nat. Belg.*, 15(46):1–5.

WOOD, E. J. F., 1940. Studies on the marketing of fish in eastern Australia. *C.S.I.R.O. Pam.*, 100: 91 pp.

WOOD, E. J. F., 1950a. The role of bacteria in the early stages of fouling. *Australian J. Marine Freshwater Res.*, 1:85–91.

WOOD, E. J. F., 1950b. The bacteriology of shark spoilage. *Australian J. Marine Freshwater Res.*, 1:129–138.

WOOD, E. J. F., 1953. Heterotrophic bacteria in marine environments of eastern Australia. *Australian J. Marine Freshwater Res.*, 4:160–200.

WOOD, E. J. F., 1955. The effect of temperature and flow-rate on some marine fouling organisms. *Australian J. Sci.*, 18:34–37.

WOOD, E. J. F., 1956. Diatoms in the ocean deeps. *Pacific Sci.*, 10:377–381.

WOOD, E. J. F., 1958. Significance of marine microbiology. *Bacteriol. Rev.*, 22:1–19.

WOOD, E. J. F., 1959a. Some aspects of marine microbiology. *Indian J. Marine Biol.*, 1:26–32.

WOOD, E. J. F., 1959b. Some aspects of the ecology of Lake Macquarie, N.S.W., VI. *Australian J. Marine Freshwater Res.*, 10:322–340.

WOOD, E. J. F., 1959c. An unusual diatom from the Antarctic. *Nature*, 184:1962–1963.

WOOD, E. J. F., 1962. A method for phytoplankton study. *Limnol. Oceanog.*, 7:32–35.

WOOD, E. J. F., 1964. Studies in microbial ecology of the Australasian region. *Nova Hedwigia*, 8:5–54, 453–568.

WOOD, E. J. F., 1965. *Marine Microbial Ecology.* Reinhold, New York, N.Y., 238 pp.

WOOD, E. J. F., 1966. Plants of the deep oceans. *Z. Allgem. Mikrobiol.*, 6:177–179.

WOOD, E. J. F. and CORCORAN, E. F., 1966. Diurnal variation in proto-plankton. *Bull. Marine Sci. Gulf Caribbean*, in press.

WOOD, E. J. F. and DAVIS, P. S., 1956. Importance of smaller phytoplankton elements. *Nature*, 177:438.

WOOD, P. C., 1961. The production of clean shellfish. *Health Meeting Chelmsford, 1961*, pp.8–11.

WOODS, D. D. and LASCELLES, J., 1954. The no-mans-land between the autotrophic and heterotrophic ways of life. In: B. A. FRY and J. L. PEEL (Editors), *Autotrophic Microorganisms*. Cambridge Univ. Press, London, pp.1–27.

WRIGHT, R. T., 1964. Dynamics of a phytoplankton community in an ice-covered lake. *Limnol. Oceanog.*, 9:163–178.

YCAS, M., 1955. A note on the origin of life. *Proc. Natl. Acad. Sci. U.S.*, 41(10):174–176.

ZOBELL, C. E., 1936. Bactericidal action of sea water. *Proc. Soc. Exptl. Biol. Med.*, 34:113–116.

ZOBELL, C. E., 1937. The influences of solid surfaces upon the physiological activities of bacteria in sea water. *J. Bacteriol.*, 33:186.

ZOBELL, C. E., 1938. The sequence of events in the fouling of submerged surfaces. *Dig. Federal Paint Varnish Prod. Clubs*, 178:379–385.

ZoBELL, C. E., 1946a. Functions of bacteria in the formation and accumulation of petroleum. *Oil Weekly*, 1946 (Feb. 18).

ZoBELL, C. E., 1946b. *Marine Microbiology*. Chronica Botanica, Waltham, Mass., 240 pp.

ZoBELL, C. E., 1947. Bacterial release of oil from oil-bearing materials. *World Oil*, 126(13):36–47; 127(1):35–41.

ZoBELL, C. E., 1950a. Assimilation of hydrocarbons by microorganisms. *Advan. Enzymol.*, 10:443–486.

ZoBELL, C. E., 1950b. Part played by bacteria in petroleum formation. *J. Sediment. Petrol.*, 22:42–49.

ZoBELL, C. E., 1950c. Bacterial activities and the origin of oil. *World Oil*, 130:128–138.

ZoBELL, C. E., 1952. Bacterial life at the bottom of the Philippines trench. *Science*, 115:507–508.

ZoBELL, C. E. and ALLEN, E. C., 1935. Attachment of bacteria to submerged slides. *Proc. Soc. Exptl. Biol. Med.*, 30:1409–1411.

ZoBELL, C. E. and BECKWITH, J. D., 1944. The deterioration of rubber products by microorganisms. *J. Am. Water Works Assoc.*, 36:439–453.

ZoBELL, C. E. and FELTHAM, C. B., 1934. Preliminary studies on the distribution and characteristics of marine bacteria. *Bull. Scripps Inst. Oceanog. Univ. Calif., Tech. Ser.*, 3:279–296.

ZoBELL, C. E. and JOHNSON, F. R., 1949. The influence of hydrostatic pressure on the growth and variability of terrestrial and marine bacteria. *J. Bacteriol.*, 57:179–189.

ZoBELL, C. E. and MORITA, R. Y., 1957. Barophilic bacteria in some deep-sea sediments. *J. Bacteriol.*, 73:563–568.

ZoBELL, C. E. and OPPENHEIMER, C. H., 1950. Some effects of hydrostatic pressure on the multiplication and morphology of marine bacteria. *J. Bacteriol.*, 60:771–781.

ZoBELL, C. E. and RITTENBERG, S. C., 1948. Sulfate-reducing bacteria in marine sediments. *J. Marine Res. (Sears Found. Marine Res.)*, 7:602–617.

ZoBELL, C. E. and UPHAM, H. C., 1944. A list of marine bacteria including descriptions of sixty new species. *Bull Scripps Inst. Oceanog. Univ. Calif.*, 5:239–292.

INDEX

Acetes, 204
Achnanthaceae, 77
Achnanthales, 77
Achnanthes, 94, 97, 196, 204, 216, 218, 220
Achromatiaceae, 54
Achromobacter, 45, 49, 51, 213–215, 240, 241, 243, 257, 259
Actinocyclus, 71, 93, 95, 152, 177
Actinomyces, 46, 53, 232, 253
Actinoptychus, 96, 201
Actipylea, 268
Adansonian system, 19, 45, 46
Adsorption, 12, 26, 30, 80, 150, 163, 186, 273
Aeromonas, 45, 49
Agamont, 120, 273
Agar, 28, 42, 51
Agarbacterium, 19, 35, 42
Agar digestion, 144, 145
Akinetes, 90
Algae, 7, 11, 28, 32, 70–132, 147–169, 214–220, 262–266
Alginomonas, 42, 48
Algonkian, 9, 262, 265
Alkaligenes, 42, 49, 255
Allergy, 165
Allochthonous, 273
Allogamous, 273
Alternaria, 65, 223, 227
Aluminum, 267
Amazon River, 151
Amerosporae, 64
Amino-acids, 4, 5, 26, 55, 85, 160, 164, 165
Ammonia, 85, 141, 142, 160
Amoebae, 117, 173
Amphidinium, 166, 189, 201

Amphilothaceae, 76, 109
Amphipleura, 204
Amphiprora, 94, 97, 216
Amphiproraceae, 77
Amphisolenia, 107, 108
Amphisoleniaceae, 76
Amphora, 94, 97, 194, 196, 204, 216–218
Anabaena, 82, 88, 164
Anaerobes, 4, 6, 31, 44, 47, 48, 149, 174, 191, 212, 221–223, 238, 243, 258, 264, 266, 269, 273
Anaulus, 91
Animal Exclusion, 39
Anisolpidium, 63
Anomoeoneis, 97
Antibiotics, 73, 158, 192, 234
Antarctic, 30, 63, 69, 74, 124, 133, 136, 152, 155–157, 178
Antithamnion, 193, 219
Aphanocapsa, 87
Aphanothece, 87
Aphotic, 16, 273
Apistonema, 111, 113
Arachnoidiscus, 95
Arafura Sea, 134, 157
Araphidineae, 81, 96, 97
Arctic, 30, 152–154
Arripis, 243
Artemia, 162, 163
Arthrobacter, 42, 52, 58, 241, 252
Ascomycetes, 61, 62, 64, 65, 67–70
Ascophyllum, 132, 167
Aspergillus, 65, 227
Astasia, 115, 117, 201
Astasiaceae, 78
Asterionella, 83, 101, 157, 170, 184
Asterolampra, 95